China: The Land and its People

china

The Land and its People

R. R. C. de Crespigny, M.A., Ph.D.
Lecturer in Chinese
Faculty of Asian Studies
Australian National University

ST. MARTIN'S PRESS
NEW YORK

For information, write:
St. Martin's Press, Inc.
175 Fifth Avenue, New York, New York 10010
Library of Congress Catalog Card Number 76-180738
First published in the United States of America in 1971

AFFILIATED PUBLISHERS:
Macmillan & Company, Limited, London—
also at Bombay, Calcutta, Madras and Melbourne—
The Macmillan Company of Canada, Limited,
Toronto
Printed in the U.S.A.

This book is dedicated to
Anne

Contents

Plates

Maps

Figures

Preface

Fifteen years ago, when George B. Cressey published his great geography of China, he gave it the title *Land of the 500 Million*. Today, an educated guess would set the population of the country at 750 to 800 million and still increasing. The sheer size of China, whether it be measured by expanse of land, numbers of people, or potential power in Asia and the world, makes her difficult for Australians to comprehend, and it is still harder sometimes to appreciate her problems and to sympathise with her aspirations. This book is an attempt to set out, in short space, the essential pattern of the country in the hope that as we learn more of China we may go some way further to understanding her people and coming to terms with them.

For any geographer, there are two special problems in dealing with present-day China. Firstly, the startling lack of statistics: on account of practical difficulties and also for reasons of state, there are essentially no reliable figures for production or internal finance published on the mainland since the late 1950s, and even our estimates of population must be based on varying judgements of natural increase since the last effective census in 1953. Only for the off-shore island of Taiwan, under a rival government to the Communists in Peking, are there any acceptable figures now available.

The second problem is that of place names. Since Chinese is written with characters and not with an alphabet, there are a variety of ways by which the sounds of the language may be rendered into Western transcription. Most books published in this century have used the so-called Post Office system, which is inaccurate and unscientific but now has the advantage of popularity and common recognition. The system is still followed by the Government of the Republic of China in Taiwan, and it was used in *The Times Atlas of the World*, Mid-Century Edition, 1958. More recently, however, in the Comprehensive Edition of 1967, the *Times* has adopted the Wade-Giles transcription, so that the capital of China, written Peking in Post Office, is now Pei-ching. In the meantime, on the mainland the official Pinyin system, adopted by the Communist government in 1958, calls the city Beijing, phonetically more accurate but strange to the untutored eye. For those who read about China primarily in the English language, either in texts, magazines or daily newspapers, the Post Office system will be the more familiar, and I have followed it throughout this book, with the *Times* Mid-Century edition as the guide and model.

In one other matter I follow the policy of *The Times Atlas:* the question of political boundaries. There are differing claims along almost every part of China's borders, but I have tried to describe the situation as it exists, and both in the text and in the maps I have sought to acquaint the reader, in the words of the editors of the *Atlas*, 'with the authority he will find in operation at any given point, whether it is or is not that which his patriotism or conscience is ready to acknowledge'.

Of all those who have helped and advised me with this work, I thank particularly Professor A. T. A. Learmonth, formerly of the Australian National University and now of The Open University, Walton Hall, England, Mr David Pettit of Melbourne Church of England Grammar School, and also Mr Peter Daniell and Miss Pam Millwood, of the Department of Geography, School of General Studies, ANU, who prepared fine maps from very amateurish suggestions.

RAFE DE CRESPIGNY

Canberra
November 1970

Acknowledgements

The publishers wish to acknowledge photographs from the following sources:

Camera Press for permission to reproduce Plate 33; China Publishing Company, Taipei (Pl. 54); Dragonfly Books, Hong Kong (Pl. 49); Foreign Language Press, Peking (Pl. 40); The Geographical Magazine (Pls 29, 35, 37); The Globe and Mail, Toronto (Pl. 43); Government of the Republic of China (Pls 52, 53, 55); Hong Kong Government Information Services (Pls 46, 47, 48); Gun Kessle and Jan Myrdal (Pls 12, 20, 26, 34); Pacific Communications Ltd, Hong Kong (Pl. 19); Mrs P. Reichl (Pl. 27); The Victoria and Albert Museum, London (Pls 45 (i)); Wen-wu Publishing Company, Peking (Pls 31, 36).

McGraw-Hill Book Company for the use of Table 3 and Map 15 from George B. Cressey, *Land of the 500 Million*, 1955.

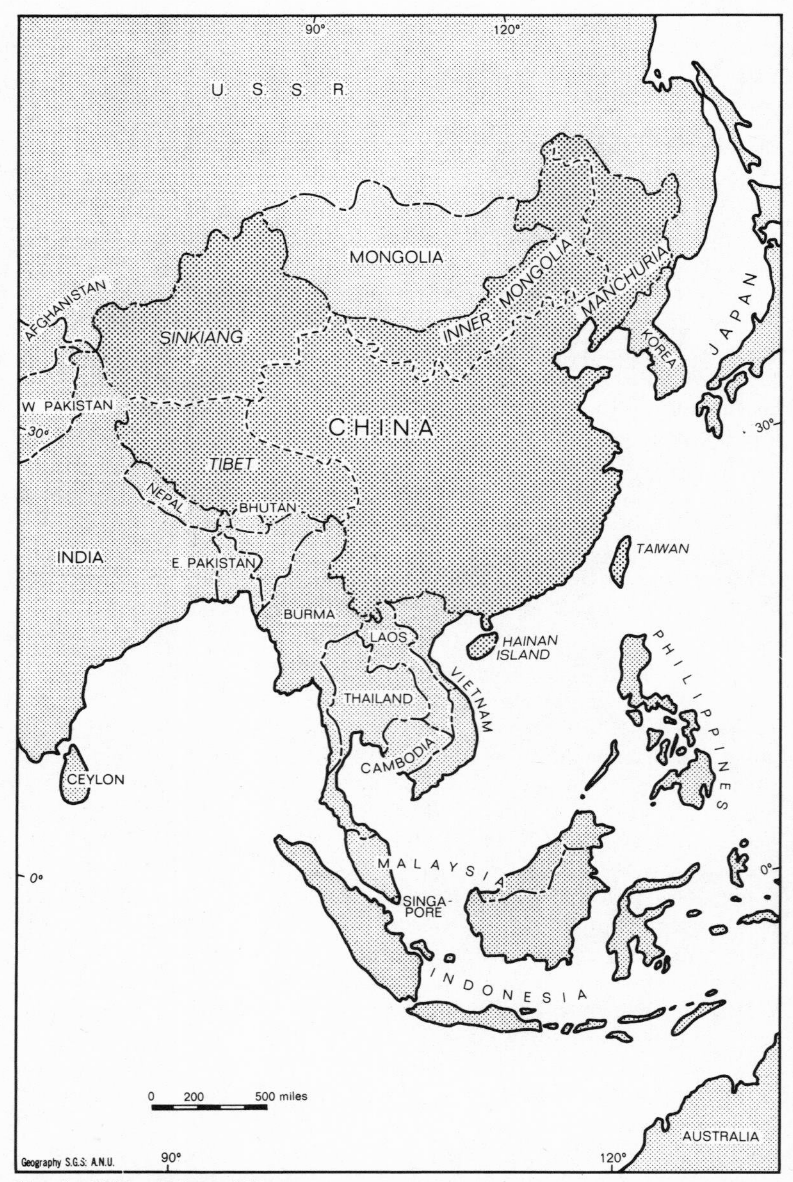

Map 1 China and her neighbours.

The present area of China is probably the largest ever effectively controlled by a single government, though there are some territories (Outer Mongolia, North Vietnam) which have been ruled by a Chinese empire in the past but which are outside the present borders. Considering that the land frontiers of China are almost ten thousand miles long, and considering also the disturbed history of the past century and a half, it is not surprising that there are some areas of dispute and possible conflict. Politically, China seems predominantly a land power, but the coastline of the country is more than three thousand miles long, and the provinces of the south and south-east have a long tradition of seamanship, trade and overseas settlement. At the present time, the off-shore island of Taiwan is politically separate from the mainland, but both the Communist government at Peking and the Nationalist government in Taipei are agreed that Taiwan is an integral part of China. Each in its own way looks forward to reunification.

1 The Nation of China

The latest estimate of the population of the People's Republic of China is 750,000,000, a figure which represents one quarter of all the people in the world today. There are almost as many people in China as there are in India, Russia and Japan combined; and there are sixty Chinese for every Australian.

In land area, China's 3,657,765 square miles make it the third largest country in the world. Only the USSR, with more than 8.5 million square miles, and Canada, with 3.8 million, are larger. In comparatively recent times, the government of China has also claimed suzerainty over the whole of Mongolia, although the present People's Republic of Mongolia, otherwise known as Outer Mongolia, is now independent. Were this territory included, the Chinese realm would exceed 4.3 million square miles.

Within this enormous country may be found every extreme of geographical feature. Two of the longest rivers in the world, the Hwang Ho (Yellow River) and the Yangtze, flow from the highlands of Tibet eastwards to the sea. Mount Everest, highest in the world, is on the border of China with Nepal, and the Turfan Depression, the second lowest area of dry land, lies in Sinkiang. The borders of Inner Mongolia and Manchuria exceed latitude 53°N, and the Gulf of Liaotung and the Bay of Korea are blocked by ice during the winter months each year. To the south, the island of Hainan is within 20 degrees of the equator, and the ports of Canton, Hong Kong and the coast of Fukien are lashed by tropical typhoons in summer. Mainland China's coastline is 3,300 miles long, and on the landward side her frontiers stretch 9,300 miles, from Vietnam in the south, by Laos, Burma, India, Bhutan, Nepal, Pakistan and Afghanistan to the USSR in the west and north and Korea in the north-east. From Tien Shan to Vladivostok and the Amur, China's border with Russia and her close ally the People's Republic of Mongolia is more than five thousand miles.

Politically, this vast area on the mainland of Asia is ruled by a single government with its capital at Peking. Geographically, it is natural to contrast the great territories of Outer China, that is Tibet,

Sinkiang and Inner Mongolia, with the more densely settled and developed lands of Manchuria in the north-east and the eighteen provinces of China Proper. Some one hundred miles offshore, the island of Taiwan is controlled by a Nationalist government hostile to the Communists of the mainland, but both sides of this political division agree that Taiwan is an integral part of the Chinese world.

Population growth

Of all the features of China, it is the numbers of her people and the rate of their increase that presents the greatest problem both for the country herself and for the nations around her. During most of recorded history, from the first census figures preserved for the year A.D. 2 down into the eighteenth century, the population remained fairly steady between fifty and sixty million. A significant rise appears to have begun under the Ch'ing dynasty, and throughout the three centuries of this last empire, despite war and natural disasters, the steady increase in the number of people placed a constant strain on the economic resources of the government and on its political control of the nation.

In 1911, at the beginning of the Republic, it was reliably estimated that there were 374,000,000 Chinese. Forty years later, in 1953, after a period of civil disturbance, foreign war, widespread flooding and serious earthquakes, a full census was organised by the new Communist government. It was the general opinion that the figure would fall somewhere between 450,000,000 and 500,000,000, but the final total was a fifth as much again: 602,000,000 Chinese, including twelve million living abroad. Throughout the 1950s, with one of the world's highest birth-rates of thirty-five per thousand, and a death-rate declining every year (twelve or thirteen per thousand), the growth of China's population was estimated at thirteen to fifteen million a year. More recently, the rate of increase has slowed, but there is no reason to doubt that the people of China numbered 750,000,000 by the middle of the 1960s, and they have quite possibly reached 800,000,000 in 1970.

Faced with such a situation, any government would find itself in a quandary. Communist China has proved no exception. In many ways, the rising population is a tribute to the discipline of the new regime, to the restoration of political order, and to the efficient control of natural resources. Such achievement is in itself enough to encourage the growth of population. The Chinese government had also intervened in matters of social concern, raising the status of women and putting a final stop to such ancient practices as foot-binding, arranged marriages and the exposure of female infants at birth. Although the equal rights of women are now firmly enforced by law, both in Mainland China and on Taiwan, the lingering effects of discrimination may still be found in census figures, for recent estimates suggest that men outnumber women in China by 52 to 48 per cent. (In Australia the ratio is 50.3 to 49.7.) The general increase in numbers was seen as a result of the stability of the government, and the old apologists of over-population pointed out that for every new mouth there was also added another pair of hands to work for the development of the nation. At one time, indeed, it is said that encouragement to factories to increase their output was extended also to maternity hospitals, so that several of these establishments carried banners 'More, bigger, better, faster'.

In 1959, however, a warning appeared. For three years in succession, a series of poor harvests brought the first major grain shortage of the Communist regime and compelled a policy of food imports which has continued to the present. In an agricultural economy such as that of China, the need to import staple foods has proved a political embarrassment and a heavy drain on foreign exchange. Within the country, the pressure of population on scarce resources has encouraged a change of policy towards family planning. Young men and women are now actively discouraged from marriage before reaching their late twenties; many husbands and wives, for reasons of employment, may live apart, and over-frequent pregnancy in women is criticised as a hindrance to their work in building the

Plate 1 Two-fifths of the present population of China has been born since the advent of the Communists to power. Children in a kindergarten attached to a knitting mill are taught the thoughts of Mao Tse-tung while their parents are at work. *(China Pictorial)*

future of the country. Slowly, over recent years, the attitude of the government of China towards its mounting population has turned from acceptance to discouragement.

In this field, however, official policy can never be completely effective. Good government may encourage a rising birthrate, as we have seen, but it is difficult to introduce legislation and social pressures which may be effective deterrents to population increase against a myriad individual emotions and the cold statistics of demography. It is unlikely that the situation will improve for some time, if only because two-fifths of the present Chinese population are under twenty and have been born since the Communists came to power.

An age pyramid, broad at the base, may indicate great potential energy, but it is also a clear sign of a continued rise in population. Both the numbers of the Chinese people and their comparative youth are a potential source of trouble for a developing nation whose chief needs are stable population and steady, real economic growth.

The civilisation of China

With such a vast area, larger than all Europe, and such an enormous number of people, the sub-continent can well be considered a world of its own. So it has been, indeed, for more than three thousand years. The Chinese names for their country, *Chung-kuo* 'The Middle Kingdom', or *Chung-hua* 'Central Flower Country', reflect the attitudes of the original cluster of civilised states in the Hwang Ho valley and plain—states entirely surrounded by alien and, to them, barbarian peoples. From these beginnings, the political realm of China has extended across the mainland into Central and Northern Asia, and the culture of China has influenced the whole of East and South-East Asia.

In historical terms, the civilisation of China is comparatively young. The earliest written fragments found on Chinese soil date no earlier than the second millenium B.C., and while there are many legends, there is little reliable history until the time of the sage Confucius, about 500 B.C. Contrast this with the civilisations of Mesopotamia and of Egypt, already constructing the Great Pyramid in the years before 2500 B.C., and it may be seen that the antiquity of China compares rather with the later classical age of Greece and Rome. To this extent, the common belief in the long history of China is false and misleading.

On the other hand, unlike the world of the Middle East, the Mediterranean and Europe, China has had no great interruption to the continuity of her history and civilisation, and there has been no permanent political division among her people. China has suffered invasion and long periods of disunity, but there is nothing in her experience to match the *Völkerwanderung* which destroyed the Roman Empire, nor has there been any division so complete and long-lasting as that between the nation-states of modern Europe. From anthropological evidence, it appears that the people of China today are of much the same physical types as their predecessors on the same soil four thousand years ago, while in philosophy and politics the unity of the civilised world has been for them a constant theme and a steady ambition.

In considering the reasons for such remarkable social cohesion, two factors appear essential: the Chinese system of writing, and the agricultural techniques of the Chinese peasant. While it is misleading to describe Chinese characters as pictographic writing, it is important to note that, in contrast to the alphabet of the West, it is almost entirely non-phonetic. A Chinese character represents a meaning to the reader by the pattern of its strokes, but there is no specific connection between the shape of a character and the sound by which it is pronounced. It is possible, in fact, to read and understand a Chinese text without knowing one single word of the spoken language and, though the Mandarin dialects of the north are entirely different from the speech of the southern Chinese, educated men, scholars and officials can communicate without difficulty by writing. It is obvious that this non-phonetic writing has proved of immense value to the establishment and maintenance of a universal empire. Moreover, the development of characters has placed Chinese culture in a dominant position among its neighbours.

In the West, there has been more than one form of alphabet and more than one method of writing, but in the Far East Chinese characters have had no competition. As people developed a need for writing, it was the Chinese script that they adopted, and with the Chinese script there came inevitably Chinese influence. Those tribes close to centres of civilisation in China proper were inevitably drawn into the orbit of this world, and even such distant countries as Japan and Korea, whose modern scripts are merely an adaptation of the Chinese, have been continually affected by Chinese example.

On the other hand Chinese writing created problems. To read a book, a man must know five thousand characters, far more difficult than learning the twenty-six letters of our alphabet. The present government has embarked on a long campaign both to encourage the wide use of the 'National' Mandarin language and also to increase literacy by the use of simplified characters. Romanisation programmes have had more limited success.

More important perhaps than writing is the basic style of Chinese peasant society. From earliest times, China has been an agricultural nation, and climate and soil have both demanded and encouraged

Plate 2 The pictographic style of Chinese writing is still important as a communications link between people throughout the country speaking different, mutually unintelligible dialects of the same language. Literacy is now claimed to be 65 per cent. Wall newspapers, as at this shipyard in Shanghai, play an important role informing the people of recent events and of government policies. *(China Pictorial)*

large-scale works of irrigation. In the friable loess soil of the Hwang Ho valley and its tributary, the Wei Ho, and also in the fertile expanse of the North China Plain, dykes have been raised and canals dug to control the flow of the great river and to bring essential irrigation to fields of wheat and millet. Further south, in the subtropical valley of the Yangtze and in the rugged hills beyond, the same techniques of water control have been used to fill and drain the paddy-fields for rice. In both regions, the natural resources of the land have encouraged settled farming and large-scale co-operative works. On the one hand, the peasant is tied to his land by the need to maintain it and by the long tradition of labour which binds him to the past. On the other, the development of water-control technology has required competent administration and a flair for practical invention. On the firm base of subsistence agriculture, the Chinese have achieved a remarkable political organisation and an extraordinary record of technical achievement.

In the hundred years before the Communist take-over in 1949, China often appeared weak and incompetent in her dealings with foreigners and in her internal politics. In many ways she has fallen behind the advanced technology of the nations of the West, and despite great economic plans it is clear that she finds it extremely difficult to develop a strong industrial base. More than four-fifths of her people are still dependent on agriculture for their livelihood, and her present political isolation has imposed on her the remarkably difficult task of pulling herself up by her own bootstraps to a position of full prosperity and power. Technically, China may be described as an under-developed nation, but if it is remembered that the Chinese people in the past have been the first inventors of gunpowder, printing and paper, and that in recent years they have successfully tested an atomic bomb, it is impossible not to feel respect for their achievements. It becomes clear that the passive history of the last century is unlikely to be the pattern for the future.

In any consideration of China's geography, her people must be of paramount concern. Their numbers, their customs, and their present-day work will be a dominant influence on the economic development of their country and on the future of all Asia. In sum, perhaps the most important point to remember is that the people of China have a long history behind them and that they have in the past achieved a level of civilisation equal to and in many respects superior to that of the West. The Chinese farmer works soil tilled by generations of his ancestors. He is surrounded on all sides by the engineering works that they have constructed and by the graves, the temples and the traditions that they have left behind them. A short century of weakness and humiliation at the hands of foreigners has left a legacy of resentment and hatred but, more important than that, there remains a well-justified pride in the past and a perhaps overweening confidence in the future.

The ancient empire

The region now ruled from Peking represents perhaps the greatest area that has ever been effectively controlled by a Chinese government. There is no part of the present Chinese state that has not at some time or another been included within the empire, and there are several territories which have accepted Chinese sway in the past but which now lie outside her borders. On the other hand, while there are well-established precedents for the political unity of China, the past two thousand years have also seen long periods of regional division, foreign conquest, and civil war.

The earliest records of Chinese history, supported by the evidence of archaeology, place the origins of Chinese civilisation in the Hwang Ho valley, the modern provinces of Shansi, Shensi and Honan. From this heartland, where the early Chinese developed the techniques of agriculture, the art of writing, and the elements of their religious beliefs, their culture spread rapidly over the North China Plain and southwards to the Yangtze. By 500 B.C., a flourishing culture of bronze craftsmanship was challenged by the introduction of iron; and local kingdoms, with able clerks to assist their administration, steadily increased their power and battled for supremacy. At the end of the third century B.C., the state of Ch'in united all the civilised Chinese world, and although that empire was soon destroyed, the Han Empire which succeeded it maintained its state four hundred years. The memory of these first great empires has remained an inspiration. To this day, the Chinese people describe themselves as *Hans*, to distinguish the non-Chinese people such as Tibetans, Mongols and Manchus; and the European word 'China' is very probably derived from the ancient state of Ch'in.

There is a common Chinese saying:

> When the empire is divided it seeks to unite,
> When it is united it tends to divide.

The fall of the empire of Han saw the beginning of a new period of division, with a succession of ephemeral Chinese dynasties in the south, and nomad invaders dominating the north. In the seventh century A.D., China was reunited under the T'ang dynasty, which was succeeded by Sung three hundred years later. At first, Sung ruled the greater part of China, but early in the twelfth century the emperor was driven south by a new incursion of nomad people, and in 1280 the Mongols under Kublai Khan swept from the north, crushed the last elements of Chinese resistance, and placed all the nation under alien rule. During the eighty years of Mongol dominance, Marco Polo came across Asia to the court of the great Khan, and he has left in his *Travels* a description of the great city of Hangchow, formerly capital of the Sung, and then 'without doubt, the finest and most splendid city in the world'.

The Mongols had conquered China by the sword, but they could not maintain their government without Chinese support. As the first fury of conquest faded, Chinese resistance grew. In 1360 the native Ming dynasty regained the empire, and although it was destroyed in 1644 the Ch'ing dynasty of the Manchus, which was proclaimed in its stead, preserved the unity of the empire and extended Chinese power on the frontiers.

Beneath the facade of political unity, however, and behind the lines of imperial frontiers, the reality of China was not always as neat as scholars would make it. One of the major features of Chinese history, unnoticed by those concerned chiefly with political forms, has been the spread and the increase of China's population. In Ch'in and Han times, though the emperor claimed to rule south China and though his garrisons controlled the land as far as present-day Vietnam, the settlement of Chinese people was stretched thinly along the rivers. The mountains were a refuge for the non-Chinese people, original occupiers of the land, and a base from which they could maintain resistance against the incursions of the newcomers. As time passed, however, and the pressure of settlement mounted, cultivation gradually spread from the river valleys up the slopes of the hills. The non-Chinese people, whether by conquest, by intermarriage, or by conversion to a superior and more prosperous culture, became adapted to the new way of life. This steady process of colonisation, as old as Chinese civilisation itself, has now perhaps reached its final phase on the last frontiers of south China, the east coast of the island of Taiwan, and the few Autonomous Regions in Kwangsi, Kwangtung and Yunnan.

Such an expansion as the Chinese people achieved in the south, however, was never possible in the north. For reasons of climate and terrain, the steppe country of Mongolia, the oases of Central Asia and the highlands of Tibet have always resisted Chinese-style settlement, and the peoples of those regions have remained alien to the Chinese in culture and in economic resources. With the development of technology, the advanced civilisation of China now dominates Tibet and Sinkiang, and the frontier of Chinese colonisation is being pushed steadily forward into Mongolia. Yet this development has taken place only in comparatively recent times, and it is not so many years since the fear of barbarian raids cast a shadow on the lives of Chinese peasants.

That threat was finally removed at the end of the eighteenth century, when the armies of the Ch'ien-lung Emperor destroyed the last vestiges of Mongol military power, and the territories of Tibet and Central Asia were placed under effective imperial control. China's interest in the lands to her west had been established centuries earlier, for the Han dynasty had set garrisons along the Great Silk Road past the Takla Makan Desert in present-day Sinkiang, and the T'ang had contested Central Asia with the armies of Islam from the west. It was in many ways ironic that the triumph of China over her traditional enemies on the Inner Asian frontier should have been the prelude to the humiliation of the Ch'ing empire at the hands of Europeans invading from the sea.

In the history of China during the nineteenth and early twentieth centuries, two factors combined to render the nation weak and apparently defenceless. Firstly, the countries of Europe, which had

had some contact for several hundred years before, now burst upon the East armed with the weapons and resources of the Industrial Revolution and eager for trade to swell the profits of their mercantile empires. Secondly, the Ch'ing Empire of the Manchus, two centuries after its establishment, was showing all the signs of administrative decay. To consolidate its position in China, the government had remained conservative and reluctant to innovate, and had deliberately enforced a distinction between officials of Manchu origin and those recruited from the Chinese. The imperial army, although quite adequate to deal with the non-Chinese peoples of the north, faced the Royal Navy and the Army of Britain with an archaic system of hereditary garrisons that had changed very little from the first conquest two hundred years before. In such circumstances, it was not surprising that the Opium Wars of 1840 and 1860 were disastrous for China, and marked the beginning of the end of the Ch'ing Empire.

In the hundred years that followed, civil war and foreign aggression rendered the government of China almost impotent. Within the country the great rebellions of the Taipings and the Boxers prevented any effective defence against the threat from overseas, and along the coasts the representatives of Europe vied with one another to gain concessions for trade and treaty ports for settlement. In 1840, Shanghai and Hong Kong (map 24, page 128) were fishing villages; by the end of the century they had become two of the greatest and most prosperous cities in the Far East. On the other hand, though they were set on Chinese soil, they were governed by Europeans, and they served the interests of foreign traders rather than the profit of China.

As time passed, and as the Manchu government lurched desperately from one hopeful solution to another and from one crisis to the next, it became clear that the dynasty was doomed and that a new structure of power would be essential to prevent the dismemberment of the empire at the hands of the imperialists from overseas. At the time of the Boxer rebellion in 1900, when the imperial armies were smashed by contingents from Europe and the emperor was driven away from his capital, the native Chinese rebels, though killed in their thousands, maintained a defence and gave the foreigners cause to reconsider their ambitions to share in the government of a country so populous, fanatical and dangerous. In 1912, after small resistance, the imperial government was overthrown and a republic was proclaimed in its place.

The modern republic

The years that followed brought little improvement. Freed from the strait-jacket of traditional rule, the government of China was able to introduce new ideas and techniques from the West, but

Sun Yat-sen and the revolutionaries who formed the new government had few military resources to maintain their authority in the country at large. Within a matter of years, China was divided among rival war-lords, and whole provinces were effectively independent of the capital. In 1926, Chiang Kai-shek, successor to Sun Yat-sen as leader of the Nationalist party, launched the Northward Expedition from Canton, and two years later, with the alliance of Chang Hsüeh-liang, war-lord of Manchuria, the Nationalists had re-united China.

Success proved only temporary. Chiang Kai-shek was still faced by two great enemies, the Communists and the Japanese. The former, who had at one time been in alliance with the Nationalists, were driven from the cities by a purge and massacre in 1927. They established themselves in the countryside of Kiangsi Province. Under severe pressure from Nationalist attacks, the Communists abandoned Kiangsi in 1934, and in the great Long March their armies trekked westwards to Szechwan and north across Kansu, to re-establish the remnants of their forces at Yenan in Shensi. From there they maintained their position against the Nationalists and the Japanese alike.

In these early stages, at least, it was the Japanese who were the greater enemies of the Nationalist government and who appeared the more serious threat. From the time the Europeans established formal relations with the Japanese in the middle of the nineteenth century, they learned everything possible about Western techniques, and they used their knowledge to force their way into equality with the Europeans and into a dominant position in the Far East. In 1895 the Sino-Japanese War showed China's attempts at modernisation to be useless, and the peninsula of Korea fell into the Japanese sphere of influence. With victory in the Russo-Japanese War of 1905, Japan achieved a pre-eminent place in the affairs of north China, and particularly in Manchuria. In 1931, a long process of pressure and threat culminated in the Manchuria Incident, when Japanese forces occupied Shenyang (Mukden) in a surprise attack, and rapidly extended control over all the north-eastern provinces. In the following year, the Japanese invaded China from their sanctuary in the treaty port of Shanghai, and for the next thirteen years the Nationalists and the Communists in China were at war not only amongst themselves but also with the army of Japan.

By 1945, Japan had been defeated in the Pacific and her armies left Chinese soil. The Nationalists, who had survived the war at Chungking in Szechwan, tried with American help to re-establish government. The end of the Japanese threat, however, marked the beginning of the second phase of civil war, as the Communists from the north-west and the official Nationalist government struggled for power in a country which had not shown even a facade of unity for more than a generation. By 1949 the Nationalist armies were destroyed and their garrisons had been surrounded and captured. Chiang Kai-shek and the remnants of his party abandoned the mainland to take refuge in Taiwan, leaving undisputed mastery of China Proper to Mao Tse-tung and the People's Republic of China.

The borders of China

The century of foreign dominance has left its mark on the economic and political geography of the present. Within China itself, the pressure of the European traders and the establishment of treaty ports brought great numbers of people to live in cities on the coast created largely for an overseas trade which has now declined to a mere shadow of its former prosperity. At the same time, on the land frontiers of China, vast tracts had been lost because of the weakness of the Manchu Empire and the young Republic. The puppet state of Manchukuo established by the Japanese in Manchuria in 1934 removed the north-east temporarily from the control of the central government, and when the empire was overthrown in 1912 the Dalai Lama had proclaimed his independence in Tibet. Manchuria, now regarded as an integral part of China, was restored with the peace settlement in 1945, but it was not until 1951 that the People's Republic re-established the suzerainty over Tibet which had formerly been maintained under their imperial predecessors.

Other territories have not yet been regained. On the far south coast, on opposite sides of the Bay of Canton, Macau and Hong Kong remain enclaves of foreign rule on Chinese soil: Macau a grant to the Portuguese by a Ming emperor of the sixteenth century, Hong Kong ceded as a result of a series of treaties imposed on the Chinese government between the First Opium War and the end of the nineteenth century. All other European rights over China were abandoned at the end of the war against Japan, but Hong Kong is still convenient both to the Chinese and the British. With some justice, the Chinese describe the settlements imposed by war during the heyday of imperialism as 'unequal treaties'. This term, used for forced imposition of trading rights, treaty ports and grants of land, has also been applied to the Russian positions on the long frontier to the north. To the Chinese, Outer Mongolia is both naturally and historically a cause for concern, and there is resentment too that the present government of the USSR shows little inclination to reconsider boundary lines drawn more than sixty years ago by a powerful Tsarist regime at the expense of a weakened Chinese dynasty. Around the twelve thousand miles of Chinese frontier, the lines are generally fixed, but there is no region without some doubtful territory, nor free from some ancient grievance.

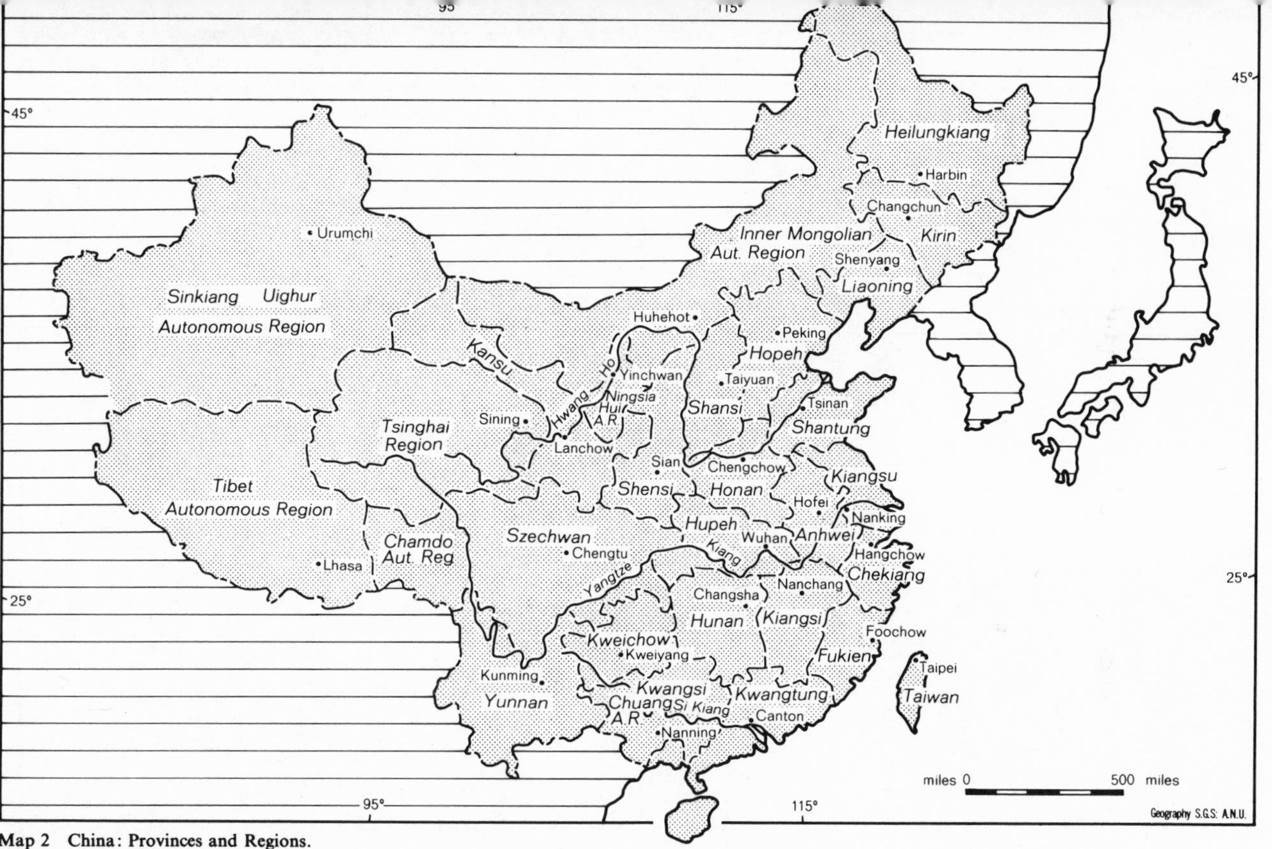

Map 2 China: Provinces and Regions.

Provinces and Autonomous Regions are shown according to the Peking government's administrative structure in the late 1960s. Reports in recent months have indicated that some northern frontier regions may be under special military control, and parts of the Inner Mongolian Autonomous Region are now subordinate to Heilungkiang, Kirin, Liaoning and Kansu provinces (see, for example, the report by Tillman Durdin, *The New York Times Weekly Review*, 28 June 1970, p.6). These changes are interpreted as defensive measures against a possible threat from the USSR, and it is not yet possible to gauge their full extent or their permanence.

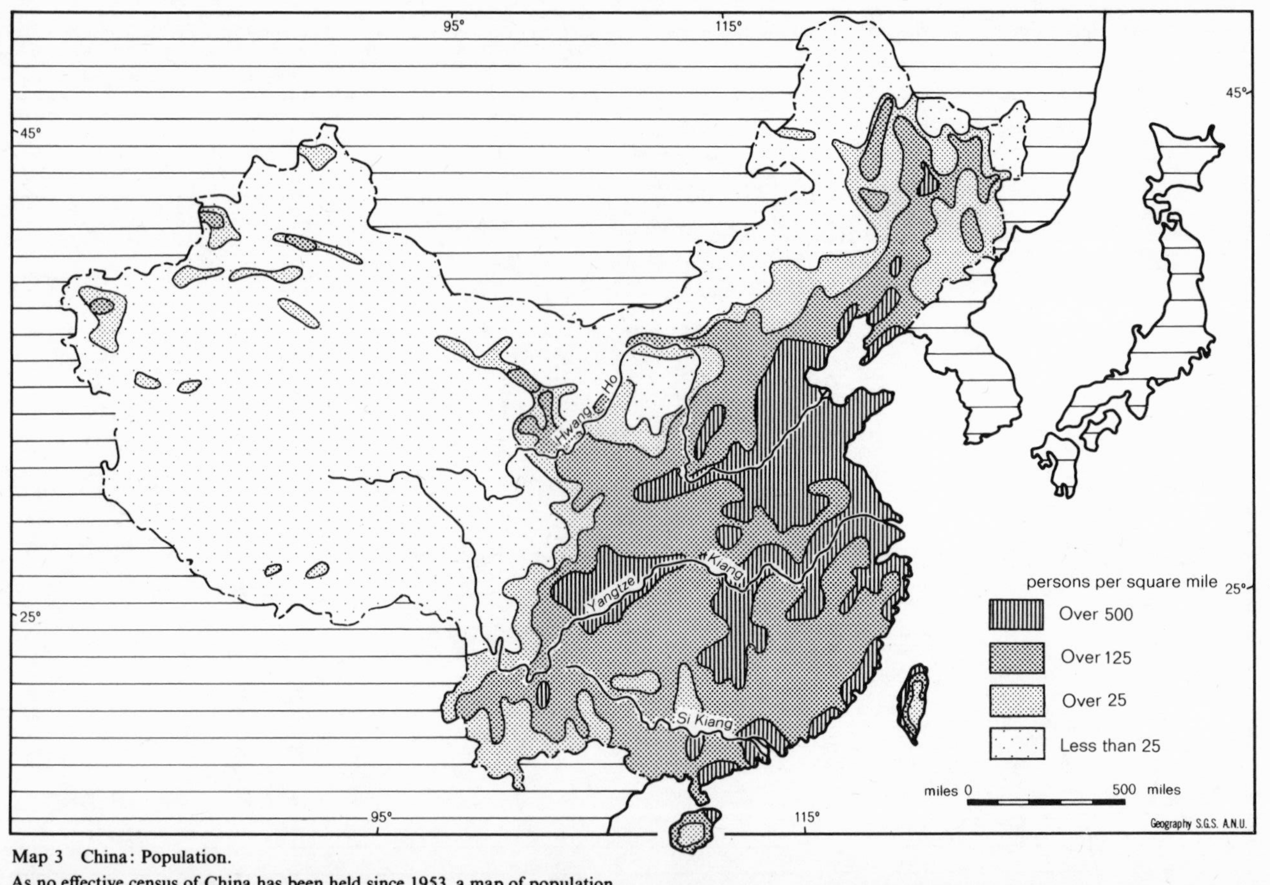

Map 3 China: Population.

As no effective census of China has been held since 1953, a map of population distribution must necessarily be generalised and based upon extrapolation

compare this map with map 6 (Landform Regions) and maps 11 and 12

Provinces, cities, and the settlement of people

Despite the lost territories, the present government at Peking now controls an area greater than any single Chinese empire of the past, and it does so through an administrative structure that owes a great deal to the institutions of its predecessors.

China south of the Great Wall, commonly referred to as China Proper, was divided in imperial times into eighteen provinces. The present government has generally continued this arrangement, excepting only the south-western province of Kwangsi, which is now an Autonomous Region, and the centrally administered metropolitan districts about the great cities of Peking and Shanghai. The territory of Manchuria in the north-east, fully incorporated to the empire by the Ch'ing dynasty, is now divided into three provinces, with equivalent organisation to those of China Proper. Below the provincial organisation, the local government units are counties (*hsien* in Chinese), some 1,500 through the whole country, and about 150 cities. Since 1958, administration below the county level has been controlled by communes, of which there are now some 26,000 throughout the countryside and in the cities.

Outer China, from Inner Mongolia through Sinkiang and Tsinghai to Tibet and Chamdo, is administered largely by Autonomous Regions and Autonomous Districts which, like those of south-west China Proper, are established under close central control to protect the rights and interests of minority non-Chinese peoples. However, if a line is drawn from the far north of Manchuria to the Burmese border against Yunnan in the south-west, though only two-fifths of China's land area would be east of the line, the territory is inhabited by more than 90 per cent of the population. The Autonomous Regions of Outer China occupy almost two-thirds of the country's area, but the minorities who comprise the bulk of their population are no more than 5 per cent of the national total.

Population density in China thus varies from uninhabited regions and those with less than ten people to the square mile over large areas of Mongolia, Sinkiang and Tibet, to urban settlements with a density estimated in one district of Shanghai at well over 300,000 to the square mile. Sixteen cities—all, except Canton, in the Yangtze valley or further north-east near the coast,—have a population over a million, and there are some 125 with 100,000 inhabitants or more. The total urban population is some 100,000,000, almost all in China Proper and Manchuria; Urumchi in Sinkiang, with about 350,000 people, is the largest city in the west.

One hundred million people, however, is less than 15 per cent of the whole population of China, and the bulk of her people live on intensively-cultivated farmland in China Proper, with population densities perhaps even more striking than the figures for the cities.

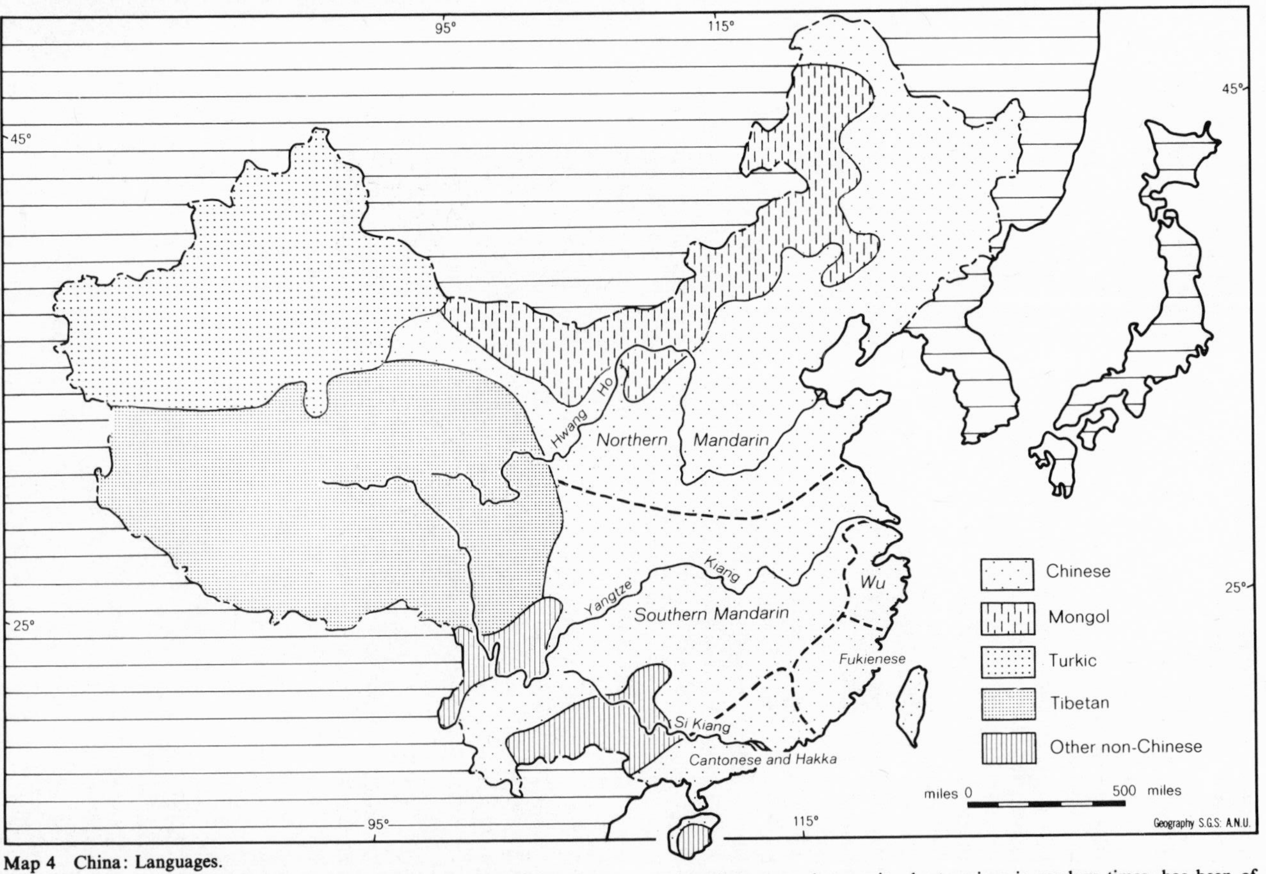

Map 4 China: Languages.

This map shows only the broad divisions of language within China. The speech of the Tibetans, the Mongols and the Uighurs of Sinkiang is totally non-Chinese, but even within China Proper the so-called 'dialects' vary so greatly in pronunciation and grammatical structure that they are perhaps better regarded as separate languages linked primarily by their use of the written language, whatever its shortcomings in modern times, has been of immense value in the past for the maintenance of political and administrative unity. One of the major projects of the present government is to encourage literacy in characters and in romanised script, and to spread the adoption of Mandarin as a national language.

Chungming Island in the Yangtze estuary has one thousand or more people to the square mile, and some of the hill farmlands of the Yangtze basin and Kwangtung Province in the south may have figures even higher. Not even the Indian province of Bengal can compare with such dense rural settlement, and average densities over the southern coastal lands, the Yangtze valley and the North China Plain regularly exceed a thousand to the square mile.

In such a country, whose economy through history has been based on subsistence agriculture, and whose present government must still be greatly concerned with food production for increasing numbers of people, it is only to be expected that population patterns will follow those of agricultural and industrial development, which in turn are related to landform, climate and mineral resources. This essential interaction must long continue to affect the people of China and their opportunities for development.

3

Two styles of work in modern China. Plate 3 Intensive agriculture on a tea plantation in Kiangsi. Plate 4 The control room of a petrochemical plant at Tsinan in Shantung. ***(China Pictorial)***

4

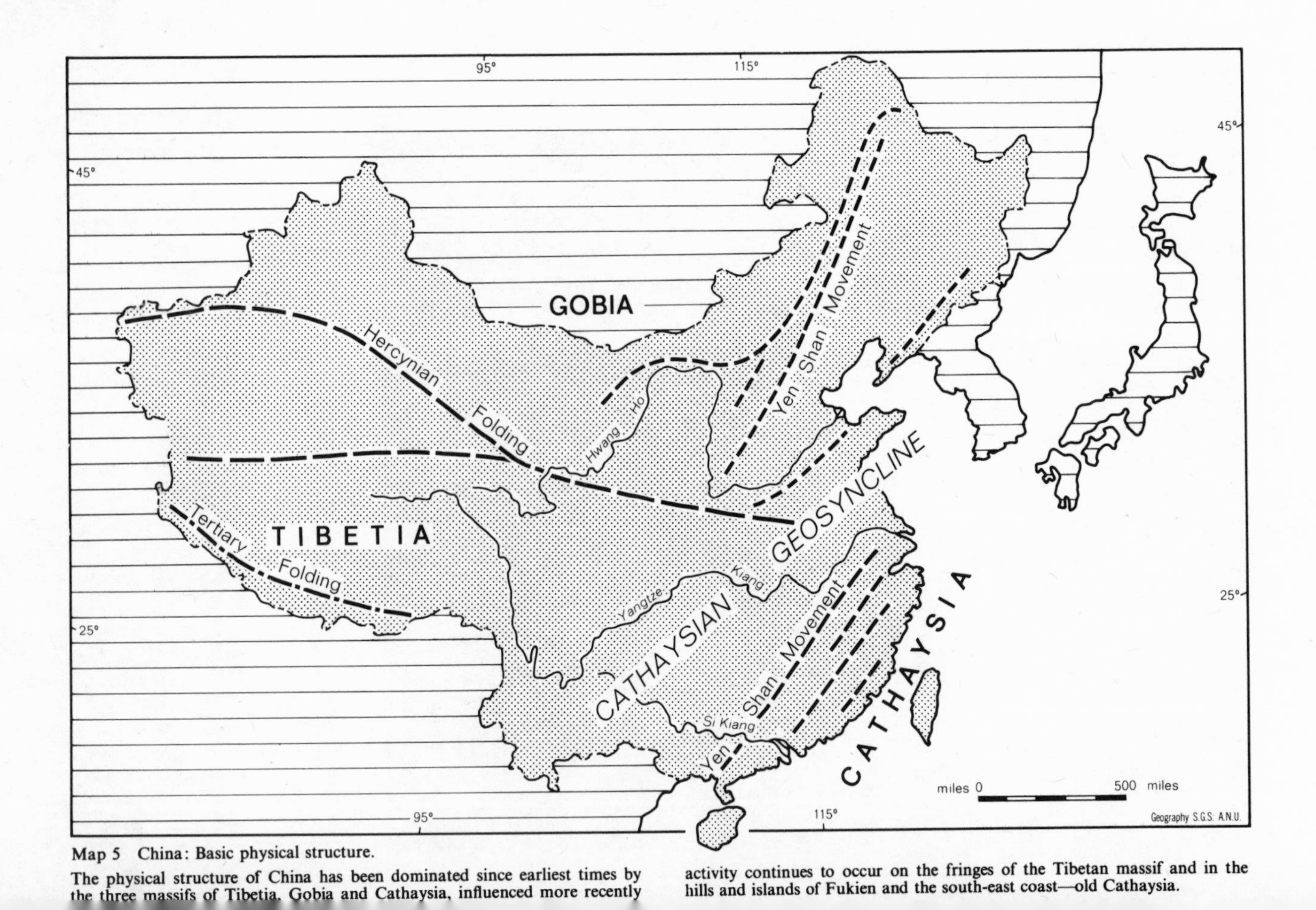

Map 5 China: Basic physical structure.

The physical structure of China has been dominated since earliest times by the three massifs of Tibetia, Gobia and Cathaysia, influenced more recently

activity continues to occur on the fringes of the Tibetan massif and in the hills and islands of Fukien and the south-east coast—old Cathaysia.

2 Patterns of Nature and Man

Geology and landform

The physical structure of China has been dominated since the Pre-Cambrian era by three great mountain shields, called by geologists Tibetia in the west, Gobia in the north, and Cathaysia in the south-east. In earliest times, all the present area of China besides these three island massifs was covered frequently by the sea. The sedimentary rocks of the former sea-floor contain an almost continual record from Pre-Cambrian to Mesozoic times, the age of the dinosaurs, and among these rocks are layers of Carboniferous coal, remnants of sea-swamps and marshes. During the Paleozoic era, Cathaysia was warped in a geosyncline formation, and the ridges of this great folding are expressed now in the parallel belts of mountains, islands and ocean troughs running north-east and south-west through the islands of Japan and Taiwan, in the backbone mountains of Fukien Province and in the high ground of Shantung, Korea and Manchuria.

In contrast to the north-south direction of the Cathaysia geosyncline, the Upper Paleozoic period saw also a general east-west 'Hercynian' folding, which gave foundation to ridges of mountains now running from the Tien Shan and Kunlun in the west (map 23, page 113) through to the Chin Ling Shan of China Proper. These essential primitive patterns were reinforced by the Yen Shan folding in the Mid-Mesozoic period. It was at this time that the mountains of North China were forced upwards, and the east-west line of the Hercynian ridges was swung northwards through the Taihang Shan and the Shantung Peninsula to the high ground of Manchuria and the hills of Korea.

In Tertiary and Quaternary times, the major earth movements have been further folding in the Chamdo Region east of Tibet and the steady uplift of the whole Tibetan massif, a process still continuing, as witness frequent earthquakes along the fault lines from Kansu to Yunnan. There was glacial action in west China and some local glaciation in the Taihang Shan north of the Hwang Ho and in the hill country of Kiangsi Province south of the Yangtze, but

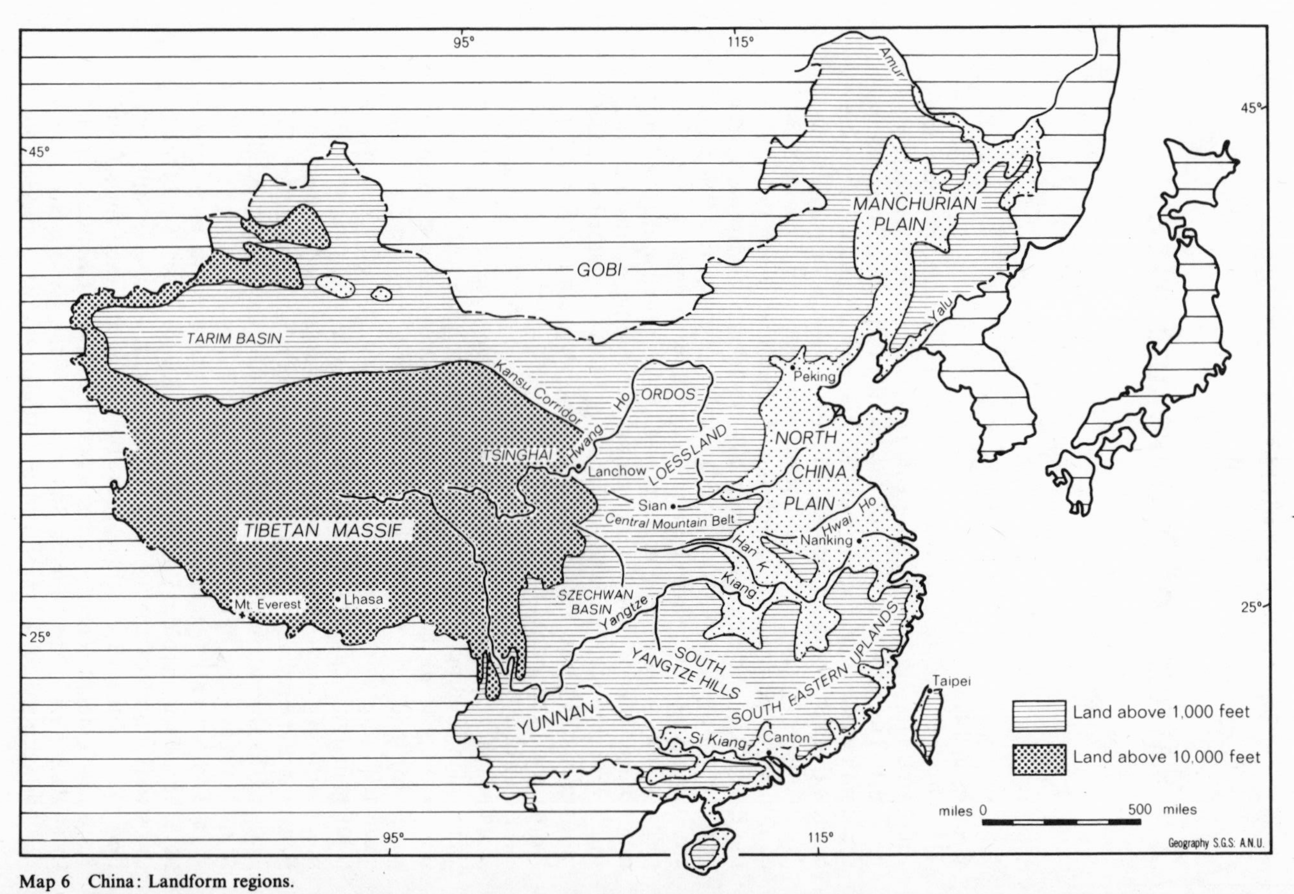

Map 6 China: Landform regions.

This map, showing the 'splayed-fingers' topography of China (see page 21)

evidence is still insufficient, and geological theories are widely divided on questions of time, extent and frequency. Overall, since the period of the Yen Shan foldings, major surface sculpture has been the work of wind and water rather than earth movement. The carriage of loess soil by the wind from the region of the Gobi to the basin of the Hwang Ho in north China appears to have begun in the Quaternary period; the process still continues, though perhaps less intensively today. It is discussed in Chapter 3. Throughout China, the great rivers, notably the Hwang Ho and the Yangtze, have established and maintained a continued pattern of erosion and sedimentary deposit along their courses, across their deltas and out to the sea.

The topography of China today is dominated by the mountain ridges running eastwards from Tibet. The effect is much like that of the fingers of a spread right hand, with the palm occupying the position of Tibet, the splayed little finger pointing south along the ridges of Yunnan towards the mountains of Laos and Vietnam, the third finger following the line of the Nan Ling south of the Yangtze, the second finger the Chin Ling Shan and its secondary extensions between the Yangtze and the Hwang Ho, and the index finger leading along the high ground of the Ala Shan, the Ordos and the Yin Shan on the north of China Proper towards the Great Khingan Mountains on the borders of Manchuria and Mongolia. The hook of the thumb represents the Tien Shan ridge which separates Dzungaria and the Tarim Basin on the north of Tibet, and the east-west pattern is continued on the north of the great Gobi Plateau by the Altai, and other mountain ranges on the borders of Soviet Russia and Outer Mongolia. In the far south-east, the Wuyi Shan of Fukien run parallel to the coast, following the trend of the Cathaysian geosyncline.

Within these ridges of mountains and hills lie great plains: the Manchurian Plain in the north-east, the North China Plain, the level ground along the middle and lower course of the Yangtze Kiang and the Szechwan Basin, but further south even the lower ground is broken by hill country. The total area of China may be divided in half between the two classification groups of mountains and hills against plains, river basins and plateaux, but much of the flat terrain is represented by steppe country in Central Asia or by alpine desert in the high ground of Tibet.

China has five rivers with a length of more than a thousand miles completely within her borders, the Yangtze, the Hwang Ho, the Si Kiang, the Tarim (map 23, page 113) and the Sungari (map 21, page 90), while the Liao Ho, in southern Manchuria, is nine hundred miles long. All the streams have had considerable effect on the topography of their basins, but the scouring of the Hwang

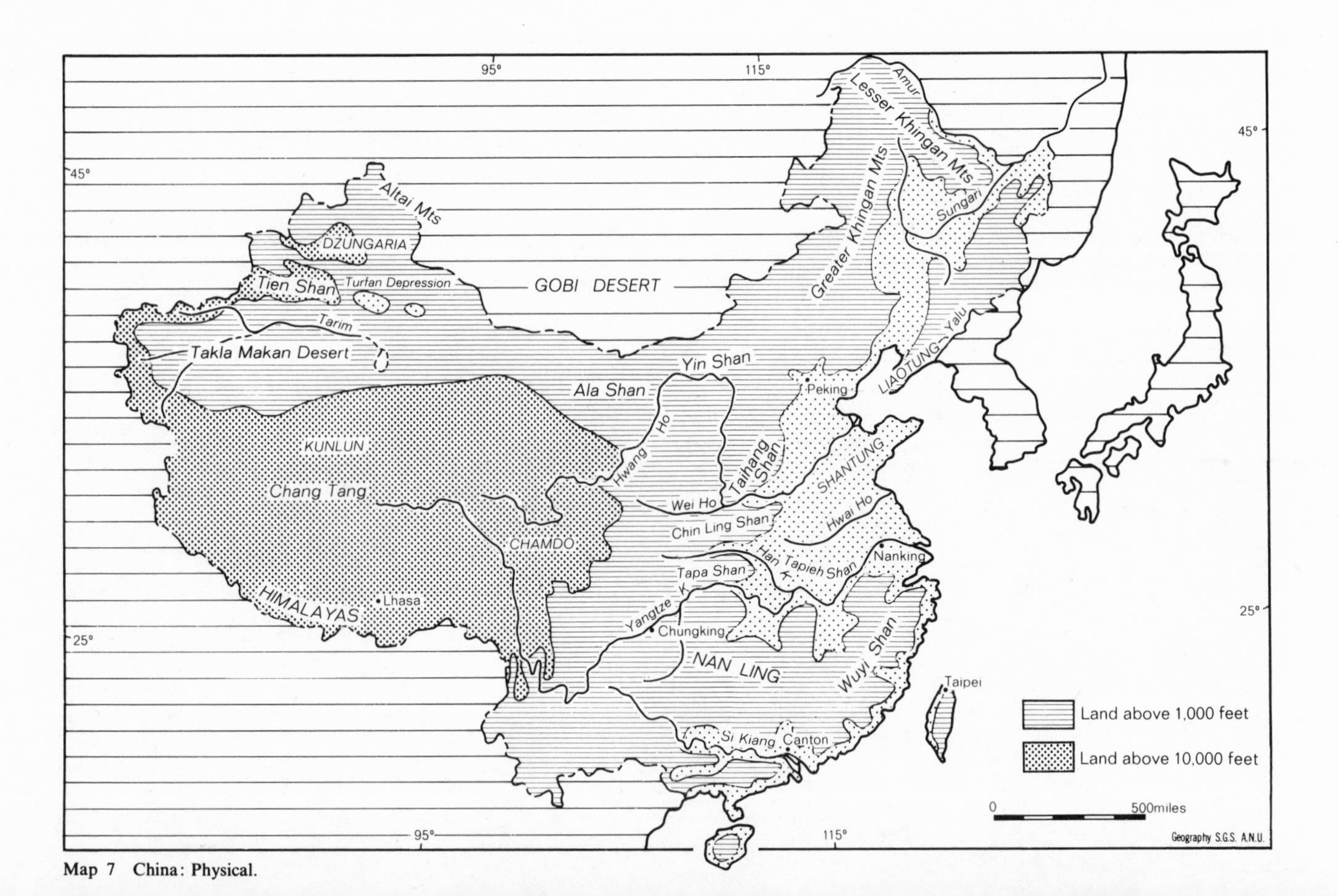

Map 7 China: Physical.

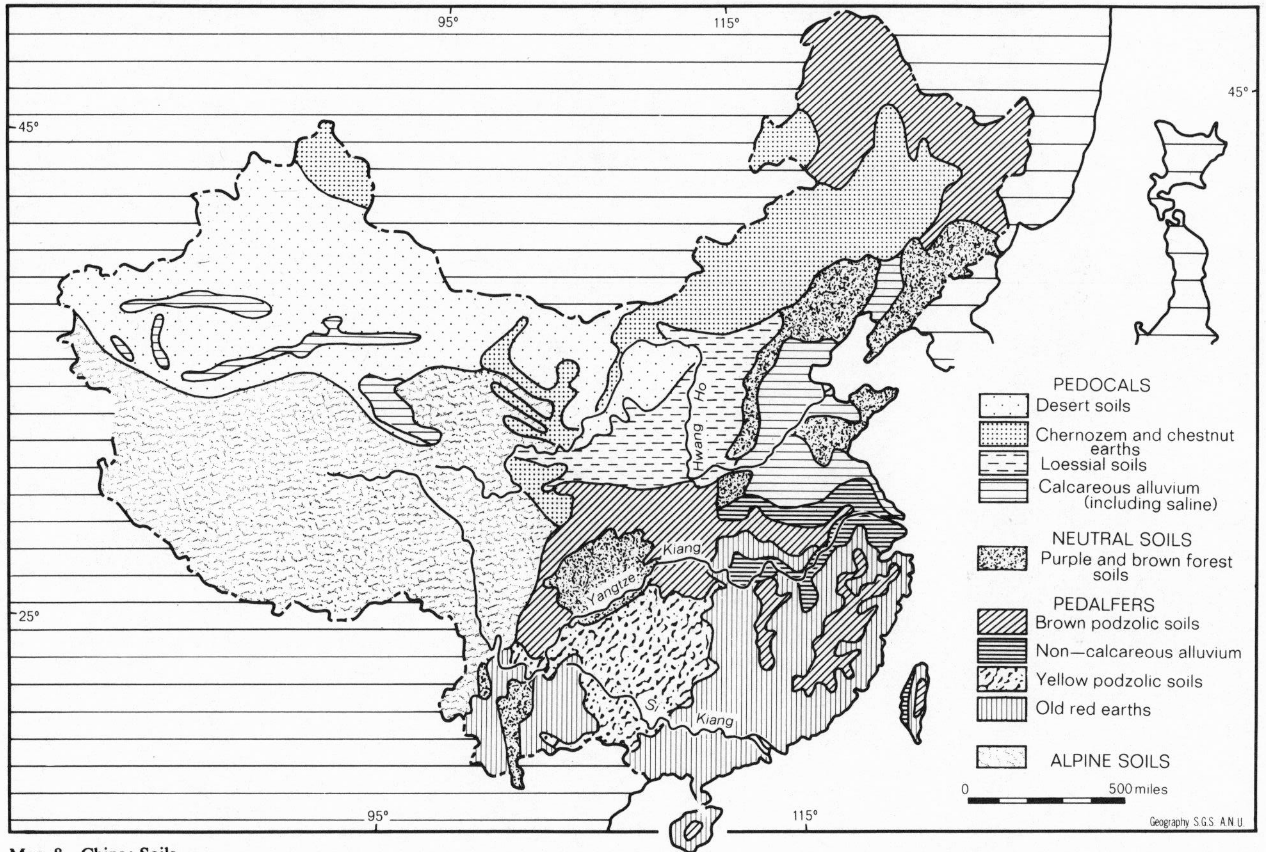
95°
115°
45°
45°
25°
95°
115°
Hwang Ho
Kiang
Yangtze
Si
Kiang
PEDOCALS
Desert soils
Chernozem and chestnut earths
Loessial soils
Calcareous alluvium (including saline)
NEUTRAL SOILS
Purple and brown forest soils
PEDALFERS
Brown podzolic soils
Non—calcareous alluvium
Yellow podzolic soils
Old red earths
ALPINE SOILS
0
500 miles
Geography S.G.S. A.N.U.

Map 8 China: Soils.

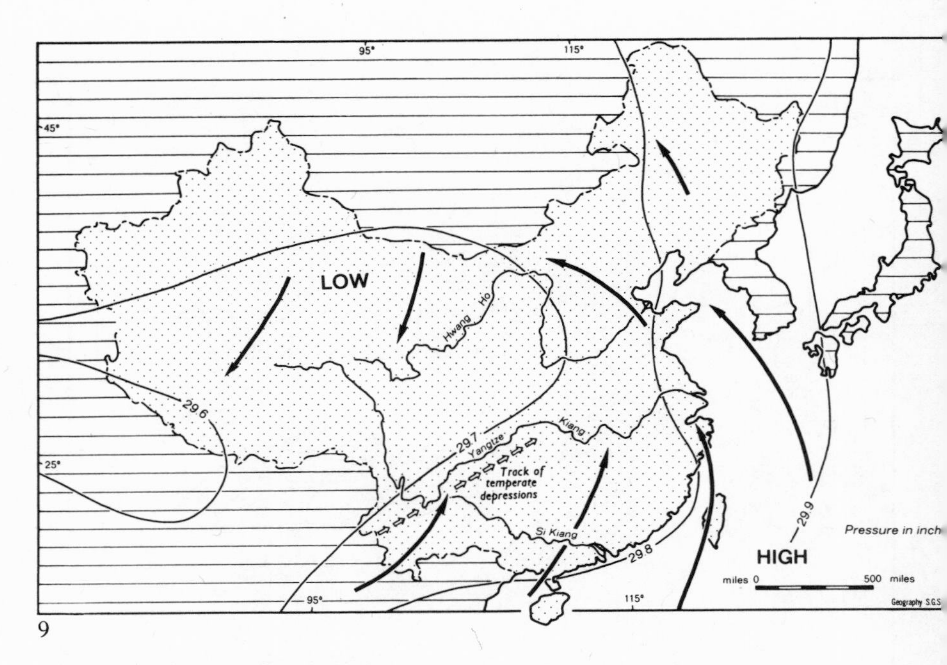

9

Map 9 China: Air movements, July, *and* Map 10 China: Air movements, January.

The monsoon pattern of climate in East Asia can be seen, firstly, in the summer movement of tropical air masses inland from the Pacific Ocean and, secondly, in the winter reversal of this movement as the high pressure region formed over Mongolia sends cold continental air masses southward. The general movement shown on map 9 for July is intensified by typhoons, which attack the southern and eastern coast of China in a season extending from May through October. (Adapted from *The National Atlas of China)*

10

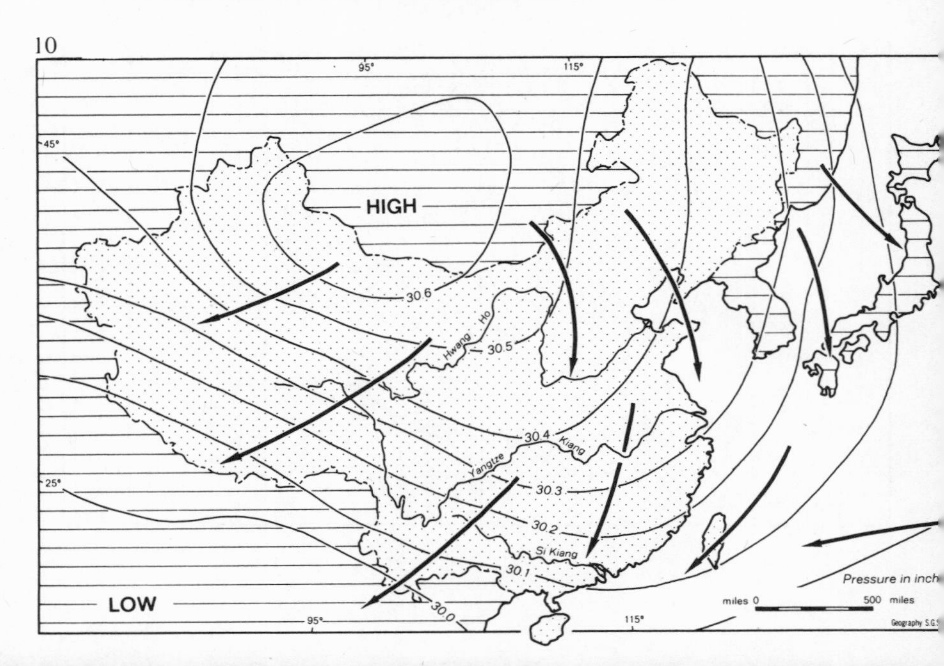

Ho in the loess soil of Shensi and Shansi, and its wide deposit in an immense alluvial fan and delta, have driven back the sea, joined Shantung to the mainland, and covered connecting mountain ridges and the coal deposits of past ages with a layer of alluvium more than three thousand feet thick. In the North China Plain there is evidence of isostatic sinking, as the underlying rock strata are pressed downward by the immense weight of sediment dropped from the Hwang Ho.

Besides the wind-borne silt of Loessland and the alluvial soils of the North China Plain and other deltas, the natural soils of China are generally brown forest in Manchuria and the north of China Proper, with varying degrees of podzolisation, and yellow, brown or red sub-tropical soils in the Yangtze valley and the south, highly leached and strongly acidic. There are some podzolic soils in the high ground of the hill country south of the Yangtze, and the purple-brown forest soils of the Szechwan Basin are essentially neutral, but the line between wheat cultivation in the north and rice in the south follows quite closely the boundary of the northern podzolic type and the leached yellow-red of the south. The Tibetan massif and its associated ranges have typical mountain and highland soil, and the great deserts of the Takla Makan and the Gobi have nothing but sand and rock. Elsewhere in Outer China, the brown, grey-brown and chestnut soils of the steppe grasslands are fertile pedocal type, and respond well to irrigation. Outside limited oasis regions, and some irrigated areas in Kansu and along the Ordos loop of the Hwang Ho, however, there is never enough rain or surface water to develop significant agriculture; and the chief influence on all Chinese farming and food production is the monsoonal pattern of the climate and the mountain ridges that affect it.

Climate

As in all the northern hemisphere, the cold winter season in China comes in December through February, and the hot summer is June to August. In a monsoon region, however, summer is the wet season, and winter, though cold, is dry. At Peking in the north of China, more than 90 per cent of the annual average precipitation of some 30 inches falls in the period from May to October, and the low winter readings are snow as often as they are rain.

In general terms, the monsoon pattern of climate is established in regions within the tropics on the eastern sides of the great continental land masses. For China, intense heating of the land during the summer causes a low-pressure area to be established over Central Asia, and warm tropical maritime air comes inland from the southern and eastern seas, saturated with moisture from its passage over the water. In south and central China, the prevailing

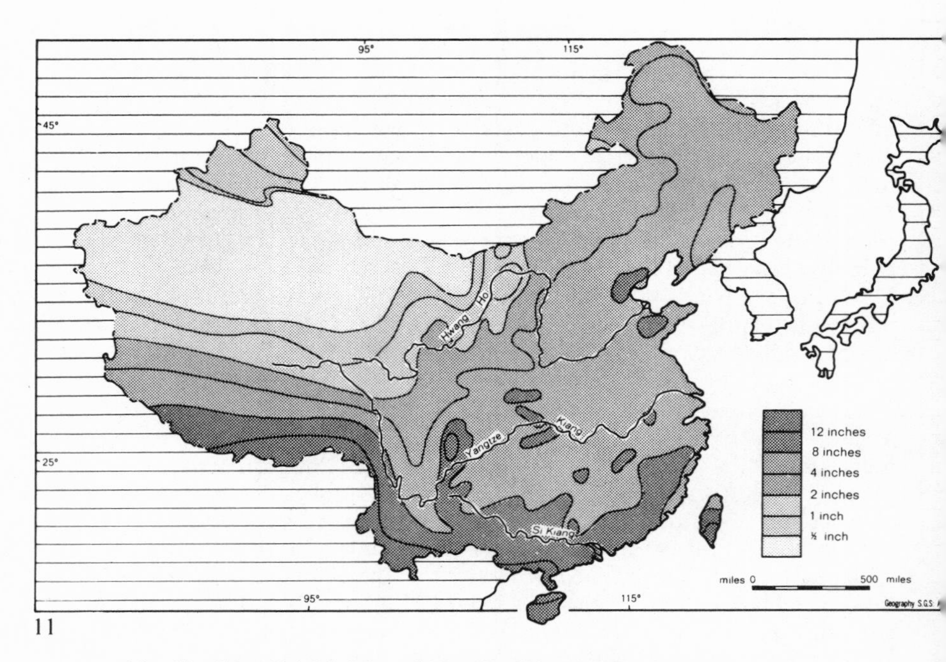

Map 11 China: Rainfall, July, *and* Map 12 China: Rainfall, January.

In the rainfall maps, it may be seen how the full effect of the air masses is influenced by the east-west mountain ridges of China. In July the moisture of the incoming air is precipitated as it passes over the Nan Ling range south of the Yangtze valley and again, as described in the text, by the frontal effect of the temperate depressions moving east along the line of the Yangtze. When the air masses reach north China and Mongolia, much of the moisture that they carried has already been precipitated. *(Adapted from The National Atlas of China)*

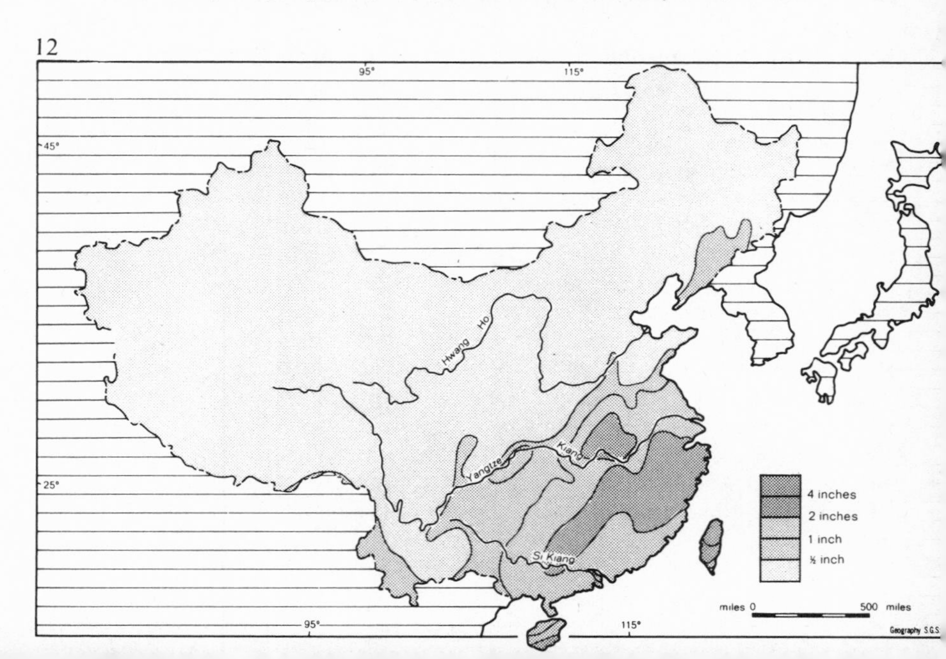

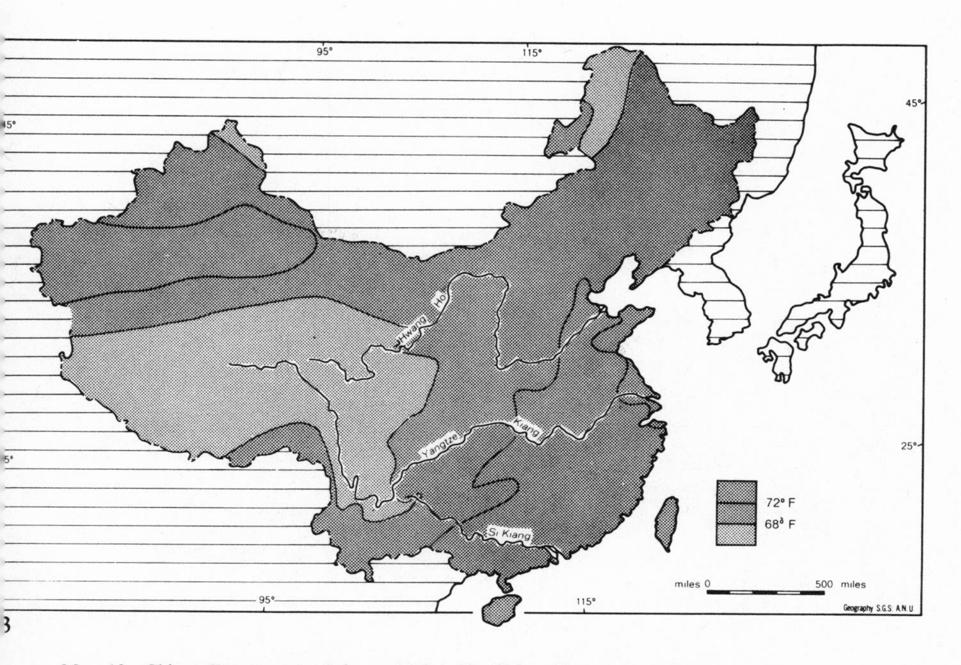

Map 13 China: Temperature, July, *and* Map 14 China: Temperature, January.

In the temperature maps, similarly, the movement of the cold continental air south in January is interrupted by the mountains, notably by the line of the Chin Ling Shan and the Central Mountain Belt. Even so, it is only the far south of China close to the Tropic of Cancer, that is frost-free throughout the year and the sea in the Gulf of Chihli is regularly frozen. (Adapted from *The National Atlas of China*)

In these maps 11-14, precipitation and temperature readings are based on records kept only since the early years of this century.

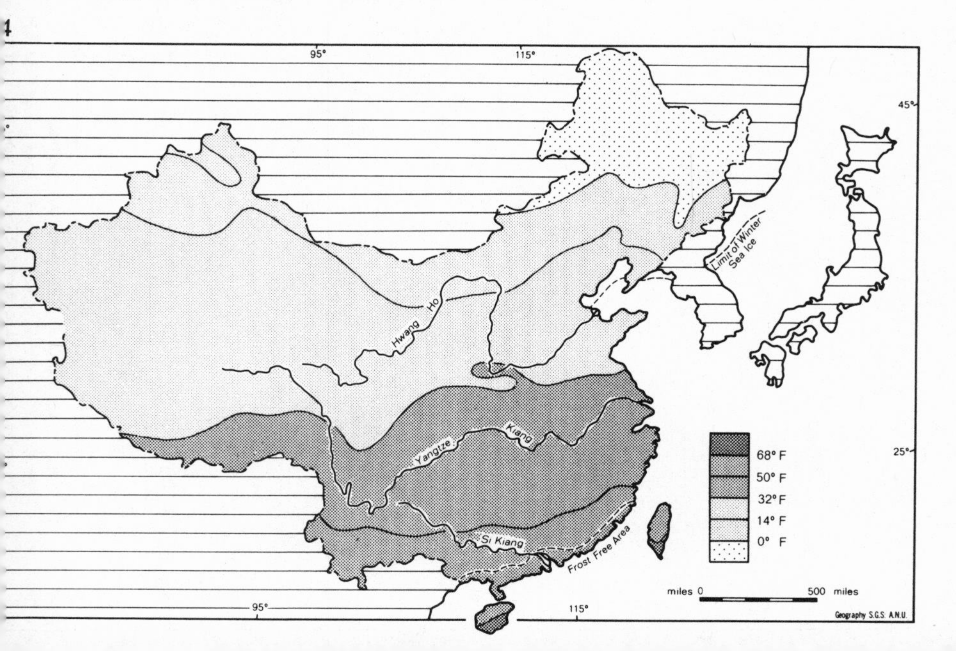

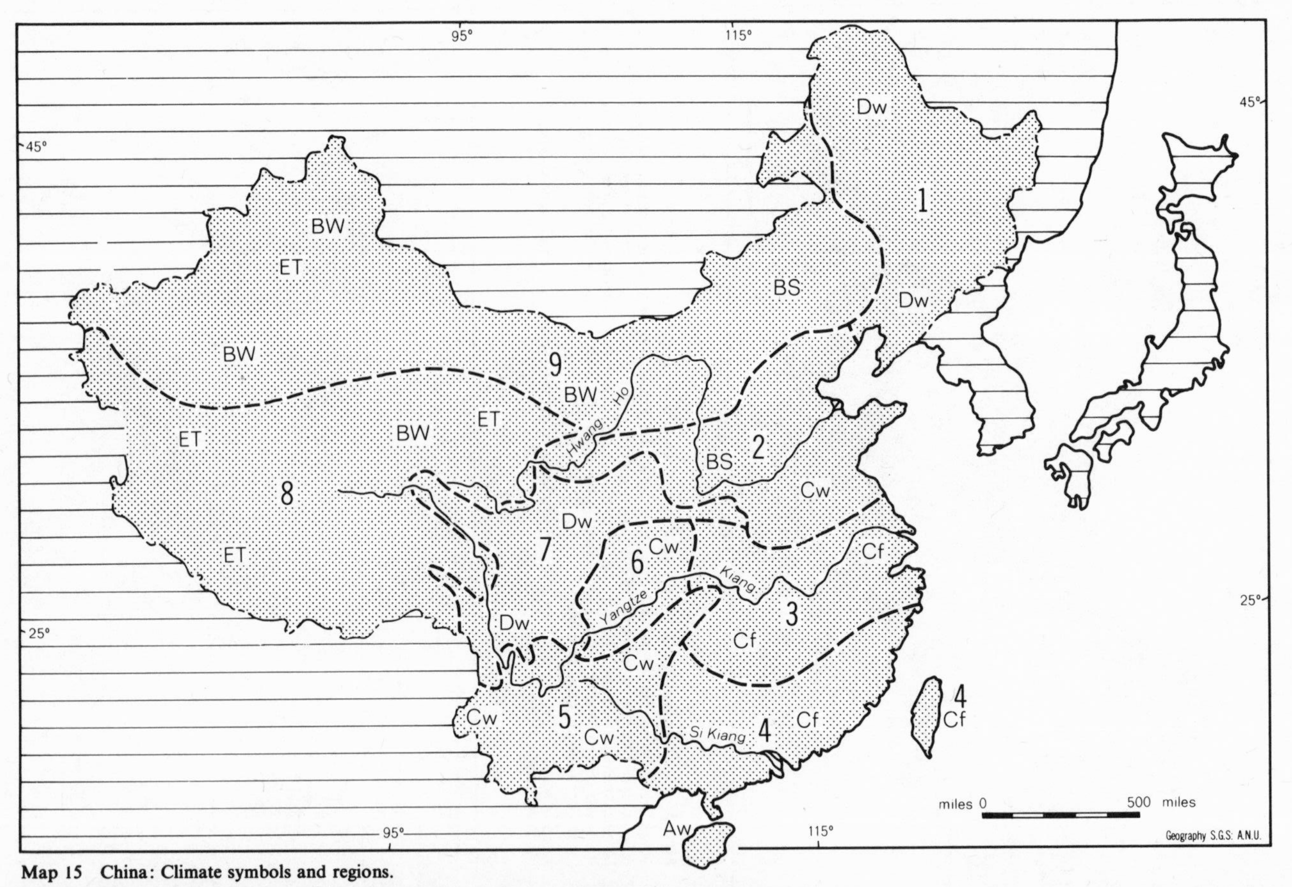

Map 15 China: Climate symbols and regions.

For discussion of the symbols used in this map and for a key to the climatic regions, please see page 30. (Koeppen symbols and climatic regions adapted

wind is southerly, but further north it is generally south-easterly. As the warm moist air masses move into the interior of the country, heavy rainfall is induced by their crossing of the mountain ridges, and also, more importantly, by the effect of cool air-currents from the north and north-east which accompany east-moving depressions across south-west China. These temperate depressions tend to form in the summer months and move slowly down the Yangtze valley. As they do, the cooler air forces upwards the warm humid air of the monsoon and heavy precipitation results. Unlike the monsoons of India and South-East Asia, the summer rainfall over China is frontal, caused largely by the effect of air masses, rather than orographic caused primarily by mountains. Along the seaboard and islands of the south and east, as in other regions of the world where great air masses come in summer from the ocean to the land, typhoons, tropical cyclones, form over the sea and batter the coasts of China and Japan from May through to October.

The essence of a monsoon, however, lies not only in the movement of warm, humid air inland during the summer, but in the complete reversal of wind direction and resulting climate during the remaining six months of the year. Each November a great centre of high pressure, largest outside the polar regions, becomes established over Mongolia, and polar continental air, with strong, dry north-westerly, northerly and north-easterly winds, comes southward across China. As in summer, the east-west mountain ridges, particularly the Central Mountain Belt between the Hwang Ho and the Yangtze, form a barrier to the full effect of this air stream. The eastward-moving depressions along the line of the Yangtze give some break from the cold, but only in the far south-east, on the coast of Fukien and the island of Taiwan and on the southern seaboard below the Tropic of Cancer, is the land frost-free throughout the year. In the north, the sea along much of the coastline from Tientsin (map 21, page 90) past southern Manchuria is frozen during winter months, and only the tip of the Liaotung Peninsula is ice-free through the year.

With the alternation of climate influence between the air masses from the ocean to the south and east and those of the dry desert and steppe of Central Asia, the monsoon system of China extends as high as latitude 60°N, and the lines of annual and seasonal temperature and precipitation, reinforced by the major mountain ridges, run roughly parallel from the north-east to the south-west. Map 15 shows climate on the basis of Koeppen symbols, where in general terms A represents tropical rainy climate, B is dry steppe or desert, C is warm and temperate with a long summer, D is cooler temperate, and E is high tundra or ice-field found in the polar regions or in high mountains. For purposes of comparison, Table 1 gives the Koeppen symbols and the average annual rainfall of the Australian capital cities and Alice Springs.

Table 1

Adelaide	Koeppen symbol Cs	precipitation 21 inches a year
Brisbane	Cf	45
Canberra	Cf	25
Darwin	Aw	61
Hobart	Cf	25
Melbourne	Cf	26
Perth	Cs	35
Sydney	Cf	48
Alice Springs	BSh	10

In simplified terms, China may be divided into nine major climatic regions, whose approximate boundaries are shown on map 15:

1 *Manchuria:* warm summers, very cold winters, low rainfall, 5 months' growing season
2 *North China:* hot summers, cold winters, low rainfall, 8 months' growing season
3 *Lower Yangtze:* hot summers, cold winters, high rainfall, 9 months' growing season
4 *South China:* hot summers, warm winters, high rainfall, 12 months' growing season
5 *Yunnan Plateau:* warm summers, cool winters, moderate rainfall, 11 months' growing season
6 *Szechwan:* hot summers, mild winters, high rainfall, 11 months' growing season
7 *Tibetan Foothills and Central Mountain Belt:* temperate climate on high ground separating the tropical south from the dry north
8 *Tibet:* cool summers, very cold winters, low rainfall
9 *Mongolia and Sinkiang:* hot summers, very cold winters, very low rainfall

Land use and agriculture

Following the patterns of climate and influencing those of soil, the natural vegetation of Outer China varies from the highland steppe and desert of Tibet, through the dry steppe and desert of Sinkiang and Mongolia, to the temperate grasslands and steppe of Manchuria,

Loessland and the frontier region between Mongolia and China Proper. In the more settled areas of China Proper, the natural vegetation is broad-leaved forest in the north, sub-tropical forest in the Yangtze valley and the south, with tropical forest in the far south and south-west, and temperate mountain forest in some of the high country of the Khingan Mountains in Manchuria, the Central Mountain Belt, and the lower ridges of the Tibetan Massif about the Chamdo Region, Yunnan and Kweichow. Almost every type of tree known in the northern hemisphere can be found in China, and the adaptable bamboo grows in the country south of the Yangtze, but save for the most inaccessible areas of China Proper the natural forest cover has been destroyed to form farmland, or waste ground with dangerous accelerated erosion. So complete is this work of man that vegetation may be best considered through the cultivation regions of rice and wheat.

In all China, fully half the area is waste, unsuitable for cultivation or for anything more than light and occasional grazing. A tenth of the land is forest, largely on the hill slopes in China Proper and Manchuria, 28 per cent is useful pasturage, but only some 10 percent, about 300,000,000 acres, is cultivated. In the far north of China Proper and Manchuria, in areas with generally less than 15 inches annual rainfall, spring wheat is sown in April for harvest at midsummer in July. In southern Manchuria and all north China as far as the Yangtze valley, winter wheat is sown in September for harvest in June. The dry climate of north China raises a hard wheat, like the Australian or Canadian, suitable for bread or for noodles. (Besides gunpowder, printing and paper, one of the less well-appreciated inventions of the Chinese is the noodle, believed to be the forerunner of Italian spaghetti and introduced to Europe through the agency of Marco Polo or some other medieval traveller.) In the Yangtze valley, where rice and wheat may be grown together, the wheat variety is softer, more suitable for cakes and biscuits.

Wheat is the predominant crop in the North China Plain. It is important in every cultivated region of north China, but a wide variety of other grains are grown as well. Millet plantings cover much the same area as those of wheat, and there is evidence from the earliest Chinese legends, which refer frequently to the god-like Prince Millet and to divination by means of millet-stalks, that millet was formerly more important. Kaoliang, which is a tall plant with a strong stalk six or eight feet high and a bushy head somewhat resembling maize, is grown chiefly in the North China Plain and southern Manchuria. The grains in the head are used for food and for animal fodder, and are sometimes fermented into wine, while the stalks are valuable for fences, walls, roofs, dam-building and for fuel. Both millet and kaoliang have the advantage of being drought-resistant, with a short growing season, and their cultivation side by side with wheat is an insurance against large-scale famine in the north.

Two crops which are grown both in the north and in the south are maize corn and soybeans. Maize is grown in a broad belt from Manchuria in the north-east to the Yunnan Plateau in the south-west, and soybeans, which can be treated to supply oil for cooking, oil for paint and soap-making and fodder for animals, is grown in almost every province, but particularly in Manchuria. Soy sauce is the common flavouring of Chinese cookery, and bean curd, frighteningly unattractive to the average Western palate, is the universal Chinese breakfast dish. In the rice-wheat region of the Hwai Ho and the lower Yangtze, barley is a useful crop, with a short growing period to harvest in May and an ability to resist wet conditions better than wheat.

Rice, however, is by far the most important single grain, with an annual production equal by weight to that of wheat, millet and kaoliang combined. To the Chinese peasant, rice is the staple grain, preferred to any other, despite claims that wheat is more valuable as a food.

Rice-growing occupies almost half the cultivated land of the whole country. South China is the major area for rice, but there are patches of rice cultivation even in the unfavourable conditions of

Map 16 China: Wheat and rice regions.

In the far north, the ground is too cold and hard for planting during the winter, and grain must be sown in the spring for harvesting some three months later in midsummer. Over most of the north of China Proper and Manchuria, however, it is possible to sow in autumn and gain the advantage of nine months growth before the harvest in June. Szechwan, the Yangtze valley and the southern part of the North China Plain are transitional regions between wheat and rice. In south China, rice is overwhelmingly popular, and there are some regions where nothing else is grown. In the north, however, while wheat is the predominant grain, it is cultivated side by side with barley, millet, kaoliang and other crops.

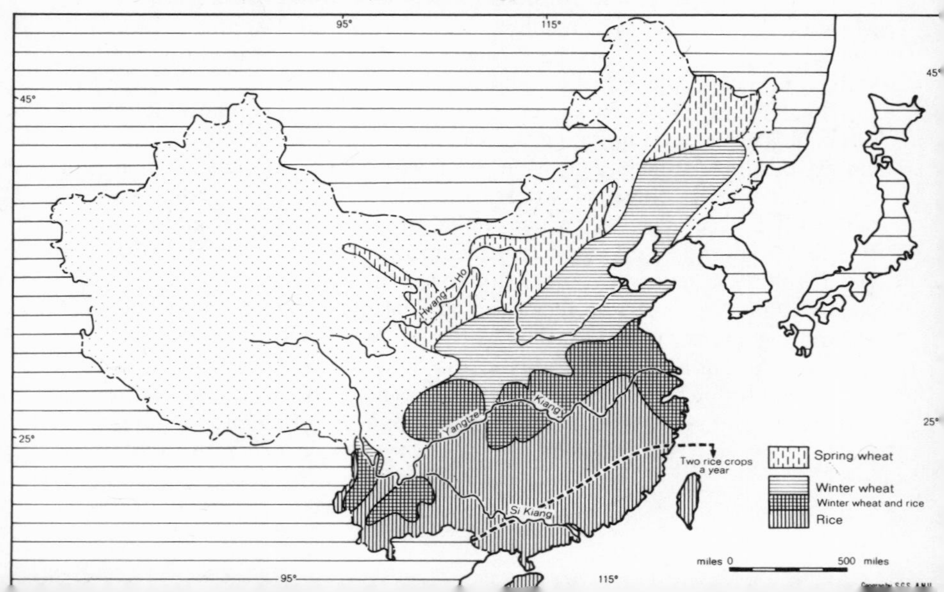

Plate 5 Wheat fields in Loessland: Tachai in Shansi Province. Hand cultivation is carried on in small walled fields, carefully terraced to minimise erosion in the friable soil. *(China Pictorial)*

Plate 6 Wheat fields in Manchuria: Heilungkiang Province. On the open plain, three mules and two men work a new mechanical harvester. *(China Pictorial)*

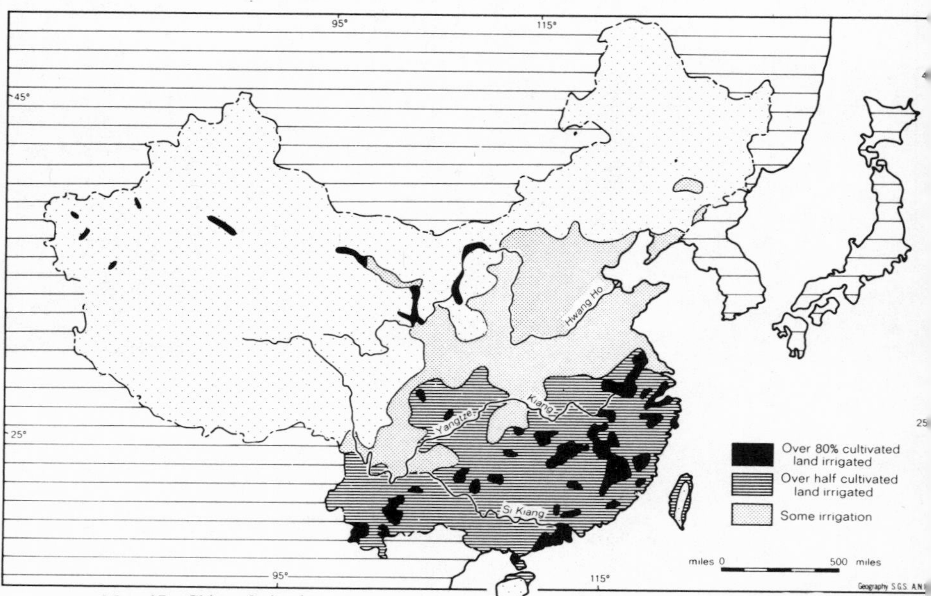

Map 17 China: Irrigation.

In the south of China, irrigation is centred about wet paddy rice cultivation, whereas water control in the north is primarily intended to alleviate the dangers of flood on the Hwang Ho. In the far north and north-west, however, irrigation is essential to cropland, and on the Ordos loop of the Hwang Ho, in the Kansu corridor and in the scattered oases of Sinkiang, local irrigation is as intensive as in any region of south China. Its spread is controlled only by the availability of water from the few rivers that flow in the steppe and desert.

the North China Plain and Manchuria. In most regions the growing season is from April to September, but in the far south, in Kwangtung and Fukien Provinces and on the island of Taiwan, two crops are harvested, one in June and the other in November. Besides the wheat and barley of the Yangtze valley, no other grain can compare with the dominance of rice in south China, and only sweet potatoes, introduced by the Europeans from the Philippines in the sixteenth century, have gained a strong position as an alternative food crop in the seaboard regions of Kwangtung, Fukien and Taiwan, in the basin of the Yangtze, and in the North China Plain.

Far the most common method of rice cultivation is by freshwater paddy, a system which requires intensive irrigation by a network of small canals with detailed attention to dykes. As we noticed in the previous chapter, one of the factors which encouraged Chinese cultural expansion from the lands of the Hwang Ho to the Yangtze valley and beyond was the ready adaptability of techniques of water control, first used to irrigate Loessland and keep the Hwang Ho within its banks, to the different but equally useful requirements of rice cultivation and the draining of marshes in the humid and tropical south. A present-day map of irrigation areas differs little from any that could be made of the past, showing flood control and irrigation works over the north of China Proper, with more intensive detail in the rice region of the south, particularly around the lakes and rivers of the Yangtze Basin, and, far out to the north-west, oasis settlement near the Ordos Region, in Kansu and in Sinkiang. Flood defences, the corollary to irrigation, have long been established, and are now maintained and intensified along all the rivers of China Proper and Manchuria.

The dominant position of rice among the foods grown in China can best be shown in tabular form. Table 2 gives the areas under cultivation and annual production, though, unfortunately, as in every application of statistics to China, figures must be taken from years now well in the past. Chinese production figures, given the confused situation of the country before and during World War II, have not for a long time been so detailed or accurate as those of Western economies, and the Communist regime, whether through desire to keep its secrets or genuine difficulty in obtaining reliable returns, has not produced any effective data for more than ten years. The figures below are estimates for the period before the Communist takeover for the whole of Mainland China, based primarily on the statistics of the National Agricultural Research Bureau, 1931-7.

Table 2

	cultivation area × million acres	production × million metric tons
rice	50	50
wheat	50	24
millet	23	10.5
kaoliang	22	13
soybeans	21.5	9
barley	17	8
maize corn	15	9
sweet potatoes	6	19

With such great areas under cultivation and so many people to feed, China is the world's largest producer of food, holding first place in the specific grains of rice, millet, barley and kaoliang, and also in sweet potatoes, soybeans, peanuts and tea. Wheat production is close to that of the United States and the Soviet Union. Most of China's production, however, goes to feeding her own population, and calculations based on Communist statistics appear to indicate that farm production is at best only holding its own with the steady increase in population.*

The grains listed above form the basic diet, supplemented as often as possible by vegetables, either grown near the houses of the people, or sometimes market gardens, or as a catch crop between the major harvests. Sweet potatoes, in particular, sown in June and harvested in November, are an important reserve of food for poorer people. Since they grow on vines spreading low to the ground, their foliage tends to keep moisture in the soil and renders them comparatively resistant to drought. In food value, however, the sweet potato is inferior to any grain, and its high moisture content can make storage difficult.

Meat is not a large part of the diet. The meat that is eaten is obtained chiefly from domestic pigs, chickens and ducks, supplemented by fish from the sea or from inland rivers, lakes and ponds. Meat, however, and the vegetable oils used for cooking, are valuable as a means of balancing a diet which would otherwise be heavily overweighted with carbohydrates. Cattle, mainly water-buffalo in the south, are used for draught animals, but there is no room in China Proper to breed them for meat. Mutton, staple food of the herding tribes in Mongolia and the northern steppe country, is regarded with distaste by the Chinese, while it is only in recent years that the value of milk has been appreciated. Some dairy herds are now maintained around the larger cities, but Chinese children are traditionally weaned on soybean curd, a rich source of vitamins, not cow's milk.

Besides these essential foods, however, several crops are grown for cash, for industrial processing and for export. Tea, which has long been used as a medicine and as a beverage, is grown chiefly in the hill territory of the Yangtze Basin, and is sold throughout the rest of the country and all over the world. Many kinds of fruit can be grown in every part of China, from the melons of the oasis regions in Sinkiang to the pineapples, bananas and mangoes of Hainan Island in the south of Kwangtung. Fruit, however, has seldom been regarded as an important crop, and it is only in recent years, both on the mainland and in Taiwan, that its value has been realised and it has been developed as a major food supplement and a crop for export. Sugar, which is grown as beet in Manchuria and the north-west, and as cane in Szechwan and the south, has long been a crop of great potential but little interest. The average annual

*For an analysis of pre-Communist and Communist statistics and probable production, see John Lossing Buck, 'Food Grain Production in Mainland China before and during the Communist Regime', in *Food and Agriculture in Communist China*, Buck and others, Praeger, 1966, particularly pp. 48-51, and appendix tables.

Plate 7 Cotton is a major industrial crop of modern China, the raw material for light summer and padded winter clothing throughout the country. Near Soochow in Kiangsu, men and women working in the hot sun remove the seeds from cotton bolls. *(China Pictorial)*

Plate 8 A workshop of the Peking General Knitwear Mill. While these women work, their children are at kindergarten (plate 1). *(China Pictorial)*

consumption of sugar in Australia is more than 125 lb per head, whereas in China it is 6 lb per head, and to a Westerner, this small use of sugar is one of the most striking differences between Chinese cooking and his own. A week in the Far East on local food rapidly develops a sense of sugar starvation which can only be eased by sticky sweet buns and large quantities of fruit cordial.

Taiwan, under Japanese occupation through the first half of this century, early developed sugar-cane production and a refining industry for the export trade, and the example is now being followed on the mainland. Though all these crops except tea are outside the main tradition of Chinese diet, they are grown increasingly for export revenue, and their processing, packaging and transport supply useful employment for the cities and towns.

Industry and communications

Among the working population of China as a whole, between 80 and 85 per cent are employed in agriculture, and the processing of agricultural produce, whether for export or for home consumption, has accounted for a great proportion of industrial development. Besides the food crops described in the preceding section, three major industrial crops are cotton, silk and tobacco, and the first two of these supply textile mills in neighbouring centres of population. Cotton is grown chiefly in Manchuria, the North China Plain and the Wei Ho valley in the north, and in the Yangtze valley, Szechwan and the hill country of Yunnan in the south. Silk, which is essentially a domestic industry, has its chief centres of production among the major settled regions of southern Manchuria, the North China Plain, Szechwan, the Yangtze valley and the delta country about Canton. Tobacco is grown in some regions of Manchuria and the North China Plain, and in south China it shares the hill country with tea plantations. The island of Taiwan grows both tea and tobacco. Of the major fibrous plants, rami flax is grown throughout the Yangtze valley, hemp is cultivated in Mongolia and the north of China Proper, and palm fibres come from the far south.

With her primary need to feed the vast population, and with the great majority of her people necessarily tied to agriculture, it will be a very long time before China's industrial and trading patterns become sufficiently developed to encourage the large-scale import of raw materials from abroad for processing and re-export. For the time being, her industrial expansion must depend on material to hand or obtainable within her own borders, and heavy industry in particular is controlled by the availability of iron ore, coal and other sources of power.

Coal is the chief material of industrial power in China. The main centres of production are in Manchuria, near Paotow and Tatung (map 19, page 46) in the north, and at Kailan and Hwainan north and south of the North China Plain (map 20, page 70). There is very likely coal under all the North China Plain, but in much of the area the carboniferous rocks are deeply buried beneath the sediment laid down by the Hwang Ho. The greater part of known reserves is in north Shansi, with other important deposits in Szechwan and the south-west still largely undeveloped. Oil has been found in the west of China Proper and in Sinkiang. A pipeline connects the field at Yumen with the refinery at Lanchow in Kansu (map 22, page 105), and a major field, with ancillary works, has been lately developed at Taching in Heilungkiang Province of northern Manchuria. Thermal electric power stations have been built at industrial centres throughout China, a great number of hydroelectric schemes are either planned or at various stages of

Plate 9 **Sugar beet is an important industrial crop in north China. The traditional carrying pole makes a contrast with the railway, the mill, and the whole scale of the operation.** ***(China Pictorial)***

completion and production, and a few short stretches of railway line, around Peking and Tatung in the north and between Paoki on the Wei Ho and Chengtu in the west, have been electrified. Otherwise, industry and transport still run largely on coal.

In the late 1950s, as part of the Great Leap Forward, cities and communes throughout the country were encouraged to establish backyard blast furnaces for iron and steel smelting. Some 25 per cent of China's output in those years was by local production. Reports of quantity surged upwards but the actual quality of the work was so low as to make the finished material almost valueless. Neither government statistics, nor perhaps economic planning, have quite recovered yet from this failure. There is still some attempt to encourage diversification of all industry, but the major iron and steel works regions are still Manchuria, Paotow along the far north of the Hwang Ho, and the Wuhan industrial complex on the middle Yangtze (map 24, page 128).

Plate 10 Workmen installing a steam turbine at a heavy machine tool works in Shanghai. ***(China Pictorial)***

Of the non-ferrous minerals, China's full reserves are not yet explored but present knowledge indicates that there are comparatively abundant supplies of those most important in present world markets. China is one of the world's largest producers of tungsten, antimony and tin, and is probably self-sufficient in bauxite, the essential raw material of aluminium, and in molybdenum. There are deposits of manganese, bauxite, molybdenum, lead, zinc and copper in southern Manchuria, but most other known reserves of all these minerals are in the territory south of the Yangtze, particularly in the Nan Ling dividing range and the high ground of Yunnan. Because of their situation, they are difficult to work and transport to processing centres, and large-scale production of aluminium, for example, will almost certainly have to wait for the introduction of cheap and plentiful hydroelectric power.

Attempts at diversification in the iron and steel industry have been paralleled by government policies in lighter industry, and they have been most successful where the new development can be related to the extractive or agricultural activities of the local area. For example, textile machinery plants have been established through the cotton-growing region of North China, side by side with the spinning and weaving mills, and Lanchow (map 19, page 46) and Chengtu (map 24, page 128) in the west of China Proper are now centres for the production of mining equipment which may be used in the new fields of coal or oil still opening up. Chemical plants have been set up in many parts of the country, producing plastics, dyestuffs and synthetic fibres, and also a great quantity of fertiliser for the surrounding farmlands. Still more closely related to agriculture, farm-machinery plants have been established at Loyang, near the head of the North China Plain, at Changsha in the south of the middle Yangtze basin (map 24, page 128), and at Urumchi, in the far west of Sinkiang (map 23, page 113), where planners have placed hopes of agricultural expansion into the steppe.*

Such a spread of industry is an obvious need for China's general development. It has taken courage to plan it and carry it out, for the greater part of the country's modernisation in the past was reserved to the great cities of the eastern seaboard, where Western capital and technical expertise were more readily available. Before World War II, many Chinese felt that these eastern cities, notably the treaty ports and the powerful metropolis of Shanghai, were rather alien settlements on Chinese soil than any development for

*For comparable attempts at development on the other side of the Sino-Soviet border, in the spring wheat regions of the virgin lands of Kazakhstan in the USSR, see, for example, J. P. Cole and F. C. German, *A Geography of the USSR: The Background to a Planned Economy*, Butterworth, London, 1961, pp. 69ff. and 218ff.

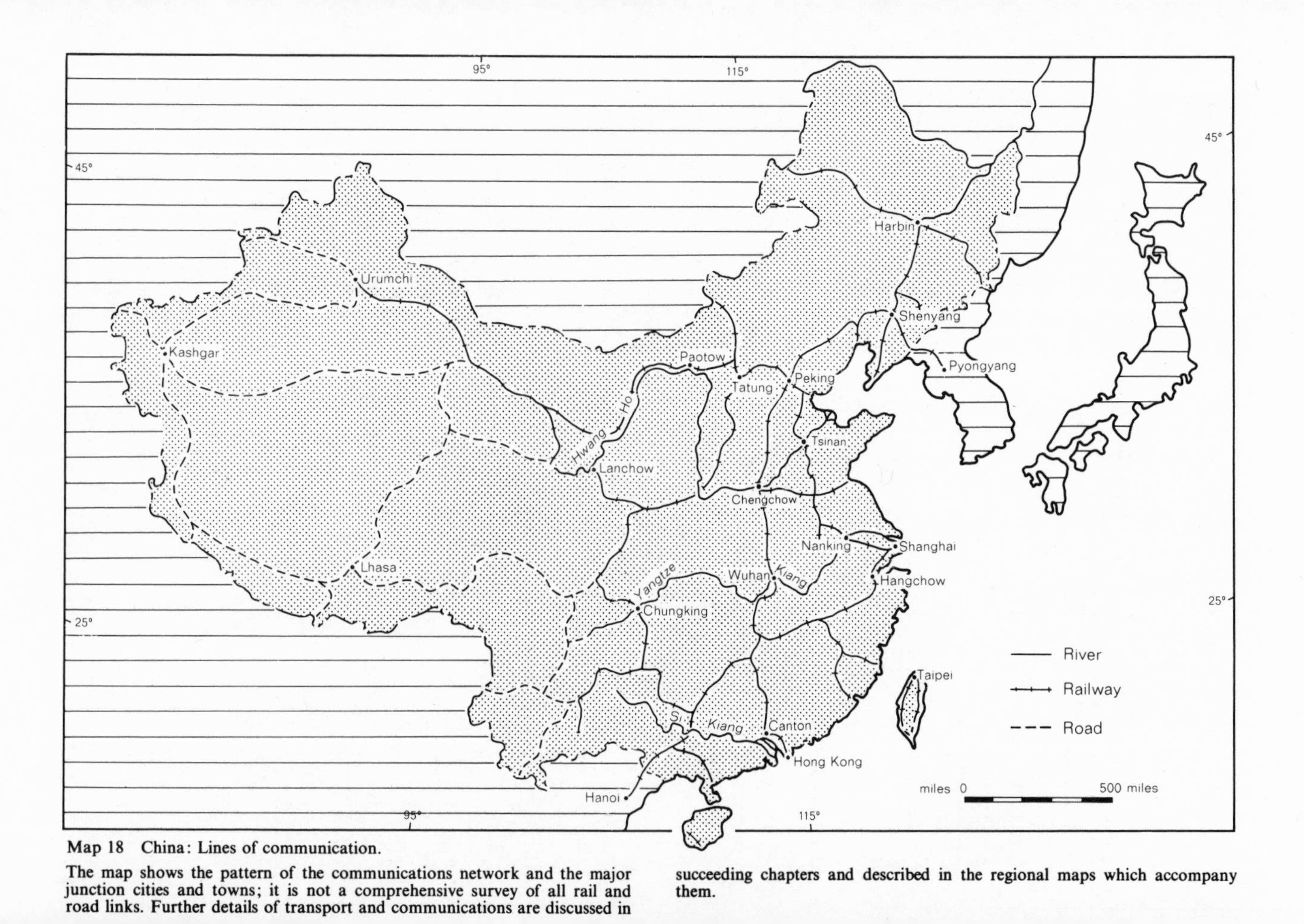

Map 18 China: Lines of communication.

The map shows the pattern of the communications network and the major junction cities and towns; it is not a comprehensive survey of all rail and road links. Further details of transport and communications are discussed in succeeding chapters and described in the regional maps which accompany them.

the nation to be proud of. Even now, the industrial complex of Manchuria, originally developed by Russian and Japanese imperialists, still dominates China's industry, and Shanghai is not only the chief centre for cotton and silk but also holds predominant place in the processing of woollen goods, with raw material obtained from the far north and west.

With its great area and population under a unified government, one of China's most serious weaknesses is that of communications. In imperial times, the chief form of transport was by water, and the Grand Canal was built from Hangchow to Peking in order to maintain the supply of tax grain from the southern provinces to the capital. All major rivers except the heavily silted Hwang Ho give passage to junks, launches and barges over much of their length; the Yangtze is navigable by ocean-going ships as far as Wuhan, six hundred miles from the sea; and even after the introduction of railways no line has yet been required along the lower course of the Yangtze nor the Si Kiang upstream from Canton.

Until World War II and the take-over by the Communists, railway development was slow, often hindered by local resentment or by government suspicion of political strings. The peasants believed that the railway tracks destroyed the auspicious sitings of ancestral gravemounds and could cause misfortune and disaster to present generations. Anti-foreign feeling among the people seemed justified on an official level when the railway system of Manchuria became a cause for war between Russia and Japan and the stations of the South Manchurian Railway Company were garrisoned with Japanese troops. Expansion has been far more rapid since the 1940s, but the total extent of China's railway network, narrow-gauge and single-track included, is no more than 25,000 miles. Only since the coming of Communist government has the Yangtze been bridged, first at Wuhan, and later at Chungking and Nanking, so that it is now possible to travel without interruption from Canton to Peking and on to Harbin.

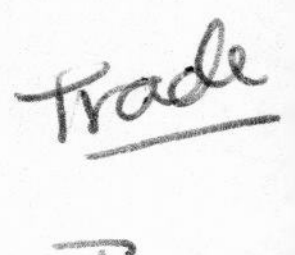

Most Chinese cities now have airports, and domestic passenger flights are supervised by charming hostesses who chant the thoughts of Chairman Mao to travellers. A great deal of movement, however, depends upon road links, often on roads with unsealed surfaces, which in Outer China and notably in Tibet are of major strategic importance for government control and military operations. Everywhere in China horses and other beasts of burden, including men, must supplement the work of trains, trucks and planes, and many of the people are connected to their neighbours and their government only by single-file tracks along steep forested hillsides and paved with flagstones, earth or mud. In general, while the essential communication links have been established across the country, they still need consolidation.

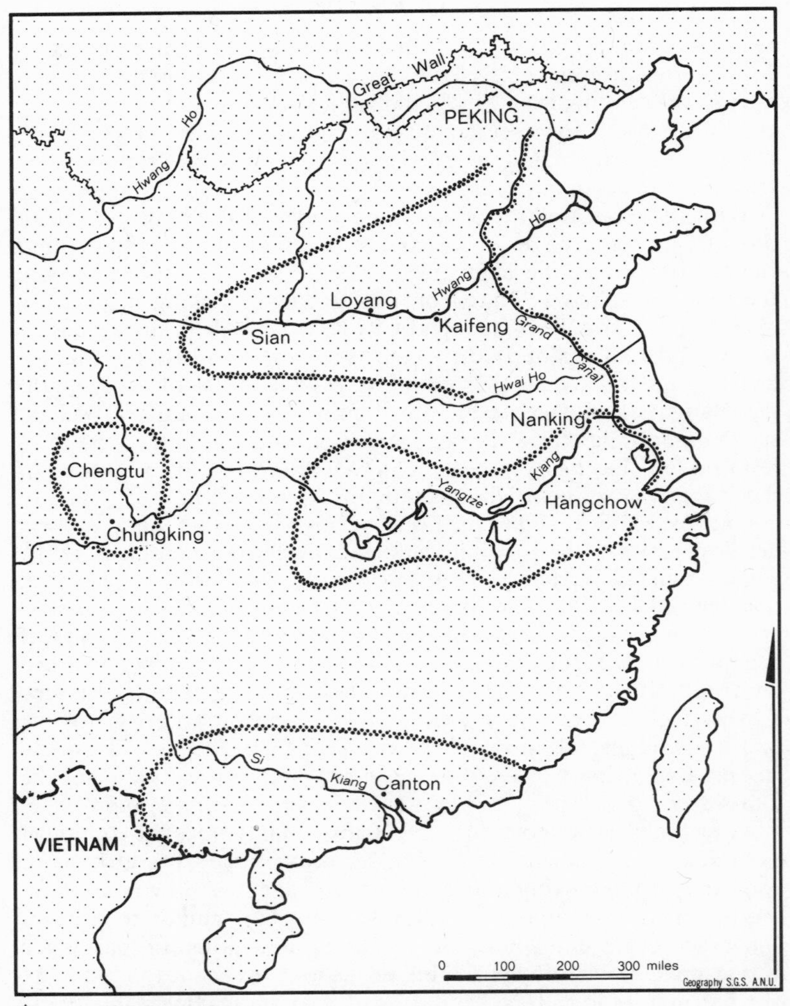

Figure 1 Key Economic Areas.

The map shows the approximate borders of the major economic areas and also the various established capitals of Chinese empires. In times of unity, the Wei valley about Sian (the 'land within the passes') and later the North China Plain with capitals at Loyang, Kaifeng and Peking, have held the predominant position. Nanking, Hangchow, Chengtu and Chungking have sometimes been capitals of separatist states in times of division, but have never been maintained for long as capitals of all China. The Grand Canal was first completed in the seventh century AD, but its work is now supplemented and largely replaced by the railway. Throughout Chinese history, the area of the Yangtze valley has been an increasingly powerful economic and occasional political rival to the rulers of the North China Plain, while the areas of Szechwan in the west and, more recently, Kwangtung in the south, have developed economic strength sufficient to maintain viable independence in any period of division. (Adapted from Chi Ch'ao-ting, *Key Economic Areas in Chinese History, as revealed in the development of public works for water control*, Paragon Book Reprint Corp., New York, 1963 (first published London, 1936))

Key economic areas

In 1936 the Chinese scholar Chi Ch'ao-ting published a book entitled *Key Economic Areas in Chinese History*, an analysis of the succeeding dynastic empires of China in terms of their dominant areas of control and their economic encouragement of these political bases. In Dr Chi's theory, to a large extent borne out by the evidence of Chinese texts, the earliest empires were controlled from the base region, the Wei Ho valley and Loessland, the area of the modern provinces Shensi and Shansi, but political power in north China over the centuries moved down the Hwang Ho to the North China Plain, first in the centre, about Kaifeng, and later, with increasing interest in the northern borders, to Peking. In times of division, the great centres of power in south China were close to the Yangtze estuary, at Nanking or Hangchow, for this region controlled communications along the Yangtze and had a forward defence line in the north on the Hwai Ho. Szechwan in the west, a fertile plain surrounded by mountains, several times held a balance of power, but it was not until very recent times that the central Yangtze Basin about Wuhan, and the far south about Canton, developed sufficient economic and political influence to rival the other great areas.

The factors which went to establish the influence of these Key Economic Areas are still effective today, though the present century has seen the addition of the Manchurian Plain and the Canton hinterland to their number, and Loessland has long declined in economic importance. In time of peace and unity, any strong government is concerned to maintain its links of administration and supply, particularly from the Hwang Ho to the Yangtze and across the Nan Ling to the far south, but in times of war or internal division, it is upon these lines that China may separate into rival states, and in the early period of the Republic ephemeral war-lord states and their armies struggled for power among the regional fragments of the former empire. Though China may appear monolithic on the map, her unity is an achievement of good government and careful administration, and every ruler, past and present, has had to work to maintain it. One belief that is unlikely to disappear is the concept of the Mandate of Heaven, which grants no divine right to any one regime, but which expects the ruler to prove himself by his ability and service to the people, and which makes rebellion lawful and justified against government that fails.

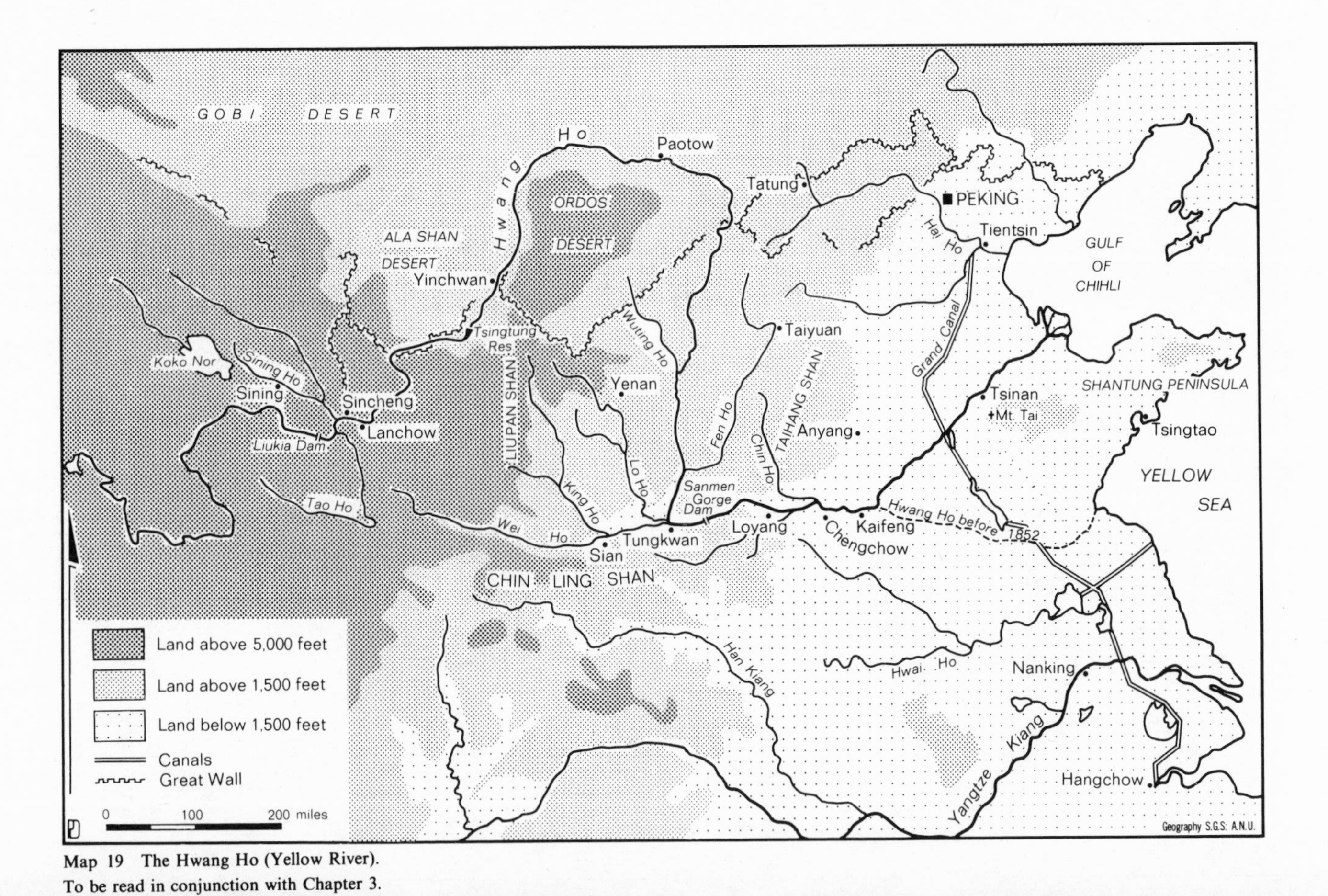

Map 19 The Hwang Ho (Yellow River).
To be read in conjunction with Chapter 3.

3 The Course of the Hwang Ho

One of the earliest geographical texts in the Chinese language, compiled during the sixth century A.D., follows the courses of the rivers, describes their flow and direction, and adds details for each place of interest that they pass. This is a very suitable approach for the treatment of north China. The Hwang Ho and its tributaries dominate the nature of the country and the lives of the people, and the muddy flow of water and silt bring both the benefits of irrigation and the disasters of flood.

The climate of north China is primarily influenced by air masses from the northern steppes and the region of the Gobi Desert, and the Central Mountain Belt about the Chin Ling Shan holds back the full effect of the tropical maritime air from the south. It is open country, with hills rather than mountains, and with a great plain to the east. Once there were forests, and the earliest inscriptions, some four thousand years old, tell of hunts for rhinoceros, elephant and deer. Now the land is generally bare, little natural vegetation remains, and in winter it is dusty and dry. Rain is unreliable and comparatively slight and with only four to six months' growing season the dry crops of wheat, millet and kaoliang generally yield no more than a single harvest. It is through this region, dry, cold and dusty, that the Hwang Ho makes its course.

From Tsinghai to the Ordos

The river has its beginning in a series of swamps and lakes about Tsaring Nor, between the mountain ridges of Bayan Kara Shan and Tsishih Shan, subsidiaries of the great Kunlun Massif, in the south-eastern corner of Tsinghai, north-west of Tibet. The stream flows south and east, rounds the Tsishih Shan, then turns west and north towards the Koko Nor. About latitude 36°N, the river turns again almost due east, crosses the border from Tsinghai into Kansu (map 2, page 13), and passes north of the city of Lanchow, capital of that province.

The source region of the Hwang Ho is over 14,500 feet above sea-level, and Lanchow is at 4,927 feet. By the time the river reaches

Kansu, it has run nearly a thousand miles of its course and has dropped almost ten thousand feet. As yet, however, it is little more than three hundred miles on a direct line from its source, and has still to travel almost two thousand miles more to the sea.

The basin of this upper section of the river receives an annual precipitation of some 10 to 20 inches. Summer is the rainy season, but all land above five thousand feet is covered in snow for six months of the year and the melting snows help to maintain the run-off. The average ratio of maximum discharge to minimum over the year is 25:1. More than half the precipitation in this basin goes to swell the flow of the Hwang Ho, for evaporation is slight and the slopes of the watershed are almost entirely formed of solid rock. In its course through the mountains, the swift flow of the river has cut great gorges, some with cliffs almost vertical, fifteen hundred feet high. By this means, the Hwang Ho gains considerable silt through erosion, although the steep gradient and turbulent flow of water in this upper course maintain a current which has no difficulty in carrying the load of sediment. There is great potential for the development of hydroelectric power, with some estimates as high as ten million kilowatts. Navigation, however, is almost impossible, and the topography of this harsh and rugged country makes any form of development expensive and difficult. It was, in fact, only in 1952 that Chinese geographers and explorers established the actual sources of the river.

Between the Liukia Dam and the city of Lanchow, the Hwang Ho is joined by two major tributaries, the Tao Ho from the south and the Sining Ho, which itself receives the waters of the Tatung Ho from the north. All three rivers have come from the mountains of the west and have similar development to the Hwang Ho. By Lanchow the river has broadened, with an average discharge of 40,000 cubic feet per second. This upper course of the river supplies two-thirds of the total annual run-off of the whole Hwang Ho catchment.

A bridge at Sincheng, also known as Hokou, 'mouth of the River', some twenty miles west of Lanchow, carries the railway and a main arterial road north-west to Central Asia. South and west of Lanchow, Kansu Province widens out. The eastern border follows the highlands of Tsinghai, and in the south the province controls the headwaters of the Wei Ho. North-east of Lanchow the Ningsia Hui Autonomous Region has a population predominantly of Mongol descent and Islamic religion. (*Hui* in Chinese means Moslem.) Kansu itself has comparatively few people, but among them are representatives of all China's five major ethnic groups. Han farmers are mingled with Mongols from the north and Tibetans on the west, while descendants of Manchu soldiers stationed in garrison towns under the Ch'ing Empire still live there. Besides these, two or three million Moslems of Arab, Turkish or Mongol descent, with some converted Chinese, distinguish themselves by religion and custom from the people around them. Both Ningsia and the Ordos Region of Inner Mongolia, outside the line of the Great Wall, are desert and steppe country, with scattered tribes of herdsmen, and the land is available for agriculture only where it can be irrigated from the river.

Downstream from Lanchow, an open valley leads through hill country, still with fair gradient and occasional gorges and falls, till the river crosses the line of the Great Wall in Ningsia Hui Autonomous Region. At this point, a hundred and fifty miles in direct line from Lanchow, the Hwang Ho is dammed into the Tsingtung Reservoir, and then for three hundred miles north and another two hundred miles east it follows the edge of the Ordos Desert.

East and south of the river lies the desert itself, with a central ridge more than three thousand feet above the plain, but at Yinchwan, formerly Ningsia City, the distance between high ground on the east and the ridge of Holan Shan on the west is fifty miles, and for the next four hundred miles, till the river passes Paotow, there is no clearly defined valley. In all this distance, from Yinchwan at 3,578 feet above sea-level to Paotow at 3,364, the river falls little more than two hundred feet.

The stream at this stage has completely changed its character. From a fast flow through gorges, it has now become a winding spread of waters, with channels meandering over an open plain. The volume of water, too, is considerably diminished by evaporation, percolation and the demands of irrigation. Here and in the Kansu corridor farming is dependent on supplementary water rather than upon the small natural rainfall, and more than four-fifths of cultivated ground is subject to irrigation. Ancient canals and modern agricultural oases stretch across the plain. By the time the river reaches Paotow, the average flow has been reduced to some 28,000 cubic feet per second, a decline of almost 30 per cent from the figure for Lanchow.

The small gradient and the steadily diminishing volume of water mean that the river is no longer able to carry the full load of sediment collected in the earlier stages of its course. Much of the material brought down from the upper basin in Tsinghai and Kansu is dropped by the river and spread along its winding course about the Ordos. Sand-bars are formed, shifting the stream from one direction to another; temporary lakes have formed in the past, and accumulated sediment. Navigation is possible, but only for craft with less than a two-foot draught, so much of the commerce is carried by barges or rafts supported on scores of inflated animal skins. From early times, this fertile crescent of ground has provided a livelihood

Plate 11 The terraced, gullied landscape of Loessland. The people of Tachai in Shansi have already brought most of their region under control with terraces and walls, but the crest of the nearest ridge shows the softer contours where work still remains to be done. *(China Pictorial)*

for generations of Chinese farmers, provided always that irrigation works are maintained and that the climate is not unfavourable. Yet the Ordos has been an outpost colonisation, separated from the main centres of Chinese culture by the desert itself, while the sediment of the river has supplied material for the north and north-west winds to carry into China as loess.

Loessland

Loess is a technical term for silt transported and laid down by the wind. Silt describes soil particles mid-way between clay and sand, a fine non-gritty dust. Silt, of course, may be produced by normal weathering and by glacial action, then carried by rivers and spread by the wind. As China has experienced no great Ice Age, it seems most probable that the loess has come from sedimentary beds of the Hwang Ho in the Ordos Desert and from the dry basin of the Gobi. Certainly, nowhere else in the world has loess played such a dominant role in a geographical region nor in the history of a civilisation.

In essence, the pattern of loess formation is as follows. Soil brought down to the Ordos Region by wind from the Mongolian Desert and steppes, or carried there and deposited as sediment by the Hwang Ho, is picked up again by the dry winds from the north. Pebbles are left behind in the desert, sand is accumulated into dunes and clay particles can be lifted high into the air. The dust storms may be experienced as far away as Shanghai and the sea. Silt particles are pressed along close to the ground, and in the desert region, where no vegetation holds the soil, each gust of wind moves the silt further south.

On the southern margins of the desert, inside the line of the present Great Wall, grass can grow naturally, and there has always been some vegetation. Here the silt is stopped and held by the stems and leaves of the plants, and a new layer of soil is set above the old. One layer of plants is smothered, but new growth comes on the raised surface of the ground, and the process of accumulation continues. The process is smooth. Unlike water-borne silt, loess shows no horizontal bedding planes. Occasionally, like the fossils of animals, the shapes of buried plants may show as irregular tubes in the loess deposit.

After ages of this process, Loessland now covers 120,000 square miles and stretches over four provinces: the whole of Shensi and most of Kansu, Shansi and Honan (map 2, page 13). The deepest beds are in northern Shensi, south of the Ordos, and in eastern Kansu south of the Ala Shan Desert. Here the beds reach 250 feet deep, and some measurements have recorded three hundred feet. The rest of Shensi and eastern Kansu is covered a hundred or two

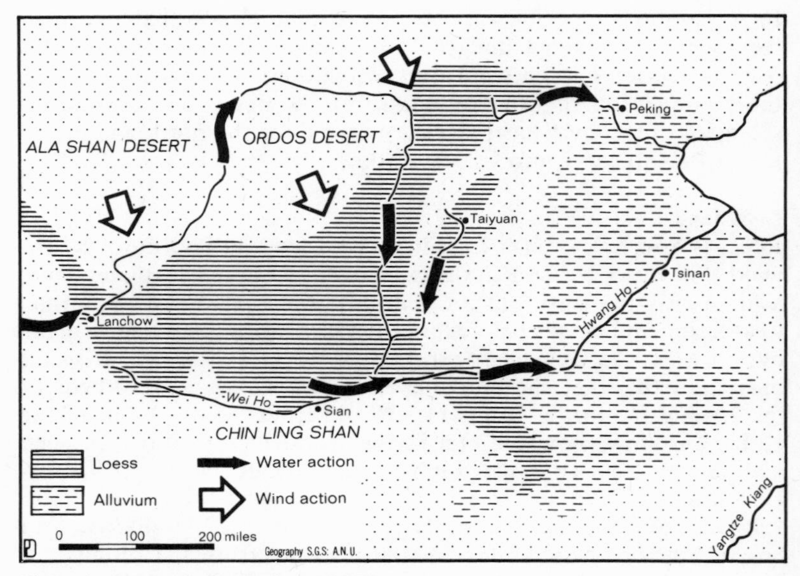

Figure 2 Loess and alluvium in north China.

Silt is carried by wind from the northern deserts to settle in the form of loess in the region north of the Wei Ho and either side of the middle course of the Hwang Ho. From Loessland, it is picked up by water erosion and carried by the Hwang Ho to spread as alluvium across the North China Plain.

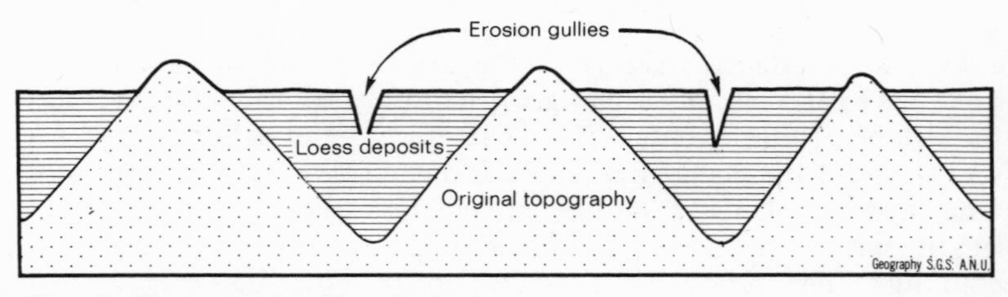

Figure 3 The topography of Loessland.

The original topography of Loessland is of rounded hills, but now only occasional peaks of the original formation can be found above ground, and the earlier landscape is buried under deposits of loess as deep as 250–300 feet. Loess itself, extremely friable, is easily eroded by the action of wind and, particularly, of water.

hundred feet deep, and in Shansi and Honan the beds average fifty feet. The process is halted by the line of the Chin Ling Shan and the Central Mountain Belt, but wind-deposited silt can be readily eroded by the action of water, and loess mixed with alluvium is spread along the valleys of the rivers and far across the North China Plain.

Both by tradition and by historical evidence, the original home of Chinese civilisation lies in Loessland: in southern Shensi and Shansi near the junction of the Hwang Ho with the Wei. It is well argued that in this region the earliest Chinese found fertile soil, easily worked with primitive implements and giving good return for comparatively small effort in ploughing and irrigation. These, in fact, are the properties of loess soil: it is fertile, friable, easily dug and cut by peasant farmers, and—for the other side of the coin—very susceptible to erosion by water.

The fine and lightly-packed particles of windborne loess give the soil a high porosity, sometimes 45 per cent. It stores water, and capillary attraction through the soil brings ground moisture to the surface, the rising water forming a solution with minerals in the soil, such as feldspar or lime. When it reaches the surface and is evaporated, a hard cement-like crust is left. The formation of such a crust is a feature of all dry lands where evaporation is in excess of rainfall, but the process is particularly effective in soils similar to loess. Partly as a result of this phenomenon and partly by reason of its cleavage and its grain size, loess has the unique property of being able to stand in vertical walls and even to hold up the roofs of caves. It is unconsolidated, and thus easy to dig. Houses and whole villages have been constructed as caves hollowed out into the faces of cliffs. Some farmers live directly *under* the fields they cultivate, and the houses are well insulated and pleasant both in winter and in summer. Earthquakes, however, are not uncommon in Loessland. In Kansu in 1920, 246,000 people were killed by the collapse of earth houses or died of starvation in the famine that followed an earthquake.

Loessland is now hilly. The original form of the land has, of course, long been buried under the layers of wind-blown silt. One mountain spur, the Liupan Shan, stretches from the Chin Ling Shan into Ningsia Hui Autonomous Region, and the Taihang Shan marks the border between the Shansi uplands and the eastern plain, but elsewhere the country is rolling rather than rugged, with alluvial plains along the main tributaries of the Hwang Ho, the Wei and the Fen. There is one open basin at Tatung in the far north of Shansi. Everywhere the land is broken by the gullies of erosion.

More than two thousand years ago, the Emperor of China commanded that all carriage wheels should be of uniform distance apart

Plate 12 Liu Ling village in north Shensi, where many of the houses are caves in the loess. *(Courtesy: Gun Kessle and Jan Myrdal)*

along the axle. The reason for this edict can still be seen in Loessland. Vehicles cut the soil crust on the roads and wind and rain carry the dust away. The track digs itself steadily deeper into the soil and the walls on either side may reach twenty or even forty feet high. Very often, when two carts meet, one must go back to a clear place or else unload. On some of these roads it is possible to travel for miles with no more than an occasional sight of the countryside around. The water of streams and rivers is as effective at cutting channels in the loess as the hoofs of animals or the feet and wheels of men.

Rainfall on the plains averages some fifteen inches a year, it is rather less towards the west, but there the higher ground brings cooler temperatures and less evaporation. Such a precipitation is marginal for effective agriculture, and many harvests are ruined in years when rainfall is below the minimum requirement. To add to the difficulty, half the year's rainfall comes in the two summer months of July and August. Then the streams and rivers pour through the hills, run-off scours the gullies of fine, unconsolidated soil, and the great tributaries of the Hwang Ho bring a volume of water and mud in suspension to join the run eastwards across the plain and towards the sea.

In such circumstances, erosion can be catastrophic; all the more so as the land is almost entirely devoid of any natural vegetation. The area is a transition region from forest-steppe, whose remains can be traced in the south-east, to a dry steppe, evident in the north-east towards the Ordos. But natural vegetation covers no more than some 2 or 3 per cent of the region, and the original flora can be judged only from the few plants that survive, many of them in a stunted condition. Centuries, even thousands of years, of ploughing and tilling have destroyed the natural vegetation and have altered the character of the soils. They have lost their natural properties and can no longer be described in terms of any of the broad soil zones related mainly to climate (map 8, page 23). They are generally described by the local name of 'black soils'.

Around Sian, in the open valley of the Wei Ho, canals and irrigation, more than two thousand years ago, first developed the prosperity of this region. The basis of the ancient network is still in use today, though new digging is constantly needed to counteract the effect of deepening river channels in the friable soil. High on the hills, above the useful levels of irrigation, men have built terraces to grow dry crops of wheat and millet, but far too often the farmers have thought little of contour lines or conservation. Natural cover has been removed from hillsides too steep for effective cultivation, and the erosion that follows has stripped the slopes of soil even below the loess deposits, and has covered the fertile flood plain with layers of useless rock and debris. In some places the effect is catastrophic. Forest has been reduced to desert in a single generation. Elsewhere, with bench terracing and strip cropping, the most serious erosion has been arrested.

The northern third of Loessland is a region of spring wheat (map 16, page 32). Some 18 per cent of the area is cultivated, and about an eighth of that receives some water from irrigation. In the south, a region of winter wheat and millet, 22 per cent of the land is cultivated, and a tenth of that is irrigated. Besides wheat, millet, and kaoliang, the farmers grow potatoes, cotton and tobacco, with rice in some irrigated areas, and also fruit, melons, peaches, and the famous apricots of Lanchow. Much of the cultivated ground is marginal farming land, which crops only in favourable years, and the high proportion of land under irrigation is a reflection of the lack of rain and its seasonal uncertainty rather than any abundance of stream flow. The two cities of Taiyuan in Shansi and Sian in Shensi have more than 9,000,000 people, and the population of the region is well over 50,000,000. As increasing numbers of people press against the confines of agricultural land with a reasonable economic return, it is the tragedy of Loessland that climate, rivers and soil combine to punish any mistake in cultivation with immediate and disastrous erosion.

Beneath Loessland lie three-quarters of China's coal reserves, high-grade bituminous and anthracite estimated at more than two hundred billion tons. The major fields are in Shansi and Shensi, with important seams curving north to the region of Yinchwan in Ningsia and north-west along the Kansu corridor. There are large deposits of iron and some fields of petroleum. Modern mines have so far touched only the accessible margins of the coalfields, and work has long been hindered by the shortage of timber for mine props. Tatung, however, in the far north of Shansi, produces high-grade coking coal to supply blast furnaces at Taiyuan to the south and at Peking, some two hundred miles to the east. Paotow, 150 miles to the west, has another large field of iron ore, with associated coal deposits at Paiyunopo, almost due north near the Mongolian border, and is now the site of major works.

In ancient times, Sian, earlier known as Changan, was the capital of the Chinese Empire. Under the great dynasty of Han, in the last two centuries B.C., and in the time of T'ang, from the seventh to the ninth century, Changan was one of the greatest cities in the world, and the population of the capital district under the T'ang dynasty is known to have been more than a million. This region of the Wei valley, with fertile soil, great works of irrigation, and a rainfall more certain than that of the rest of Loessland because of the Chin Ling Shan ranges to the south, was one of the chief granaries of the empire. Moreover, it controlled the access north and west towards Kansu and Central Asia and southwards to the Szechwan Basin around Chengtu. On the east, the territory was guarded by a ring of narrow gorges and strategic defence posts along the Hwang Ho and among the mountains on either side. It was known in ancient times as 'the land within the passes'. From there, the ruler of Changan could send his armies south and east to overawe surrounding states, while he himself rested secure within firm defences.

In more recent times, the centre of political power in China has moved further down the Hwang Ho, and Loessland has become a political and economic backwater. During the civil war of the 1930s and at the time of the Japanese invasion, the Communist armies under Mao Tse-tung found refuge at Yenan, in the northern part of Shensi, and from this secure base they were able to hold their own against the armies of Japan and of their Nationalist rivals. Since the Communist victory in the civil war, however, the region has received no special preference. Agriculturally, Loessland is in a depressed and difficult condition, and it is only through the development of heavy industry and the consequent improvement of communications that economic prosperity may return. The passes and the valleys that were so useful to ancient emperors and modern revolutionaries have also presented a barrier to transport, for the rivers, fast-flowing and turbulent, are quite unnavigable.

The railway (map 18, page 42), however, has gradually spread westwards from several points on the plain, most importantly from Chengchow in the east, along the southern bank of the Hwang Ho and the Wei, through Sian north-west to Lanchow and Central Asia. Another line runs from Peking through Tatung and Taiyuan, with an eastward link from Taiyuan to the plain, and a continuation through the valley of the Fen Ho to the great bend of the Hwang Ho at Tungkwan. In very recent years, a line has been constructed through Paotow along the Ordos loop of the Hwang Ho to junction at Lanchow. With the development of communications by air, as well as transport by rail, Loessland is becoming less of a backwater and has an increasing chance of exploiting its real economic potential.

The middle course of the Hwang Ho

From Paotow in the Ordos Plain, the Hwang Ho curves south, then runs more than four hundred miles along the border of the two provinces Shensi and Shansi. In a series of bends and loops,

Plate 13 A Shansi village in early spring, at snow-melt, still too cold to begin planting the terraced fields. In traditional domestic industry, a man and his two sons are plaiting ropes. *(China Pictorial)*

cascades and canyons, it passes through the heart of Loessland, with a fall of more than two thousand feet.

At its junction with the Fen Ho, the major tributary from Shansi in the east, the Hwang Ho emerges from the Lungmen Gorge into a relatively open reach with a more gentle slope. Then in the south of Shansi Province, where it is joined by the Wei Ho from Shensi, the Hwang Ho meets the rocky faultline of the Chin Ling Shan. Here it makes a sharp turn, almost a right angle, to the east, and runs again through deep gorges between the mountain ridges, Chungtiao Shan on the north and Hsiao Shan on the south, before emerging at the head of its natural delta, the North China Plain, near the ancient capital city of Loyang.

The Fen and the Wei are the two main tributaries in this part of the course. The Wei has a basin area of almost 45,000 square miles, and a mean discharge of over 10,000 cubic feet per second. The Fen discharge is almost 1,500, and the Wuting Ho and the Lo Ho, both from Shensi, each average a discharge over 1,000 cubic feet per second. With these and other smaller additions, by the time the Hwang Ho emerges from the last gorges at Shanhsien near Loyang, the volume of water has more than recovered its losses in the Ordos loop. The mean discharge is 46,000 cubic feet per second, 6,000 higher than the figure for Lanchow in Kansu, and 40 per cent above the flow at Paotow.

At this point in its course, however, the Hwang Ho has travelled five hundred miles through the loess region, and all the water it receives from its tributaries has been collected in basins of Loessland. The erosion which strips the hillsides of soil adds mud and gravel to the rivers. One-third of the total basin of the Hwang Ho is in loess, and observations in the northern part of Shensi Province have established that erosion by water removes a layer of soil there one centimetre thick, almost two-fifths of an inch, on average every year.

The effect of this massive erosion is reflected in the content of the river. Before it enters the loess, the river's accumulation of sediment flowing past Paotow in the Ordos is generally no more than 1 per cent by weight, with an average each year of 160,000,000 tons of material. In comparison, most other major rivers of the world carry less than 2 per cent, and any figures over 10 per cent are extremely rare. However, in its course through Loessland, and particularly through the addition of suspended material from the Wuting Ho, the Wei Ho, and the Wei's own tributary the King Ho, the Hwang Ho picks up and carries past Shanhsien 1,300,000,000 tons of sediment, six times more than either the Ganges or Mississippi. The mean content of debris each year reaches a maximum of 5 per cent each August, and it is maintained above 1 per cent from

April through December. In times of heavy rainfall and fast flow, the volume of the King Ho has been known to comprise 48 per cent solid matter; the Hwang Ho itself may carry up to 40 per cent on its middle reaches, and it has been measured at 46 per cent past Shanhsien. The material that it carries regularly each year is sufficient to cover an area seven hundred square miles with a blanket of alluvium one foot deep.

The lower course of the Hwang Ho

If Loessland, and particularly the valley of the Wei, is the ancient centre of political and military power, the North China Plain (map 20, page 70), the 'Yellow Plain', is the heartland of Chinese culture. East of the Taihang Shan, west of the Shantung Peninsula and the sea, south of Peking and north of the Hwai Ho, in an area of 125,000 square miles, more than 100,000,000 people live among the traditions and the farm-works of their ancestors. The canals that they maintain follow a basic pattern established more than three thousand years ago, the cities where many of them live can trace active settlement on the same site for more than twenty centuries of recorded history, and all around the plain, among the fields and crops, are the graves and tombs of the past. The earliest Chinese writing, scratched onto bones, cracked in fire and used for an oracle, have been excavated at Anyang in the foothills of the Taihang Shan, and the homeland of Confucius is near the sacred Mount Tai in Shantung. Even further back in time, the bones of earliest man in China, at least 500,000 years old, have been found near Peking.

One of the earliest legends of China tells the story of the Great Emperor Yü, who lived before 2000 B.C. and controlled the waters and put an end to the floods that had ravaged China. The *Book of Documents*, an ancient classic of the Confucian school, contains a chapter called the 'Tribute of Yü'. This, the first geographical text of China, describes the gifts which were sent in gratitude to the great ruler from every province of the empire. It seems only too appropriate that floods and the heroic works of man should have been described so early in Chinese folklore and literature, for the problems and the danger have continued through history, and they remain unsolved today.

From Loessland, as we have seen, 1,300,000,000 tons of soil are carried each year past Shanhsien and out onto the plain. There is a slight narrowing of the stream around two islands near Mengtsing at the place called Sanmen, 'Three Gates', north of Loyang, but by the time it has passed under the modern railway bridge between Sinsiang and Chengchow (map 20, page 70) it has emerged from its valley. For the remaining five hundred miles of its course to the sea it flows either level with or above the surface of the surrounding plain.

At one time, in the geologic past, the North China Plain was a bay of the sea, and the coast-line ran along the foothills of the mountains. The rocky Shantung Peninsula was then an island, and the Hwang Ho entered the sea soon after its emergence from the last gorges near Loyang. The millions of tons of sediment brought down by the river have extended the coast-line, at a rate estimated in recent times as one mile every six years. At some time to come the Gulf of Chihli, or Po Hai, will be filled and Shantung may again become an island, this time in a sea of mud.

At present, however, as in all the recorded history of the Chinese people, and in their foreseeable future, the North China Plain is a delta of the Hwang Ho, spread thickly with fertile alluvial soil, largely loess silt in origin. When Chinese civilisation began in the valleys of Loessland, the great plain was certainly a maze of channels and marshes, and the River wandered one way or another with neither order nor control. Gradually, the Chinese, who had learnt the value of canals and dykes in irrigation work along the rivers and streams of Loessland, moved east and applied their techniques of water control to drain the marshes and fix the rivers in their courses. For the most part, they have been successful, and the soil has supported the growth and development of one of the most populous and cultivated civilisations of mankind; but nowhere else in the world do so many people live so close to the constant threat of disaster and death.

Obviously it is more convenient, and indeed essential to the farmer, if the Hwang Ho remains in a constant channel, and the Chinese have arranged that it shall do so. All along its course north-eastward to the sea, the river is guarded by great dykes. The official dykes are five to eight miles apart, and within their lines stand smaller 'people's dykes' built by farmers so they can cultivate additional land during normal years when the flow is not too great. There is only a small supply of stone on the open plain, and for long periods the river may be held between earth walls built by traditional technique.

Were the river left to wander and choose its own course, the silt brought down each year would be spread evenly over the whole area of the delta, and would extend the shore-line gradually further into the sea along a wide front north and south of the Shantung Peninsula. As it is, thirty-five billion cubic feet of silt are carried each year past Mengtsing, 397 feet above sea-level, and only fifteen billion cubic feet reach the sea. The average gradient across the plain is ten inches a mile, much steeper than the lower course of many other rivers, including the Amazon and even the Yangtze. Nevertheless the load picked up by the steep scouring of the loess is too great for the river to carry, and twenty billion cubic feet of silt are left along the delimited line of its course. As a result, the bottom of the river and the land between the dykes is steadily raised, until the water is actually above the level of the surrounding countryside.

The effect is striking. Navigation of the lower reaches of the river is limited by sand-bars so most boats are small and shallow-bottomed, but the farmer in his fields looks up at the sails showing over the dyke above him. To get from one side of the river to the other he must climb the earth wall of a dyke, cross the open space between the dykes and the channel of the river, then climb over and down the dyke on the other side. In 1942 an American engineer reported on a survey of part of the course near the Peking-Wuhan railway: 'For about 80 miles . . . the flood surface of the river is about 20 to 25 feet higher than the level of the ground outside the inner dykes, and the low water surface is about 5 to 10 feet higher than the ground outside the dykes; surveys also show that the normal bed of the river at low stages averages 5 feet higher than the general level of the country.'*

Just east of Mengtsing, the Hwang Ho receives the last of its tributaries, the Ilo Ho entering from the south-west and the Chin Ho from the north. Thereafter, across the plain, there is no further gain. Other rivers cross the plain from the western mountains towards the sea, but they are not tributaries of the Hwang Ho, and indeed they receive some of its water by seepage through the dykes and levees. As the river passes the Shantung Mountains, to the north of the ranges about Mount Tai, a few small streams add to its volume, but over the whole plain there is an average loss of more than 350

*John R. Freeman, 'Floods in China', *Proceedings of the American Society of Civil Engineers*, XLIX (1942), p. 1422, quoted in George B. Cressey, *Land of the 500 Million*, p. 251.

Figure 4 Dykes on the North China Plain.

The cross-section shows how the silt deposits dropped by the Hwang Ho raise the bed steadily above the original level until it flows within its dykes well above the plain.

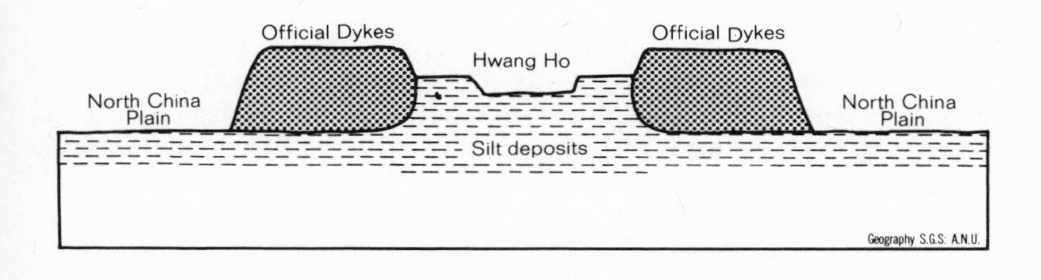

cubic feet per second. The plain is not part of the basin of the Hwang Ho. On the contrary, it receives water from the river, and great areas of inhabited ground, tens of miles from the existing course, lie below the water-level.

Flooding on the Hwang Ho

The control of the Hwang Ho on its course across the North China Plain, even in equable conditions of rain and water flow, would ultimately become impossible. There is, in the end, a limit to the height that earth dykes can be raised, and eventually the deposit of sediment must bring the water of the river too high for the levees to keep in check. The danger of flood, however, recurs every year because of the drastic changes in flow and load of sediment when the summer rains fall in Loessland.

In the upper reaches of the Hwang Ho, from Tsinghai into Kansu and along the Ordos bend, the flow is comparatively steady and not excessively laden with sediment: the variation between minimum and maximum flow at Lanchow in Kansu is estimated at 1:25, and that at Paotow is 1:20. However, just as Loessland supplies all but 160 million of the 1,300 million tons of sediment that is carried to the head of the great delta each year, so it is the rain in southern Shensi and Shansi that gives the Hwang Ho its enormous increase in flow during July and August. At Shanhsien in Honan the ratio of mean minimum to maximum flow is regularly 1:110 and it has risen as high as 1:150, based on a minimum discharge of 5,000 cubic feet per second and a maximum of more than 775,000. Chinese accounts of the flood in 1843—admittedly hard to believe and still in need of checking—claim that the discharge at one time reached 1,270,000 cubic feet per second. This would give a variation of more than 1:250, a record for any major river in the world.

Not only is there immense difference in flow, but the volume of water can increase at extraordinary speed as run-off from the rainfall over a wide area is collected by several tributary streams and brought into the main channel at the same time. In 1933 the discharge of the Hwang Ho past Shanhsien on 7 August was a little over 175,000 cubic feet per second; two and a half days later it was over 650,000. With the comparatively steep gradient, the flood crest can move at a speed of six to twelve miles an hour, giving little time for downstream defences to be prepared before the torrent of water reaches them. After short downpours in Loessland, the rush of flood water often passes along the plain and is gone with the same speed that it came, but in 1949, for example, when there were heavy rains over an extended period, the high flood discharge of 350,000 cubic feet per second continued for ninety-three hours. Only by great effort were the levees held and widespread flooding prevented.

Many times in the past the Hwang Ho has broken its banks and changed its course, and at one time or another the mouth of the river has been as far north as the region of Peking and as far south as the valley of the Hwai. A map of the various recorded courses would appear like the ribs of a fan stretching across the plain, with a node point in the region of Kaifeng. Until the last great change of course in 1852, the river ran almost due east from Kaifeng and entered the sea south of the Shantung Peninsula. About that time, the British were in dispute with the Chinese government, and a fleet was sent to give a show of force opposite the mouth of China's greatest river. It was not for some while, and then with much embarrassment, that the commander realised he was blockading the wrong coast-line.

The change in 1852 was the last full change of course by the river, but there have been major floods since that time, most notably in 1938 when the dykes on the south were broken deliberately by the Nationalist armies as they retreated before the invading Japanese. For nine years the floodwaters went south into the valley of the Hwai and thence to the Yangtze, until the line of dykes was restored in 1947. Within the last hundred years the mouth of the river has shifted 250 miles north and then, briefly, five hundred miles south, roughly comparable to a transfer of the Murray mouth between Mount Gambier and the north of Spencer Gulf in South Australia; this in a region with a population up to 80,000,000 people.

Whether or not a change of course is involved, a break in the river banks allows water to flow in a winding, braided series of streams ten or twenty miles wide, and a proper channel may not be re-formed for ten years or more. Farms and houses are covered by water and mud, and without efficient relief those people who die of starvation may outnumber those who are drowned. Often enough, refugees from the great areas of flooding have disrupted the life of people in the higher safe areas around; and, many times in the past, rebellions fierce enough to overthrow the government of a great empire have arisen from the disorder and despair of China's sorrow. When the flood-gap is closed and the fields are drained, people return to their land and resume their occupations, for the soil is good, despite the danger, and the Chinese have great affection for their farmlands.

Control of the river

Centuries of experience have made the Chinese people expert in the art of water control by dams and canals. They are no less efficient, even with the most primitive equipment, when it is necessary to repair the damage in a broken dyke. It may be an exaggeration to use the proverbial phrase 'a million men with teaspoons', but when it is necessary to close a breach and force a stream back to its course men can be recruited and organised from all the country around to work under competent technical direction.

A major break in the system of dykes can only be closed at the season of low water. When the current decreases, the open edges of the gap are steadily built inward with baskets of earth, reinforced against washaway by matting of millet stalks or kaoliang. As the opening is narrowed, the water flow gains intensity. Eventually the force of the stream may scour out the dyke until a six-foot head of water is pouring through an eroded channel several hundred feet wide and sixty feet deep. At this stage, earth and matting would be washed away, so stones must be used to maintain the edges. From this foundation, long rolls of plaited willow, bound with rope and wire into sausages three feet in diameter and forty or sixty yards long, and filled with stones, are rolled into the gap to narrow the stream still further until it is no more than thirty or forty feet wide. Finally, a bridge of rope is built across the opening from one end of the dyke to the other, and on this platform there is prepared a great plug of tamped earth and kaoliang. When all is ready, the plug is lowered into the breach. If it is not swept away, hundreds of men rush in with baskets of earth and stones to make the closure hold and seal the dyke secure.

Plate 14 Water control: long rolls of plaited brushwood are used to close a dam. The illustration comes from Heilungkiang in northern Manchuria, but the technique is the same throughout China. *(China Pictorial)*

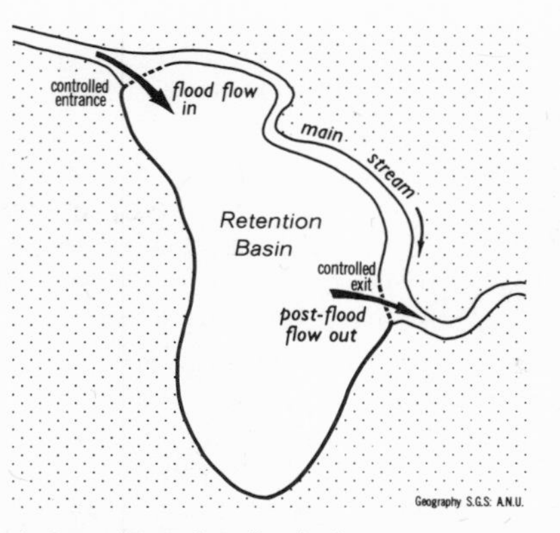

Figure 5 Flood control: Retention and settling basins.

Diagram of a flood retention basin: excess discharge from the main stream of the river can be admitted to the basin and released again after the danger is past. The technique is used both in north China and on the Yangtze, notably at Shasi and Tachiatai (page 154). By holding the water long enough for it to drop its load of silt, these reservoirs can also be used as settling basins to raise the ground on either side of the main stream, and a series of such settling basins would eventually build permanent defences against flood. Apart from the constant labour to build new basins as each was filling, however, resettlement of people to make way for these works will always be a major difficulty on the heavily populated North China and Yangtze plains.

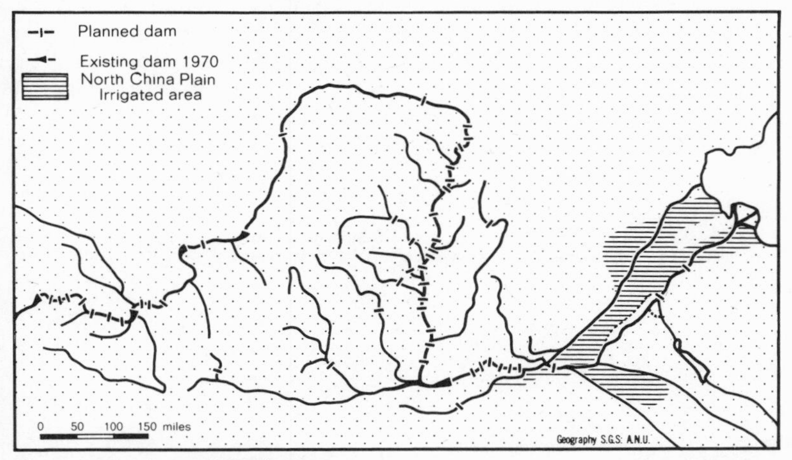

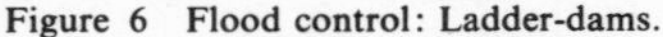

Figure 6 Flood control: Ladder-dams.

The map is adapted from the 1955 *Report on the Multi-purpose Plan for Permanently Controlling the Yellow River and Exploiting its Water Resources* presented by Teng Tse-hui, then Vice-Premier of the State Council. The central feature was the Sanmen Dam near the junction with the Wei Ho, but the report also called for the development of ladder-dams on the main stream and tributaries of the Hwang Ho, particularly in the erosion-susceptible areas of Loessland and, downstream, for irrigated areas and close control of the Hwang Ho and the Hai Ho in the northern part of the plain. Since the withdrawal of Russian technicians in the early 1960s, work on the project has largely fallen into abeyance. The Sanmen Dam is only part-completed, and those dams which have been built on the upper reaches of the Hwang Ho in Kansu and Ningsia are related rather to the requirements of hydroelectric power for the new atomic industries developing at Lanchow than to the needs of water control on the Hwang Ho itself. The ladder-dams in Loessland remain on the drawing board, and it is not yet certain that the problems of siltation will be overcome successfully even when work takes place. Even after the departure of the Russian technicians in the early 1960s, however, the Hai Ho project was carried through, and the drainage system of the North China Plain has been immensely improved. Within the limits of traditional techniques of water control, the present government has been energetic and effective (see, for example, plates 14, 16 and 18), but there are few signs yet of a breakthrough in dealing with the old problems of silt and flood along the Hwang Ho.

Just as legends claim that the Great Yü, controller of the flood-waters, was founder of China's first imperial dynasty, so modern historians, seeking some answer for China's long unity as an empire, find an explanation in the great works of irrigation and water-control. To harness the river and maintain it in its course required constant co-operation from immense numbers of people, and great administrative ability from those who controlled them. For over two thousand years, the Chinese officials, cultured, literate and elegant in manner, established and maintained their position in society by their ability to organise the people and to supervise them in great works of engineering with primitive equipment. Of all these works, from the Great Wall against the nomads of the north to the palaces and houses of the emperors and their courts, the most important to the Chinese people, and the foundation of their administrators' power, have been the dykes of the Hwang Ho across the plain.

However, although the Hwang Ho is controlled within certain limits, there is no immediate possibility that floods can be entirely prevented, and in this densely-populated plain every flood is a disaster, in terms of lives lost, of farmland out of commission, and of the ever-present threat of famine. Under the Ming dynasty, the great engineer Pan Chi-hsün urged that the Hwang Ho should be restrained in a single channel as narrow as possible between the official dykes. By this means, it was thought that the stream would use its natural slope to the full, gain velocity, and be able to carry

Plate 15 **At Linhsien County in Honan, in the Taihang Shan, intense terracing forms the base for an orchard. The trees will help to control slope erosion as well as producing fruit.** ***(China Pictorial)***

Plate 16 Water control: the Nankutung Aqueduct in Honan, on the newly constructed Red Flag Canal, brings water from the Chang River in Shansi to Linhsien in Honan. *(China Pictorial)*

the silt from Loessland all the way to the sea. Pan's opponents argued for the opposite treatment: the dykes should be set far apart to allow room for a meandering channel and a broad deposit of silt, minimising the danger of the water-flow undercutting the face of the dykes and the consequent threat of a major break.

The debate has continued, but though Pan Chi-hsün's basic policy, using the flow of water to restrict the deposit of silt, has largely been followed, traditional methods can never entirely prevent calamity in time of excessive flood. Ultimately, if the problem of the Hwang Ho is ever to be solved, it must be tackled through three great projects: to reduce the erosion of Loessland, to control the flow of the river itself, and to establish settling basins (Fig. 5) in order to trap silt and deflect the full force of flood streams.

Since the establishment of effective government, the Communists have begun work on all three of these tasks. Techniques of soil conservation have been taught and encouraged in Loessland. In 1953 the Peichinti Flood Detention Reservoir was established north-east of Chengchow, and in 1961, at Sanmen Gorge, west of Shanhsien, a major hydroelectric plant was completed. This comprises a dam almost three-quarters of a mile long, a reservoir with an area more than nine hundred square miles, and a power-station with a capacity of 150,000 kilowatts. The remainder of the Sanmen Project, however, and the whole series of ladder-dams along the river, have yet to be completed, for they were abandoned and work stopped when Russian technicians withdrew from China in 1960.

Hydroelectric plants contribute immediately to a nation's industrial development, but in time the other works of flood-control will also show their effects. It is possible, given a long period of stable government and consistent policy, that the Hwang Ho may eventually be placed entirely under the control of man, but the work will never be easy or safe. Above all, apart from the difficulties of engineering, there will always be immense social problems, for if a great chain of flood detention reservoirs and ladder-dams is to be built, then hundreds of square miles of farmland must be requisitioned and thousands of people must be moved to other districts. The lands of the Hwang Ho may one day be fertile and free from danger, but the task can only be carried out by a prosperous and powerful-government with strong centralised control. For the time being, and for many years to come, millions of people will continue to live on the open plain of north China, under regular threat of flood.

4 The North China Plain

Geology and landform

We have already considered the North China Plain as the delta land of the Hwang Ho, formed from silt deposits brought down by the river from Loessland and always under threat from the disaster of flood, the home of millions of people since the time of earliest man, and the centre of Chinese civilisation for all its recorded history. The plain today is still one of the most densely populated regions of China, and both politically and economically it maintains the same dominant position in the Communist state as it has held in all the great empires of the past.

According to recent drilling and geophysical research, the thickness of the Quaternary deposits over the plain exceeds three thousand feet in some places. Most of this material is alluvium. The surface of the plain is flat, with a slight slope towards the Yellow Sea, and the greater part of the region has an absolute elevation of less than two hundred feet. In the west, near the mountains, the plain rises no more than some three hundred feet above sea-level; in the east, towards the Shantung ranges, where a few outlying ridges of bedrock have been covered by sand and loess, the general elevation of the plain is more than a thousand feet above sea-level.

The soil of the plain, as in most of north China, is pedocal type (map 8, page 23), rich in lime and soluble minerals, with considerable alkalinity. Blown by wind and carried by water, each layer has been cultivated almost as soon as it was deposited on the plain. There has been no long period of natural climatic and botanical development, there are no recognisable soil profiles, and thousands of years of cultivation have removed all natural characteristics.

The soils so deposited and treated are often poorly drained. In the elevated areas the ground water is twelve feet or more below the surface, but over much of the region the ground water level is less than seven feet down, and in some particularly low and flat areas it is less than five. Here there is meadow-swamp. In places near the coast the soils are heavily salted. Because of poor drainage, minerals dissolved in the ground water remain near the surface

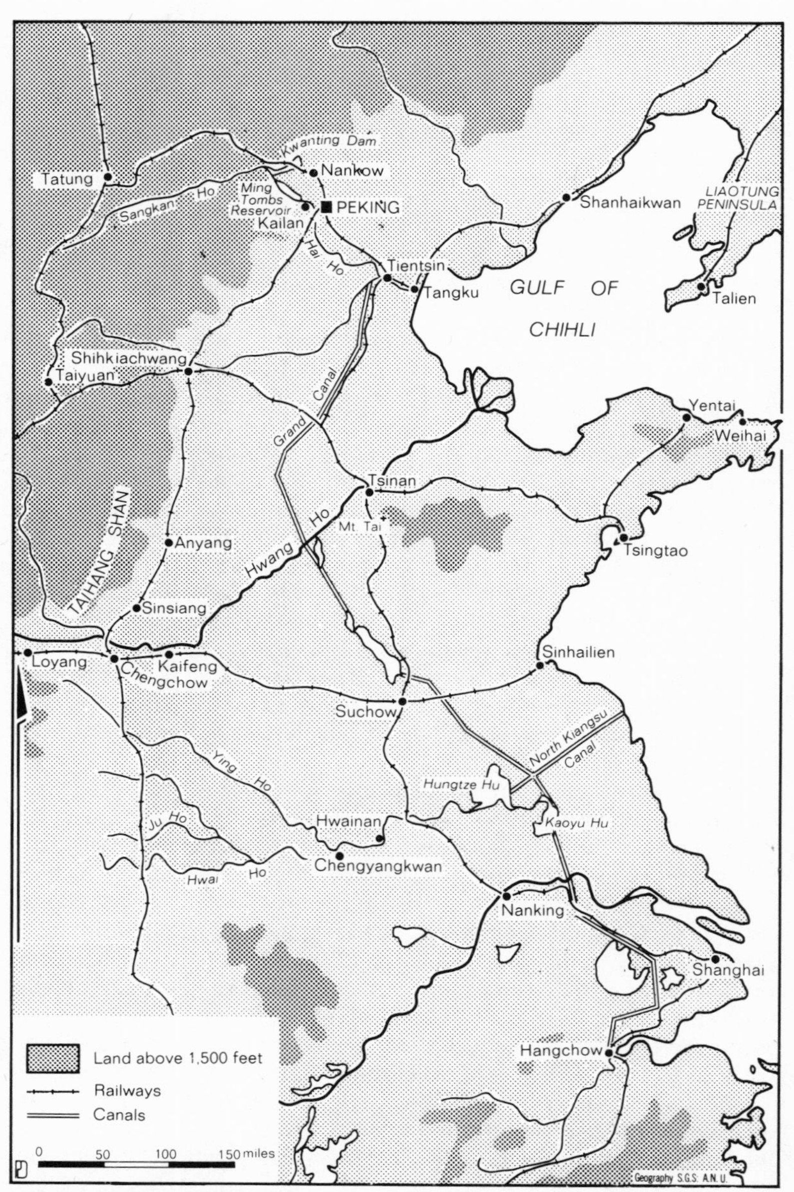

Map 20 The North China Plain.
To be read in conjunction with Chapter 4.

and are seldom carried away, while a large part of the rainfall is removed by evaporation. When they are wet, these soils become sticky; but when they are dry, they become so hard that, if the June rains come late, the farmers cannot get their ploughs through the soil, and sowing for harvest can be seriously delayed. In some districts, salt or alkali in the soil may be brought by capillary attraction to the surface and remain as a danger to the crop yield, and soil has often been ruined by these deposits. One of the mistakes of the Great Leap Forward in the late 1950s was the official encouragement of widespread well-digging across the plain. Because of the high ground water level, this is a comparatively effective way to obtain additional water, but the alkalis and salts brought to the surface by the new work had a serious effect on the soil balance and caused considerable damage to later harvests.

If the Hwang Ho has been called the Yellow River from the colour of its waters, the North China Plain is equally well named the Yellow Plain for the colour of its soil, and, indeed, everything else. It is a dusty land with comparatively low rainfall. The strong winds from the north and west during winter and spring carry fine silt in the air from Loessland, and stir the friable deposits on the surface of the plain. Dust storms are frequent, with a haze that can cover the sun, and the fine particles that coat everything in the land find their way even into closed rooms. Once there were great forests and marshes, yet now the plain is all but treeless. Cities, dykes and grave-mounds—the work of man—spread across the country and show silhouettes on the open horizon.

Climate

The climate of the plain has great fluctuations of temperature: at Tsinan in Shantung the winter minimum temperature may be 0°F, and the average for summer is 70°F, with temperatures on some days over 100°F. The rainfall is similarly variable. The annual average is 25 inches, though it is both warmer and wetter in the south of the plain. As in Loessland and the rest of north China, the heaviest rainfall comes in summer, though there are great differences from one year to the next. The lowest recorded July rainfall for Peking is 30 points, and the highest is 32.5 inches. See maps 11-14, pages 26-7.

Agriculture and the commune system

Both soil and climate lend themselves to dry farming, with crops of wheat, millet, kaoliang, maize, barley, soybeans, sweet potatoes, hemp and cotton. The climate is too dry and the soil too alkaline for rice, but the greater part of the plain supports two harvests in a year. Winter wheat (map 16, page 32) is the chief grain of north

China. In the southern third of the plain the secondary crop is barley, which stands up well to wet conditions and which can also be grown alongside rice. In the north, and also in Loessland, millet is the second crop, for it is largely drought-resistant. Both millet and barley have a short growing period.

Agriculture is carried out by intensive manual labour. In villages and communes there are oxen, donkeys and mules to help with the heaviest work, but it is the men who build the canals and guide the irrigation channels through the fields, and harvesting is almost entirely done by hand. Fertiliser, always a necessity for land which has been cultivated so long and so intensively, is now supplied partly from new chemical factories, but the greater part comes still from the traditional sources of animal and human manure. The country is short of timber so the houses of the people are generally built of pounded earth or sun-dried brick, and stalks of the coarse kaoliang plant can be woven together to give a base for walls and roofs or to stand as fencing.

With irrigation to control the water supply in all but the most extreme years, and with as many as a dozen different crops to be raised, there is little danger of a total crop failure. Besides the open field crops, the farmers grow a wide variety of vegetables and around every peasant's house there are fowls and pigs. To this day, the Chinese word for 'home' is written with a character showing a stylised picture of a pig under a roof. Even within the commune system of the present government there is room for much private barter and trade in small-scale domestic production.

The Communists, however, have made major changes, and they have been particularly effective in the North China Plain. Traditionally, Chinese peasant life was divided between intensive farmwork on small privately-owned plots of land and large-scale co-operative ventures, when whole teams of villagers worked under the direction of their leaders on the regular tasks of ploughing and harvesting or for such major projects as flood-control and irrigation. In theory, in pre-Communist China, though the peasant might pay rent for his land to members of the wealthy gentry, the proportion of his income expended in this way was not excessive; his right to his plots of land, which varied on average in different regions from three to five acres per family, was relatively secure; and the rich and powerful men of the community showed some sense of social responsibility and often provided valuable leadership.

In the twentieth century, among the chaos of war-lord rule, with a weak government distracted by civil war and foreign invasion, the traditional structure of Chinese society, already shaken in the fall of the Manchu Empire, was utterly destroyed. Absentee landlords living in the great cities were prepared to collect their rents by force, and the peasants gained neither protection nor leadership from their masters. Land reform, as in much of Asia at the present day, was an essential political and economic policy. By the 1930s there were many observers who noted accurately that land reform in China must mean Communism: no government had the financial resources to afford fair compensation to the dispossessed landowners, and only the Communist party was prepared to effect land reform without any compensation.

In the years after the Communist victory in 1949, the redistribution of land, which had already begun in Communist territory from the 1930s onward, was rapidly extended to all China. Some executions took place and many formerly rich peasant families were disgraced and impoverished, but by 1953 land reform had been effectively completed, so that those who had been middle and poor peasants, and the landless men, were now the owners as well as the tillers of their soil.

So far, it could be said that the Communists had performed a clearing operation and a re-arrangement of agricultural landholding comparable to that which had taken place at the end of civil wars and the beginning of many great dynasties in the past. From this point, however, the government attempted to introduce new patterns of organisation: first Mutual Aid Teams, through which a few households combined to work each other's land in turn, then, in 1954, Agricultural Producers Co-operatives, where five hundred people or more pooled their land, their tools and their labour, and worked together under the direction of a management committee. In 1958, at the time of the Great Leap Forward, the co-operatives were combined to form Communes, and by 1959 there were some 26,000 communes throughout the country, each with a membership of twenty thousand people or more.

At the head of a commune is a council, dealing direct on economic matters with the State Planning Organisation. The council is responsible both for marketing and purchase of material, and also for the operation of local industry, such as fertiliser plants and machinery manufacturing and repair shops.

Below the commune level there are the Production Brigades, each with some one hundred families farming perhaps two hundred acres. These brigades own the greater part of the farm tools and machinery, the draught animals and the land, and it is their duty to establish quotas for production and allocate resources among the Production Teams below them.

A production team of twenty or thirty families is the basic unit of the commune system. A farmer works within his production team to achieve the agreed quota of production, and bonus points gained for extra production by each team and each individual within a team are rewarded at the end of the harvest by distribution of consumer goods and new supplies. Each family receives a basic allocation of food and credit, but after that pay and profit goes to the man who works hardest.

In the first flush of enthusiasm, as the commune system was introduced rapidly all over China and as incredible reports of massive harvests poured into the capital, the new organisation was proclaimed a complete change from the past and the beginning of a new era in Chinese agriculture. Certainly it was a complete change, for although large-scale co-operation had long been practised in the past, it had never before been institutionalised and made a permanent basis for agricultural work. On the other hand, despite the first glowing reports, the system was not a complete success. The wonderful days of 1958 and 1959 were followed by a series of bad years and poor harvests in 1960 and 1961, which brought hunger to much of China and returned the planners and the eager statisticians to reality.

The communes now are far less important than they were at first; instead of serving as the king-pins of farming life, they are no more than a link in the chain of command from the government to the people. As an attempt to lift Chinese agriculture out of the limited viewpoint of the individual farm or village, and to establish a rural unit large enough and prosperous enough to accumulate investment capital for development and share prosperity and production over a wider area, the commune system was not entirely a failure. On the other hand, the commune and its subordinate units proved a clumsy means to control the processes of agriculture which depend, in the last resort, far more on the skill and diligence of the individual farmer than on directives sent down from above or agreements made in advance. Later instructions to the cadres repeated again and again that they should encourage the farmers to work in their own ways, and should not attempt to enforce ideal theories in the face of concrete objections from the man on the land.

Perhaps even more important, there remains the question whether individual farmers can be encouraged to work their best for the community rather than for their own pieces of land. Often, it seems, the small patches of private land around the farmhouses have been tended meticulously while the main bulk of the work in the public fields has been left uncared for. The quota-bonus system of the commune has not always proved sufficiently attractive to gain good work from the members of production teams. While some innovations, such as communal kindergartens and crèches, have freed women to work outside the home, it is not entirely surprising that communal kitchens have proved unpopular: no-one really likes to eat institutional food. In general terms, it has yet to be shown in China that agriculture by communal or Communist methods is in any way more successful than private peasant farming under a fair system of land distribution.

Communications

Ancient Chinese philosophers talked of a land where people in one village would hear cocks crowing and dogs barking in the next settlement but would have no wish to travel there. On the open plain, the Chinese seem to have come close to their ideal. The great bulk of the people live in clusters of houses—small farming villages—near their fields, with the market town no more than two or three miles away. Road networks tend to be localised and are seldom more than cart-tracks, dust or mud in summer and frozen ruts in winter. The shifting courses of rivers and streams have made ferries, fords and bridges expensive and unreliable, and even today, despite the effective central government at Peking, there are few well-paved motor roads outside the immediate vicinity of major cities. In the past, long-distance travel and transport were effected mainly by junks and barges along the rivers and canals, and since the nineteenth century it has been the railroad rather than the highway that has supplemented and developed the traditional network of communications. Even so, in its course across the North China Plain, the Hwang Ho is bridged by rail in only two places: north of Chengchow by the line from Peking along the west of the plain to Wuhan, and north of Tsinan in Shantung by the line from Peking to the Yangtze near Nanking.

It is hardly chance that the second of these trunk lines follows very closely the course of the Grand Canal, first built in the Sui dynasty, around A.D. 600. The canal links the lower Yangtze valley with the lands of the Hwang Ho, and brought tax grain to feed the imperial capital and pay the imperial officials and the army. Later dynasties extended the original waterway both north and south, so that in its furthest course it joins Hangchow in Chekiang with the northern capital, Peking. In almost every period of Chinese history, the north has been predominant in political power, but for more than a thousand years the south, the land beyond the Yangtze, has become increasingly important in the economy of the whole country. In earlier times, the transport of surplus grain as tax from the south to supply the powerful north was one of the major tasks of an effective administration in China. Even now the transport of food from the grain-surplus areas to the hungry cities is one of the chief responsibilities of the Communist government.

Plate 17 Transport: cotton barges on a canal. *(China Pictorial)*

Industry

The North China Plain has few mineral resources, though there are great coalfields in the north-east which extend into Manchuria. Kailan near Tientsin is one of the largest production centres in the country. On the level coast north and south of the Shantung Peninsula, salt-pans are used to evaporate salt from sea-water. As a preservative, salt is essential in a simple economy, and the salt trade has been a government monopoly since the days of the first empire two thousand years ago. Under the Manchu Ch'ing dynasty and in the early period of the republic, salt was one of the major sources of government revenue, and the salt commissioners were among the highest officials of the civil service. Even now, between Hangchow Bay and the Liaotung Peninsula, there are probably more salt-pans and a greater industry devoted to its extraction than in any other comparable region in the world. Far inland, there are salt lakes, particularly in the north-west near the Great Wall, and in Szechwan there are salt wells; but the bulk of China's production, second in immediate importance and value only to coal, comes from the open shore-line of the Yellow Sea.

The Hwai Ho and the Hai

In the west of China, the border between the dry north and the warm, semi-tropical south is defined by the Chin Ling Shan and its subordinate ranges. In the east, the transition region between the North China Plain and the basin of the lower Yangtze is the valley of the Hwai Ho; the tropical banana and orange trees, plentiful in the Yangtze valley and the south, do not grow on its northern bank.

The Hwai is in many ways more of a general drainage system than a river, for it carries the water from a great number of tributaries, and then, when it approaches the sea, loses course among a medley of lakes and canals. It has no established mouth. The main stream rises in southern Honan and flows in a slight depression through the plain towards the east. In the first part of its course, through Honan and central Anhwei, it receives run-off from all the plain south of the Hwang Ho, chiefly by the systems of the Ying Ho and Ju Ho. It is joined from the south by tributary streams from the Tapieh Shan. The river meanders across swampy ground, forming a belt of connected channels and lakes. As it crosses the border from Anhwei to Kiangsu it enters the largest of the lakes, the Hungtze, and then the Kaoyu, and from there, at the line of the Grand Canal, it has no further natural course.

Two main factors have contributed to this situation: firstly, the natural extension of the coast-line, and secondly, the great changes of course by the Hwang Ho, which has on several occasions usurped the channel of the Hwai, causing excess water to force its way along the Grand Canal into the Yangtze, to stand in great lakes until it evaporates, or to flood the low-lying ground. This was the pattern for more than ten years in the 1930s and early 1940s, and even when the Hwang Ho is held within its own banks, the damage it has done in the past remains to prevent the Hwai establishing its own clear path to the sea.

All along the coast of Kiangsu Province, from Hangchow Bay to Shantung, the silt brought down by great rivers has steadily extended the area of dry land, and the work of nature has been supplemented by the engineering of man. Offshore there is shallow water with sand-bars, and wherever possible the land is reclaimed by a system of dykes and levees comparable to those of Holland. Further inland also, the farmers encroach as far as possible on the great lakes along the course of the Hwai, for these, shallow with silt and showing great variation in level between high and low water, offer excellent farmland when drainage can be effective and well maintained.

It is not surprising, then, that the Hwai causes more trouble than the Yangtze, for a river that is over eight hundred miles long, with a basin area of more than eighty thousand square miles, can hardly be safe without an adequate channel and a well-defined mouth. High summer rainfall over the plain and the southern mountains causes great variation between minimum and maximum flow. The regular channel of the river is quite unable to take the peak load of water: the discharge maximum in flood at Chengyangkwan in Anhwei, for example, has been measured at 460,000 cubic feet per second, and the capacity of the channel is hardly 300,000 cubic feet per second.

Traditional methods of embankment and dyke defences have had fair success in containing all but the major floods on the Hwai, but there is as yet no adequate means to avoid calamity in time of particularly heavy floods, and these may be expected every ten or

twenty years. When the Communists established effective government after the civil war, one of the major works in their First Five-Year Plan was the improvement of the Hwai Ho. The chief outlet to the sea is now the North Kiangsu Canal which drains the Hungtze Hu. Other water flows along the Grand Canal and the Kaoyu Hu to reach the sea through a network of canals and rivers flowing east or south to the Yangtze. New dams and locks have been built to control the water, and hundreds of miles of dykes have been raised and strengthened. New channels are planned and immense work is still needed, mainly in the continued development of a great system of reservoirs to hold the floodwaters and, further upstream, of controls to retain the water for increased irrigation in the drainage area and to prevent constant soil erosion.

To the north of the North China Plain, the Hai is the largest river of the drainage system running from the northern hills and Taihang Shan in the west to the sea-coast of the Gulf of Chihli (Po Hai). Many of the rivers which flow across the plain follow ancient courses of the Hwang Ho, and their existing channels are all affected in various degrees by the north-south line of the Grand Canal leading to Peking. The Hai Ho itself, whose drainage area of some eighty thousand square miles extends north and west about Peking, ends its six-hundred-mile course south-east of Tientsin in a channel at one time occupied by the Hwang Ho. Like the Hwang Ho, but unlike the Hwai, the greater part of the Hai's lower course follows a bed raised constantly by alluvial deposits, and always requiring protection by dykes. On a smaller scale it resembles the Hwang Ho, with similar problems of summer flood and sedimentation.

Plate 18 Water control: building a canal to control a tributary of the Hwai Ho in the south of the North China Plain. The construction is carried out almost entirely by manual labour, with no large earth-moving machinery. Note the division of labour: digging teams inside the channel, teams to carry the material in wheelbarrows to the crest of the dam, and consolidation teams at the top. The placards carry such slogans as 'Long live the invincible Thought of Mao Tse-tung'. *(China Pictorial)*

In 1963, after the greatest flood recorded for two centuries, the government determined to carry out the Hai Ho project, which involves reorganisation of almost every river system north of the Hwang Ho. New outlets have been created to the sea, and great areas of alkaline waste and coastal marshland are being treated to return them to productivity. So far the scheme has greatly reduced the dangers of flood, and has offered newly reclaimed, fertile and irrigated land to more than 50,000,000 people. Smaller than many of the schemes embarked upon with Russian advice, its success has been a triumph for the independent policy of the Chinese Communist government.

North of the Shantung Peninsula, the sea-coast of the North China Plain presents the same opportunities for reclamation and the same difficulties of salt-marsh and shallow ground as the Kiangsu coast-line in the south. Harbours are few, and while the Hai Ho serves as the port for Peking and small ships can anchor at Tientsin, twenty miles from the sea, this is more a matter of commercial necessity than natural circumstance. The major part of China's overseas trade is carried out from the great cities and the natural harbours of the Yangtze and the southern coast.

Peking and the cities of the north

In a pre-industrial society, there are two chief reasons for the growth of a city: as a trading centre or as a unit of political control. In either case, the site will be a nodal point for some local transport network and a significant link on a chain of long-distance communication. For its continued existence, however, the pre-industrial city depends upon the country that surrounds it. Economically, its prosperity from trade depends largely on the produce of the farmer; politically, wealth, power and growth are a function of profits from administration and gains from tax.

In large measure, China is still at a primitive stage of industrial development, and on the North China Plain there are far more people living in villages around the countryside than in the cities and market towns. At the time of the last effective census, in 1953, the population of the plain numbered over 80,000,000 people, but only the cities of Peking and Tientsin had more than a million inhabitants, and the next largest, Tsinan where the railway crosses the Hwang Ho in Shantung, had 500,000 to 600,000. Altogether, at that time, there were some fifteen cities with more than 100,000 people, and a combined population of seven or eight million, no more than a tenth of the numbers of the whole region. The cities have grown larger. Peking and Tientsin are both now probably more than three million, yet it does not seem that the overall ratio of rural-urban population has changed.

Plate 19 Peking on the North China Plain, with classical square layout of streets and houses, great walls, and a distant, dusty horizon. *(Courtesy: Pacific Communications Ltd, Hong Kong)*

The predominance of Peking and its close neighbour Tientsin is a function of both politics and economics. Nankow Pass, on the main road to Mongolia, is fifty miles north-west of Peking, and Shanhaikwan, the narrow gateway to Manchuria between the mountains and the sea, is two hundred miles due east. Peking's strategic position close to the northern borders and at the centre of an arc of natural defences has made it important to every Chinese empire. Before 500 B.C. the site of the modern city was already the capital of a great state; under the early dynasties military headquarters and garrisons were maintained here; and when the Mongols conquered China in the thirteenth century they established their administration at Peking. The Chinese dynasty of the Ming, which drove out the Mongols in the fourteenth century, first made their capital at Nanking on the Yangtze, but soon returned north to Peking, the 'Northern Capital'. So close to the frontier with the Manchus, Peking was an excellent headquarters for controlling defence against the emperor's major barbarian enemy. But as the military power of Ming declined, Peking became dangerously exposed. In 1644 the treachery of a Chinese general allowed an army of Manchus through the pass of Shanhaikwan and they were able to establish their power through all of China, claiming as they did so that they ruled from the same seat as their predecessors.

After the revolution in 1911, the new republic set its capital at Nanking, and the former capital was renamed Peiping, 'Northern Peace'. When the Nationalists were driven from the mainland to the island of Taiwan, the Communists returned the government to the north and restored the name Peking. At present, the Nationalists, and their allies the Americans, commonly refer to the city as Peiping.

In climate, Peking can be harsh, with occasional snow in winter and in spring and summer the ubiquitous yellow dust. The annual

Figure 7 Peking.

The sketch map shows Peking as the archetype city of the North China Plain. Established as a centre of government and administration, on open ground with no important irregularities of terrain, the city has broad boulevards and regular protective walls. It is interesting to compare the plan with that of a treaty port city such as Shanghai (figure 8, page 162).

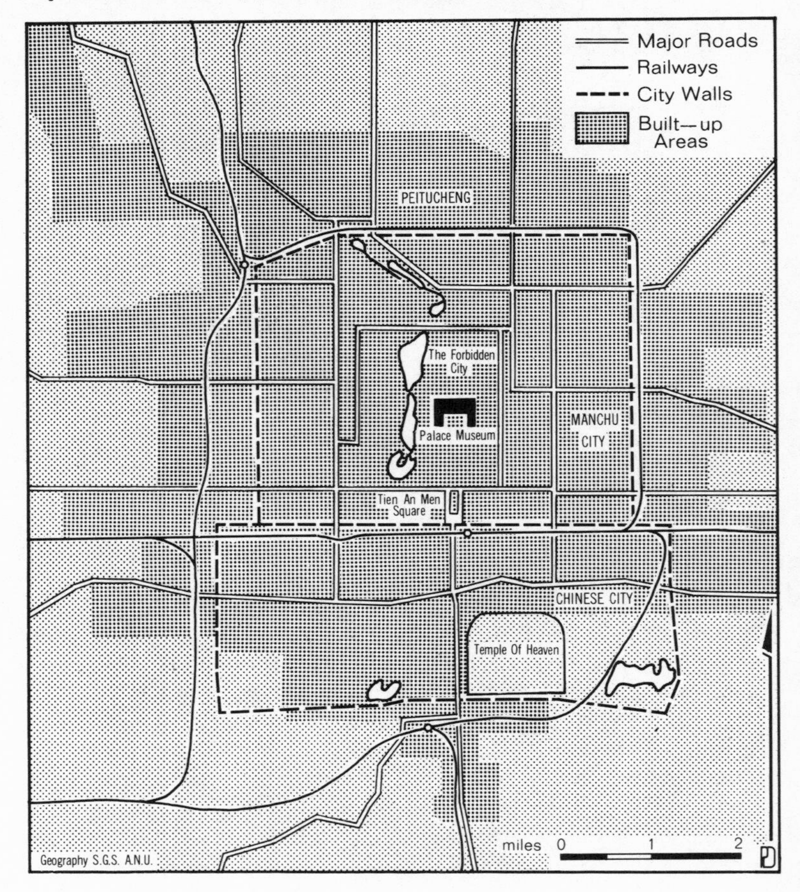

rainfall averages some 20 inches, but may vary greatly from one year to the next. Autumn, after the heaviest rains and before the November frosts, is the most pleasant season. After centuries of imperial patronage, with trees and wide boulevards first laid out by the Yung-lo Emperor six hundred years ago, Peking is one of the finest cities of the world and a superb example of traditional Chinese town-planning. Like almost all the cities of the plain, where town-sites are flat and little affected by hillslopes or rivers, Peking is planned on a grid system within great squares of defensive walls facing north, south, east and west. In former times, the ruler sat with his back to the north, and his throne-room, his palace and the city beyond were placed about him in regular fashion.

Peking is really three cities (fig. 7, page 82), with modern suburbs scattered around outside. In the north there is the walled Inner 'Manchu' City, and inside the Manchu City is the Imperial 'Forbidden' City, former palace of the emperors. South of the Manchu City is the Outer 'Chinese' City, surrounded by lesser walls, and containing the Temple of Heaven, where the emperor, Son of Heaven, would worship at midnight on the winter solstice. The Imperial City, the Temple of Heaven, and the Summer Palace outside the city have now been restored and turned into museums and pleasure-grounds for the people. Fitting to the capital of one of the world's greatest empires, the walls and squares are massive and wide. During the Boxer Rebellion in 1900, when foreigners in the Legation Quarter of the Manchu City were besieged by rebels, the wall of the city was a battleground, with guns mounted to fire along the rampart. At the present time, when the leaders of the government join the people to celebrate a national festival with a parade and display in Tien An Men Square before the Forbidden City, several hundred thousand people can be fitted into this 'Square of the Gate of Heavenly Peace'.

Like all Chinese cities, Peking has busy shops open to the street and the houses with gardens are behind walls. Chinese houses are seldom more than one or two stories, generally with a blank wall facing the street and courtyards inside surrounded by rooms and apartments. From outside, all may seem dull and forbidding to the passer-by, but behind the wall there are flowers and trees and a quiet sense of community. In the shopping streets and lanes, on the other hand, the counters are open to the street and the shopkeepers commonly live above their premises.

Under imperial rule, Peking was the centre of culture, and the Imperial University was the finest in the empire. Despite changes of government policy the tradition of learning has been maintained. Under Communist rule almost a score of colleges and technical institutes, each with five thousand students or more, have been

Plate 20 A bicycle park in Loyang, ancient capital of the Chinese empire. Shops are open to the street, and the shopkeepers live above them. *(Courtesy: Gun Kessle and Jan Myrdal)*

established alongside the earlier foundations, such as the Medical College and the National University, both of which began as missionary schools for Western learning.

Most of these institutions are found in the western suburbs. On the east side there are blast furnaces, machine shops and textile factories, for this region of the North China Plain has important resources of coal and in any great city manpower is readily available for industrial development. One of the most impressive works of the new regime in the 1950s was the Ming Tombs Reservoir project, north-west of Peking in the high ground near the Great Wall, and the related Kwanting Dam, which controls and stores the water of the Sangkan Ho and Yungting Ho and provides a major source of hydroelectric power.

Tientsin, some eighty miles by road south-east of Peking on the Hai Ho, was formerly the seaport for the capital, but silting has become so severe during the present century that only small ships can now be unloaded on the river wharves. Tangku, at the mouth of the river, has become the port for Tientsin itself and an artificial harbour, capable of sheltering vessels of ten thousand tons, has been constructed there. Although in winter months the port is ice-bound, the hinterland of Tientsin, with Peking close at hand, and an extensive system of railway communications through the north of the plain and into the western mountains, have helped to make Tientsin and Tangku among the leading Chinese ports, with Talien in Manchuria and Shanghai and Canton in the south.

It was during the nineteenth century, in the period of European influence on China, that Tientsin became a major link in the communications system between the Western countries and their embassies and missions at the imperial capital. The Convention of Peking in 1860 opened Tientsin to foreign trade and residence, and the original Chinese city was soon surrounded by British, French, German, Russian, Japanese and other concessions. The population grew as migrants from the countryside came to the city to serve the foreigners and to work on the wharves and railways. With such a labour force available, light industry has developed and continued to expand; there are flour and paper mills, rug manufacture, and a variety of processing plants handling raw material from the country and goods imported from abroad.

Peking and Tientsin, with their population enlarged by imperial interest and foreign trade, have naturally developed considerable local industry. It is noteworthy, however, that except in the region of Peking and Tientsin major industrial progress has had small effect on the comparative growth of population in other great cities of the plain, for the delta region of the Hwang Ho has no great mineral wealth to attract large new settlement around plants for heavy industry. Hwainan, in the south of the plain, has important coalfields, but the three cities ranking after Peking and Tientsin—Chengchow, Kaifeng ana Tsinan—have a long history of settlement on their sites. They owe their present prosperity chiefly to their importance in the communications network, near major crossings of the Hwang Ho. In the same way, the city of Loyang, further to the west at the head of the delta and now an important centre for the manufacture of cars, tractors and agricultural equipment, was the capital of China almost two thousand years ago. In many ways, despite changes of government and the coming of industrialisation, the essential patterns of agriculture and population on the North China Plain are much as they have been for centuries past. The raw materials for an industrial revolution in China are to be found in the hill country of the Taihang Shan to the west of the plain, in the Shantung Hills to the east, and in the north-east, in central and southern Manchuria.

The Shantung Hills

Geologically, the Shantung Hills are a southward extension of the mountain ridge from Heilungkiang Province in eastern Manchuria through the Liaotung Peninsula across the narrow strait between the Gulf of Chihli and the Yellow Sea, while a western link may be traced to the Chin Ling Shan. The flat delta of the North China Plain has buried the connecting strata, but the Shantung Hills stand as a sharp rocky outcrop, similar in many ways to the original formation of Loessland in the west yet without the massive deposits of wind-borne silt.

The geographic region covers some thirty thousand square miles, with a population of over twenty million. It is divided into two parts by a down-faulted block or graben, and along this lowland the railway from Tsingtao runs north-west into the North China Plain. On the west, the massif about Mount Tai extends like a salient into the plain, and the ancient and modern courses of the Hwang Ho must flow to the sea either north or south of the high ground.

Mount Tai, 5,056 feet high, is the sacred mountain of China. Geologically, it is a fault scarp, rising sharply from the surface of the plain, with lesser ridges and peaks no more than two or three thousand feet high extending towards the east. Confucius lived near here, emperors have come to worship with great state sacrifices, and for thousands of years pilgrims and tourists have climbed the six thousand stone steps to the temples at the peak, to gaze across the plain and stare down on the lesser hills round about.

On the slopes exposed to wind from the plain there is a thin surface of loess, but elsewhere the natural soil is the neutral brown soil, common to all the hill country from Shantung to Liaotung, to the Jehol foothills of western Manchuria and to the Taihang Shan across the plain (map 8, page 23). Erosion, however, is severe. The natural vegetation, chiefly pine forests, has largely disappeared, and the rainfall, averaging annually some 25 inches, is sufficient to wash away any exposed soil from the steep mountain slopes and to choke the valley floors and gullies with useless debris. The steep slopes of the Shantung Hills, with their isolated pine trees, rocky crags and paths, and a hermit's hut or tiny temple poised artistically above some dark and cloudy abyss, have been the inspiration for great numbers of traditional Chinese landscape paintings, but few of the trees now remain, and the soil-wash from such slopes is very great.

Though the population of the region is far smaller than that of the North China Plain, the settlement is just as intense in relation to resources, and cultivation has been extended up to and often beyond the limits of economic conservation. Much of the country is now barren and denuded of soil and heavy terracing is often needed to preserve the remnants of fertile ground. Elsewhere, there is still good land, and the patterns of human settlement are as close as production will allow. In the spring millet, kaoliang, peanuts and cotton are sown, and successful crops depend on good summer rains, some 20 inches between May and October. Too little, and the crops will be dried out; too much, and they may be washed from the soil by flood or beaten down by torrential downpour. In September, after the autumn harvest, winter wheat and barley are sown, covering some two-thirds of the arable land. Then, all through the growing period until the harvest in June, the water in the soil must be preserved by mulching and by light irrigation from wells lest the crop dry out in the near rainless season of spring. Almost all the work of the farm is done by hand—planting, hoeing, watering, harvesting and threshing—and draft animals are not even so common as they are on the North China Plain. Silk, a domestic industry, is produced by worms fed with oak leaves instead of the mulberry leaves used elsewhere. Since classical times, silk has been the home product of the Chinese peasant, though the main centres of the industry are now in south China. The increase in synthetics is having considerable effect on demand for the natural material.

The hills of Shantung, chiefly in the west near Tsinan, have large coalfields, with reserves estimated at 1,600,000,000 tons and an annual production of some 10,000,000 tons. The region thus takes third place behind the north China fields around Kailan near Peking and the mines of southern Manchuria. There are major deposits of iron ore in the same area, and secondary deposits on the south coast near Tsingtao.

The Shantung Peninsula, with its rocky backbone of mountains, has good harbours for fishing. Shrimp, mackerel and bass are three main catches. Drag netting is carried out all the year round, although in winter the temperature of the water approaches freezing point and there is a migration of fish to the south beyond the Yangtze estuary. On the northern coast of the peninsula, Yentai and Weihai are the two major cities, but Tsingtao, in the south, with a population well over a million, is the most important centre of the region. Tsingtao is connected by rail with Yentai to the north-east and Tsinan to the west, and it has important railway workshops, a fine harbour with dock facilities for very large ships, and a processing industry for textiles. Through Tsinan, Tsingtao has access to the main communications routes of the North China Plain, and its hinterland extends well beyond the province of Shantung. Tsinan, the capital of the province, is situated in the region of the North China Plain rather than of the Shantung Hills.

In 1898 Tsingtao and a considerable part of southern Shantung was granted as a concession to the German government by the imperial court, and in a countermove Great Britain took control of Weihai. The foreign occupation was of some benefit to the region, for the Germans dredged and deepened the harbour of Tsingtao, built a considerable part of the modern city and established a major re-afforestation programme. In general terms, however, the people of Shantung Province fared worst at the hands of foreigners in the century of imperialism before World War II. Further south, the great cities of Shanghai, Canton and Hong Kong, and the ports of the Yangtze and the Fukien coast, all made a profit from the European trade with the great hinterland behind them. Shantung, however, was a region of conflict for naval bases and for political interest. Later, at the outbreak of World War I, it exchanged German rule for the still more aggressive occupation of the Japanese. It is not surprising that Shantung was one of the strongholds of the anti-foreign Boxer Movement in 1900 nor, after the fall of the empire in 1912, that many peasants of Shantung abandoned their crowded, distressed homeland and migrated across the Yellow Sea to the open territory and new opportunities of Manchuria in the north-east.

5 Manchuria

Manchuria, known to the Chinese as 'the north-east', is a lowland plain surrounded on three sides by mountains and drained by great rivers which flow southwards and eastwards into the sea. To the west lie the high steppes of Mongolia, to the north and east is Russian Siberia, and south-east is the People's Republic of North Korea.

Her geographical position has made Manchuria a pawn of diplomacy and war for all this century, and the present government of China maintains a natural concern with the security of its territory and the definition of its borders. At the time of the Boxer Rebellion in 1900, Russia attempted to persuade the weakened Imperial Government in Peking to cede Manchuria. The Tsarist defeat in the Russo-Japanese War of 1904-5 changed only the source of the threat and did nothing to relieve the danger. Thirty years of Japanese pressure and encroachment culminated in the Manchuria Incident of 1931, when the Japanese army drove Chinese forces from that territory and established the puppet state of 'Manchukuo'. In 1945, at the defeat of Japan, Manchuria was returned to China, but not before the armies of the Soviet Union had occupied the territory and taken away with them, under the guise of reparations, almost every piece of industrial and mining equipment that could be moved. When the Chinese Communists took over, much of Manchuria's pre-war development had been destroyed. There remained a tradition of technology, vast known deposits of the raw materials for industry, an excellent railway system within a controllable geographical region, and a nagging fear of renewed foreign invasion.

Industry and communications

It is the industrial development of Manchuria that makes the region of primary importance to China, for deposits of coal and iron ore lie close together in several places and Manchuria is the country's major centre of heavy industry. The foundations for this supremacy were laid in the period of Japanese occupation; by 1943, when production was at its peak, it was estimated that industrial output included 25,000,000 tons of coal, 1,725,000 tons of pig-iron and

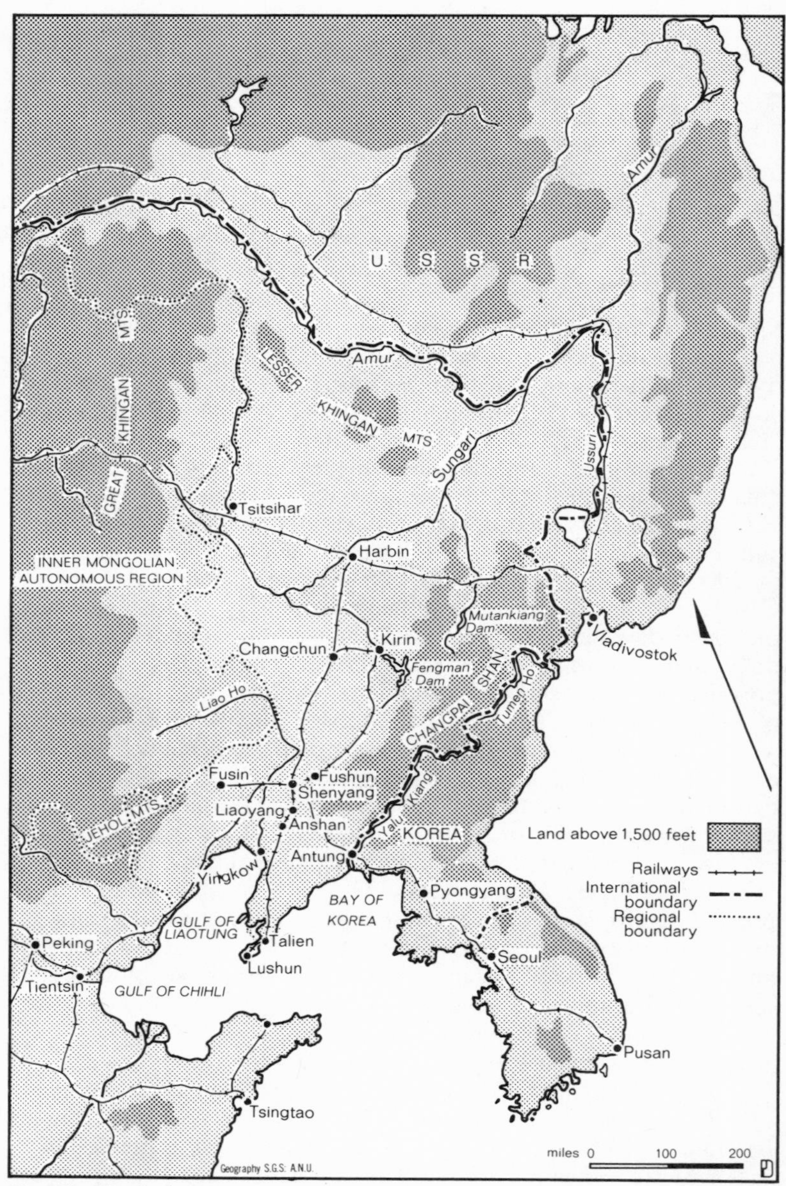

Map 21 Manchuria.
To be read in conjunction with Chapter 5.

more than 835,000 tons of steel ingots. The devastation caused by Russian plunder and the Chinese civil war reduced production so far that it was not until 1953 that output returned to the wartime level it had reached ten years before. Estimates of national production of coal and steel over the twenty years since the Communists came to power would indicate amazing increases: American and Japanese sources, for example, suggest a rise from 32,000,000 tons of coal in 1949 to more than 320,000,000 tons in 1969. The year 1949, however, is not a good choice for such comparisons, since at that time Manchurian production was at its lowest ebb. The great open-cut mine at Fushun, which had produced 10,000,000 tons of coal in 1944, produced no more than 2,500,000 in 1949, while present-day claims suggest an annual production of 20,000,000 tons.

In their work of reconstruction, the Communist government received considerable assistance from the Soviet Union, whose experts did something to repair the devastation their armies had wrought a few years earlier. Some two thousand Russian technicians and twenty thousand skilled Chinese were brought to Manchuria, and by 1955 there were eight blast furnaces in operation, with two more under construction, and heavy rolling mills producing steel girders for construction work and steel bars for tubing. The plant is modern, and although the design and initial equipment came from Russia it is Chinese skill and technology that has expanded the works and developed production further.

The two major factors which encouraged the Communist government to restore Manchuria's prosperity and develop its industrial base were firstly the availability of raw material for industry and secondly the comparative efficiency of communications. The coalfields of Manchuria are not as good as the known reserves of Shensi and Shansi in either quantity or quality, but they are still enormous, and they are far more accessible than those to the west. Fusin and Fushun, the two great open-cut mines of Liaoning Province in southern Manchuria, are estimated to have reserves of 4,000,000,000 tons with 950,000,000 tons of good bituminous coal, exposed to open-cut mining in seams of extraordinary thickness. At Fushun, now the major field of extraction, the coal seam varies between 120 and 360 feet in thickness, with an average of 240 feet, and it is at present exposed along a cutting four miles long and some three-quarters of a mile wide. The cutting could be extended another four and a half miles. The coal lies beneath a layer of oil shale some 250 feet thick, and a surface stratum of green shale about the same thickness. During the period of Japanese working, an oil refinery was built to process the oil shale. The green shale is now being used for water-softening.

Plate 21 Anshan Iron and Steel Company, Manchuria. Granulated waste slag is being stockpiled for further use. *(China Pictorial)*

Fushun is closer to the centres of production than most other fields and, although the seam slopes downwards and working is gradually becoming more difficult, it will continue to be an important mine for some time to come. Elsewhere, besides Fusin, there are estimated reserves totalling well over 2,000,000,000 tons of bituminous coal, mainly in the eastern hills and in the south-west towards the border with China Proper. There are also considerable reserves of molybdenum, copper, lead, zinc, graphite and bauxite, and in southern Manchuria there are estimated reserves of iron ore totalling some 4,500,000,000 tons. All but some 60,000,000 tons, however, is low-grade. In this region there are also adequate

Plate 22 Drilling team No. 32143 at Taching oilfields, in Heilungkiang Province, north Manchuria. *(China Pictorial)*

quantities of limestone, dolomite and fire-clay, the auxiliary minerals needed for iron and steel production.

The second factor encouraging industry in Manchuria is the network of railways centring around Shenyang, formerly known as Mukden, the capital of Liaoning Province. The South Manchurian Railway Company, which was developed by the Japanese after they defeated the Russians in 1905, had by 1943 almost 9,500 miles of track, with a double-track central route from Talien through Shenyang to Harbin. This was more than all the rest of China's railway system put together and, despite the destruction of rolling stock through war and plunder, the established system of communications made southern Manchuria a natural site for further development. Shenyang is now the centre of this system, linked by rail with the coalfields of Fushun, Tunghwa and Sian on the east, Fusin and Peipiao on the west, and further afield with Peking, Tientsin and the north of China Proper. Talien, often known as Dairen, and its secondary port, Lushun (formerly Port Arthur) at the tip of the Liaotung Peninsula, both have good rail connections with the north and east and possess the only harbours on the northern coast of the Gulf of Chihli which are ice-free throughout the year (map 11, page 26). While winter sea ice may affect the shallow waters at the mouth of the Hai Ho and close the port of Tientsin, and the Gulf of Liaotung and the Bay of Korea are regularly frozen, the tip of the peninsula has deep water close inshore to the east and the few extra degrees of southern latitude keep the water warm enough not to freeze over. By contrast, at Vladivostok, the great eastern port of the Soviet Union, which is significantly further north on the Sea of Japan, the harbour freezes to a depth of two feet in winter. In modern times, Vladivostok is kept open by ice-breakers, but it was the Russian interest in obtaining a year-round port at the eastern extension of their empire which caused conflict with Japan and China in the early years of this century, and the major sea and land battles of the Russo-Japanese War were fought to determine possession of the Liaotung Peninsula.

The role of the cities

Under the Communist government, Talien and Lushun which in 1950 had a combined population well over a million, are administered as one municipality. Besides the railway, docks and shipyards, there is considerable light industry including a chemical fertiliser plant constructed under the First Five-Year Plan. In the Gulf of Liaotung, Yingkow at the mouth of the Liao Ho is an old-established port which has now lost much of its importance due to silting from the river and to the growth of its great neighbour on the south. On the east, in the Bay of Korea near the mouth of the Yalu Kiang, Antung like its satellite Tatungkow is primarily a timber port and now also serves the developing industrial region on the border with North Korea.

On the main north line from Talien, and fifty miles south of Shenyang, Anshan is the chief centre for heavy industry and structural steel. Coal and iron ore are brought by rail from every part of the region, but fair quality iron ore is mined at Huolienchai, less than fifteen miles away, and the coal at Fushun is only eighty miles distant by rail through Shenyang. The largest blast furnaces in China are at Anshan, and in 1958, the last year of statistics before the Great Leap Forward, Anshan's steel output was 3.22 million tons. It was claimed to have exceeded 4,000,000 tons in 1960. Besides the local needs of industry in Manchuria, the Anshan furnaces and rolling mills have supplied the girders, bars, tubes and angle irons for the bridge across the Yangtze at Wuhan, for the No. 1 Tractor Plant at Loyang, the iron and steel works at Paotow, and the pipe-lines from Lanchow to the Yumen oilfield in Kansu. By force of circumstances, the machinery at Anshan is almost entirely post-war, up-to-date and largely automated, and the efficiency and productivity of the plant compares favourably with similar units in any industrialised country.

With a population well over a million, Shenyang itself, besides its importance as a railway junction, is the major engineering complex for machinery tools. Standardised equipment such as lathes and presses is mass-produced here and distributed all over the country. At Harbin, the other great city of the Manchurian Plain, of comparable size to Shenyang and three hundred miles north of it, industry is concentrated on final products rather than on factory equipment. The No. 1 Machine Building Plant at Harbin produces heavy turbines and generators for hydroelectric power stations, and agricultural machinery ranging from combine harvesters, ploughs and winnowers to tractors and water-pumps. There are also major repair shops and schools for apprentice mechanics, who are trained to work in rural communes and maintain the machinery on the spot. At Changchun there are motor vehicle factories, and at Tsitsihar in the north-west there are railway workshops.

Kirin, due south of Harbin on the main road and connected to the railway system by a branch line, is the chief producer of chemicals and the centre of an extractive industry which uses as raw material the pine forests of the eastern mountains. The Kirin Chemical Company has three modern plants for production of chemical fertiliser and insecticides; for calcium carbonate used in steel working; and for dye-stuffs. In the city and nearby there are smaller plants which re-work the waste products from these industries and process wood from the surrounding forests to make resin, turpentine and pine-wood oil.

The eastern mountains are also the area where China has most actively developed her hydroelectric potential. The position of Manchuria in this regard is much the same as for coal and iron: there is certainly great potential for development elsewhere, but the impetus gained from foreign investment has put the region ahead of most of the rest of China. Twenty miles south of Kirin is the Fengman Dam and on the Sungari River there are power stations, first built by the Japanese, repaired after the war, and now holding a generating capacity of 567,000 kilowatts. North across the mountains, the Mutankiang Dam on a tributary of the Sungari has a hydroelectric plant with a capacity of over 380,000 kilowatts. North-west of Harbin, near the border with Inner Mongolia, the Kumotsin Dam above Tsitsihar is a project of the Second Five-Year Plan, and in the far south the Shuifeng Reservoir on the Yalu Kiang is close to the coalfields and the secondary industrial area served by the port of Antung.

Landform

Central Manchuria is a lowland plain drained by two major river systems. In the north, the Sungari River collects tributary streams from high ground both east and west and then flows north-east to the Russian border. In the south, the Liao Ho flows east and south from the high ground of Jehol to the Gulf of Liaotung. South-east of the plain, the Eastern Manchurian Uplands are dominated by the Changpai Shan, whose highest peak Paitou Shan, with a crater lake, is 9,190 feet above sea-level. Elsewhere, the secondary elevations seldom rise above 3,000 feet. In the south of this hill country, the border with Korea follows the line of the Yalu Kiang and the Tumen Ho to the Bay of Korea and the Sea of Japan respectively. In the north the mountain range is broken by the valley of the Sungari River.

From the Manchurian Plain, the Sungari flows through a gap in the mountains to join the Amur, which marks the line of the whole northern border of Manchuria. Soon after its junction with the Sungari, the Amur is joined by the Ussuri, flowing northwards along the border of the Soviet Maritime Province and then into the sea opposite the island of Sakhalin. Between the great rivers and the mountains, a triangle of low-lying and marshy but fertile ground has been the scene of Chinese and Russian border clashes, with rival patrols firing across the winter ice-fields of the frozen rivers and struggling for the possession of little islands in the middle of the stream.

In the far north and the west, the Khingan Mountains are one of the least-visited areas of China. The Lesser Khingan range, due north of the plain and south of the Amur River, comprises for the most part rounded hills, with few elevations over 3,000 feet. The Great Khingan presents a comparatively sharp escarpment to the Manchurian Plain, but the western side of the range is more gentle country, no more than a thousand feet above the Mongolian Plateau. To the north, near the Amur and the Lesser Khingan range, the peaks of the Great Khingan are more than 7,500 feet high, but further south the mountains become narrower and lower. The railway running eastwards from Harbin crosses the mountains into Siberia with a series of long grades and at the top a tunnel. South of the railway the range declines to hill country near the headwaters of the Liao Ho. This saddle between the Khingan Mountains and the Jehol Mountains of south-west Manchuria has been the traditional route for nomad peoples and their armies entering Manchuria from Mongolia.

The Manchurian Plain is six hundred miles from north to south, and about half that distance in average width. It is rolling country, easily eroded, quite unlike the flat alluvial delta of the North China Plain. The Jehol Mountains in the south-west divide Manchuria from China Proper, a low spur from the Eastern Manchurian Uplands establishes the watershed between the Liao Ho and Sungari, while all the land between the surrounding mountains has low hills and undulating plains. The Liao Ho is shallow and silted, giving passage only to small native craft, but the Sungari and the Amur are readily navigable by large river steamers. In winter, all the Manchurian rivers are frozen over and serve as seasonal roadways for carts and motor-cars.

Climate

The winter temperature of Harbin in January averages −2°F, and at Shenyang it is 9°F. Minimum temperatures can reach thirty or forty degrees below zero. Summer averages in the two cities in July are 72°F and 76°F, with maxima around 90°F. Annual rainfall is 21.5 inches at Harbin and 26.5 inches at Shenyang. In general, Manchuria has a cool temperate climate, with a hot rainy period in summer and cold dry winters. See maps 11-14, pages 26-7. Like the rest of north China, the climate in winter is dominated by the great high-pressure area around Lake Baikal (map 10, page 24), which sends great waves of cold dry polar continental air eastwards over the Khingan Mountains to the plain, as strong winds which continue from September through April and May. In summer, the pattern is to some extent reversed, for although the low-pressure area is less pronounced in Mongolia, tropical maritime air is brought in from the high-pressure cells over the Yellow Sea and the Sea of Japan, warm winds blow from the south, and there are summer rains averaging 4 to 5 inches each month from July to September (map 9, page 24). The effect is almost that of a monsoon, and no other region of eastern China has such a contrast in seasonal climate.

Settlement and agriculture

Until very recent times, Manchuria was a land of prairie grassland and broadleaf forest, with conifers and deciduous forest on the high ground of the mountains. There was some Chinese settlement in the south but until the last years of the Manchu dynasty, even though the territory was an established part of the Chinese Empire, the people of China Proper were kept by imperial edict from the lands of their conquerors. Those who were allowed in came as labourers rather than peasant farmers. Though the controls were slackened in the later part of the nineteenth century, much of Manchuria remained grazing country, empty but for scattered tribes of nomads and their flocks.

At the proclamation of the Republic in 1911, all restrictions on migration were removed, and settlers from the lands of the North China Plain and the Shantung Peninsula poured into the fertile country to their north. In the two years 1927 and 1929 the number of immigrants exceeded a million and, although some 30 to 60 per cent of the travellers were only seasonal workers, the increase in population was still enormous. It was estimated in 1904 that Manchuria contained some 17,000,000 people. By 1930 the figure was 34,000,000, and at the census of 1953 there were 47,000,000. Almost all the available territory is now farmland, and the population must now be in the vicinity of 60,000,000.

Many of the colonists were fugitives from political disorders. Besides those from China, great numbers of Russians came to Manchuria in the aftermath of the Russian Revolution; so many that Harbin became the largest white city in Asia. Koreans, the majority of whom entered during the period of Japanese control, now form the largest foreign group. The Japanese, who administered the country before World War II, have almost entirely gone. There are several million Mongols and some Tungus, related to the peoples of neighbouring Siberia, but there are comparatively few Manchus, for the Manchu language and culture are disappearing just as their grazing lands are swallowed up in the steady expansion of Chinese agriculture. The restrictive policy of the Manchu emperors was intended to preserve the identity of their own people, and events since 1911 have shown they were right.

The comparatively recent arrival of such large numbers of people has affected the settlement history of the great cities as well as the development of farmland. Unlike those of north China, the cities of Manchuria owe much of their importance to the requirements of modern industry rather than to their position in a traditional communications network of trade and politics. Harbin, for example, was built by the Russians in the late nineteenth century at the point where their Chinese Eastern Railway crossed the Sungari River. Shenyang, though already important as the former capital of the Manchus, was considerably re-oriented with a new town built around the railway yards. In contrast, the ancient city of Liaoyang, formerly a key point on the route from China to her presumptive tributary of Korea, is now of minor importance.

With the increase in population, the area of cultivated land has shown comparable rapid increase, from 16.5 million acres in 1915 to 31 million in 1932 and an estimated 42.4 million in 1950, when the total harvest was 18 million tons of grain and 2.6 millions were surplus for export to the rest of China. The climate is too cold for more than one crop a year (map 16, page 32). Wheat, maize and tobacco are planted in April when the subsoil is still frozen, and soybeans, kaoliang and millet are planted in late April and early May. The crops may be seriously affected by too little rain in the spring or by excessive rain in midsummer, and though autumn is usually warm and dry, the harvest must be completed in September or crops left standing will be killed by night-time frosts.

The most important crops are soybeans, kaoliang, wheat and millet. Some cotton is grown and the Korean settlers still cultivate rice, despite the unfavourable climate. Manchuria is famous for soybeans and was the world's leading exporter before World War II. The beans contain 40 per cent protein and up to 20 per cent oil. After processing, protein-rich soybean cakes are used as cattle food or as fertiliser, and the oil is suitable for soap, paints, chemicals, margarine and the universal Chinese condiment of soya sauce.

The soil of Manchuria is of the same brown earth type as that in north China (map 8, page 23). Some parts of the plain have exceptionally rich chestnut brown soil mixed with black earth, and the centre of the plain, originally covered by grassland, has high humus content and is excellent for settled agriculture. In most of the region the moderate rainfall leaves the soil largely unleached and high in mineral plant food, though in the drier west, soils tend to be alkaline and capillary action in the dry windy climate removes water and leaves salts which can harm the crops.

As yet, the pressure of immigration does not appear to have seriously overcrowded the land. In the period before the Communist take-over, peasant holdings averaged an acre per head, more than twice the ratio for China Proper. Since the 1950s further colonisation has been organised on a co-operative and communal basis and, as in other provinces, individual holdings are taken over by the state.

With a recent history of settlement, and with some open land still to be developed, Manchuria has been a safety valve for many of the problems of China's people. Besides its industrial wealth the region has generally been able to send a net export of food supplies and agricultural produce to the rest of the country. A question for the future, however, will be the final effect of population increase on ultimately limited resources of farmland. For the last seventy years and more, Manchuria has afforded room for expansion and relief from the most pressing problems of over-population. In time it may become as densely peopled as the North China Plain, and then new areas and resources will have to be developed.

Plate 23 Vegetable garden on a pioneer farm in Kirin Province, Manchuria. *(China Pictorial)*

In the mountains about the central plain, one danger of swift colonisation has already appeared. As well as converting prairie to farmland, settlers have also entered the hill country and slashed away great stretches of the natural forest to open their fields. In the Jehol Mountains and the Eastern Manchurian Uplands, on either side of the southern portion of the plain, hills and valleys have been denuded of timber, and gullies of erosion have formed where forests once stood. Almost all the damage has been done in two generations. The Communist government, with a long-term programme of replanting and controlled forestry, is attempting to restore the original cover. The Eastern Uplands in particular, with an annual rainfall of thirty or forty inches, is an excellent region for permanent forestry, and with replanting and steady conservation it could supply a major part of China's requirements for timber.

Anxious prosperity

In the present state of China's economic development, Manchuria is of the utmost importance. Here is the base and heart of her heavy industry; here, despite unfavourable climate and increasing population, is one of her chief food-surplus regions, conveniently close to the great cities of the north. Economically viable in its own right, the region is essential to the maintenance of China's prosperity and to any hopes of future development.

Manchuria's position in Asia, however, makes the territory a

potential source of conflict between the rival empires of China, Russia and Japan. In the present century, Japan has fought both Russia and China for this land, and there is some reason to suggest that China's firm intervention in the Korean War in the early 1950s was no more than a defensive response to a threat she saw approaching from the same direction as in the past. In many ways, by their conquest of Japan, the Americans took the place of the Japanese in the strategic picture of the Far East, and the United Nations' campaign in support of South Korea could well be interpreted by the Chinese as a new advance against her vital territory.

To a government in Japan, Manchuria may be considered a distant defence zone to guard the traditional Japanese sphere of influence in Korea. As in the 1930s, it may also be a useful area for colonisation and a potential source of imperial advantage, but Japan's chief areas of interest lie closer to home. For a Russian government, concerned with its great possessions in Siberia, Manchuria is no less important than it is to the Japanese. In the days when they controlled the Chinese Eastern Railway, Russian trains could move direct from the region of Lake Baikal, across the Great Khingan Mountains, through Harbin to Vladivostok. The alternative route through present Soviet territory is a long loop north of the Amur River and the Khingan Mountains, then southwards up the Ussuri valley. Should Russian influence extend still further south, the harbours of Talien and Lushun would provide ice-free anchorage all the year and thrust Russian power effectively into the centre of the Far East.

Russia's designs on Manchuria have never yet involved major war with China. However, it required Japanese armies to remove the Tsarist forces from Talien and the Soviet occupation and looting of Manchuria in 1945 can leave no reassuring memory, even to a Communist Chinese government. With so vital a territory at stake, it is not surprising that the rulers of Peking are remarkably sensitive to any threat. The importance they attach to Manchuria may be reflected in the contrast between Chinese intervention in Korea and their careful quiescence over Vietnam, or between their often desultory shelling of the Nationalist-held offshore islands, Quemoy and Matsu, and their explosive reaction to the threat of Russian encroachment along the Ussuri River. Beyond these immediate causes of conflict, however, lie the Chinese people's long resentment and constant anxiety concerning the tribes of Inner Asia and the security of the northern borders.

Plate 24 Incident on the Ussuri River, north-eastern Manchuria, 1969. When the rivers freeze in winter, the ice is heavy enough to bear wheeled vehicles for communications or for war. A Soviet armoured car is attacked by a group of Chinese frontier guards and fishermen. *(Down with the New Tsars)*

6 Outer China: Mongolia, Sinkiang and Tibet

The geographical area of China Proper is bounded by the sea to the east and the south, by the Great Wall to the north, and by the highlands of the Tibetan Massif to the west. Beyond these frontiers are the lands of Outer China, inhabited by peoples very different in race, language and culture from the Chinese, who have maintained their independence for hundreds of years in the past, but who have several times also acknowledged the sway of outside rulers, and who have now been brought under the control of the government at Peking.

In legendary times, the Chinese emperors administered a world arrayed in concentric rings about the capital, from the direct subjects nearest home to the tributary barbarians on the edges of the earth, and all within the 'four seas' were rightfully subject to the one Son of Heaven. More recently, the Europeans who came to Canton in the sixteenth century were regarded as barbarians from the south, and the influence of the traditional Chinese view of the world may be seen in the north-south division between 'Inner' and 'Outer' Mongolia, separated by the Gobi Desert but named in accordance with their closeness to Peking, and the occasional reference to 'Nearer' (i.e. East) and 'Further' (i.e. West) Tibet, also based on the view from China Proper. Sinkiang, the third region of Outer China, takes its name from the Chinese 'New Territory', for although it had several times been controlled by Chinese armies under earlier dynasties, it was not brought fully under the government of the Manchu Ch'ing until the nineteenth century.

Since the earliest records, all these regions and their peoples have been in some relationship with China. Often until recent times, they preserved their independence, and the Mongols in particular were not only the enemies but at one period also the masters of the Chinese. Now, however, with improved technology and means of communications, and with the growing population of China Proper, the Han Chinese have established their dominance over the nomads of the mountains and the steppe, and over the oasis peoples of Central Asia. So long as China Proper remains united under a competent government, the outer territories will surely be held in control. As an alternative, it is possible that conflict with some other great power may change the ownership of these lands, but it is now most unlikely that their people will ever again have significant control over their own destinies. Even the Mongolian People's Republic, in Outer Mongolia, separated from China earlier in this century and now an independent state recognised as a member of the United Nations, is guarded by Russian arms and advised by Soviet officials, and has perhaps rather less freedom of international manoeuvre than any satellite of Eastern Europe.

It is their small populations, of course, that place these regions at a disadvantage in dealing with the present-day giant states—China, Soviet Russia, and also India. In this great area, from Manchuria to Afghanistan and from the Gobi to the Himalayas, almost 1,500,000 square miles have a population of some 12,000,000 people, an overall density rather less than ten to the square mile.

Considering the nature of the country, this is not surprising. Here, in the heart of Asia, the two great shields, the Gobi Plateau and the Tibetan Massif, thousands of feet high and well separated from the sea, both have a dry climate, often cold, with annual rainfall averaging generally less than 10 inches and in some places less than one. Between the sand and stones of the Gobi and the snow-covered wilderness of Tibet lie the two basins of Sinkiang separated by the Tien Shan ranges; steppe country in Dzungaria to the north, and the desert of Takla Makan to the south. Isolated valleys in Tibet and a few oases in the deserts give some opportunity for settlement and offer staging posts along the ancient roads, but the people are too few and too isolated to resist effectively any outside power. Improved communications now permit the government of China to control the steppe and the desert, to exploit the minerals and natural resources, and even to alleviate, by colonisation, some of the pressures of population in China Proper.

Mongolia

The geographic region of Mongolia is a plateau surrounded on all sides by mountains. In the south and east, the Ala Shan, the Yin Shan and the Great Khingan Mountains make a natural division from north China and Manchuria. In the west, the Altai Mountains extend a ridge along the border of the Sinkiang Uighur Autonomous Region. Far to the north, beyond Ulan Bator, capital of the People's Republic of Outer Mongolia, another series of mountains, some over ten thousand feet, enclose the territory.

The mountains to the west, on the outskirts of the Tibetan Massif, rise 15,000 feet and more above sea-level and the Great Khingan Mountains are almost as high, but the mountains to

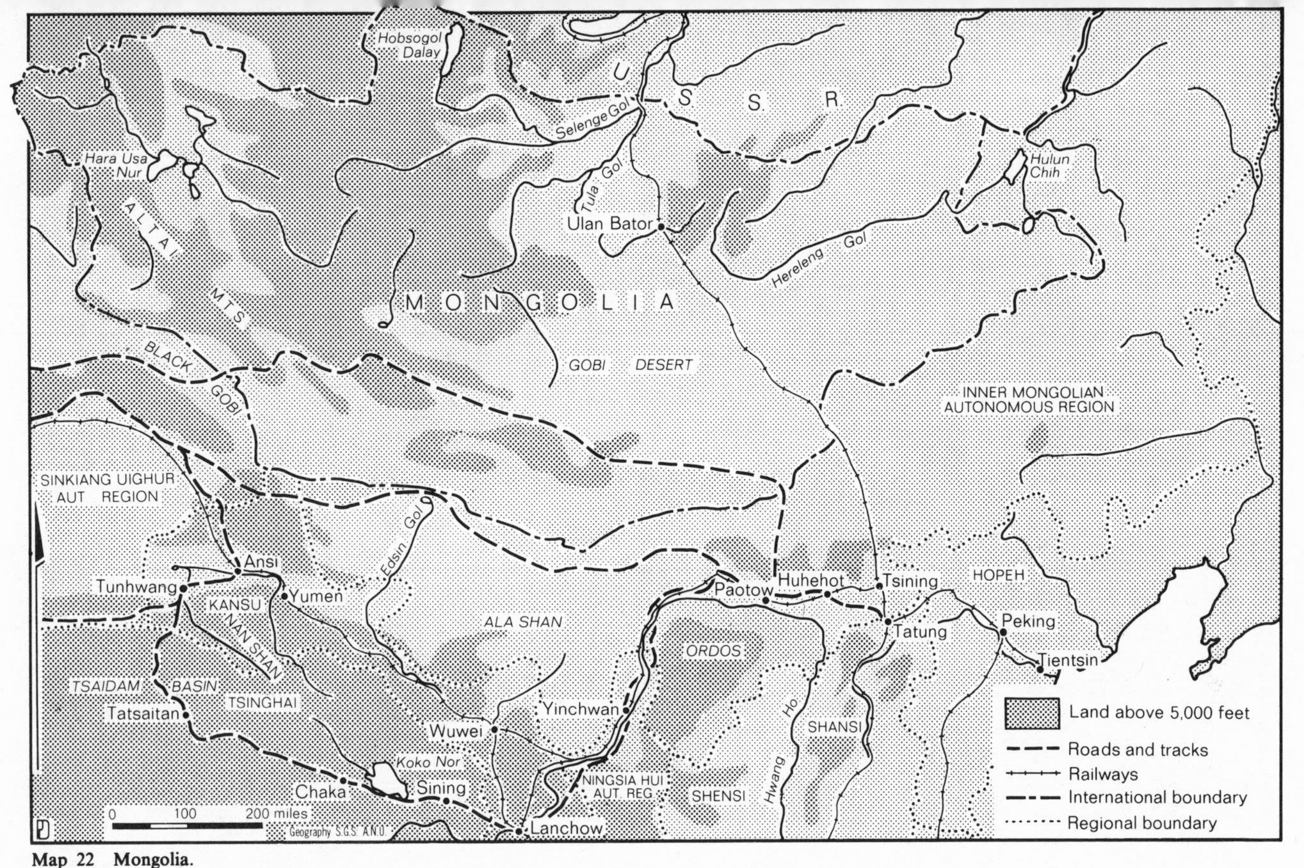

Map 22 **Mongolia.**

To be read in conjunction with Chapter 6.

the south average only 4,500 to 6,000 feet, with the highest peaks at 7,000 to 8,000 feet. On all sides, the land slopes quite gradually towards the centre of the plateau, which at its lowest point is some 2,000 to 3,000 feet above sea-level.

The centre of this region is the Gobi depression, the word Gobi being a Mongol term which describes the form of the country rather than the region itself. Gobi are wide, flat-floored basins, underlain by soft materials, subject constantly to erosion by the wind; these formations cover most of geographical Mongolia. The Gobi Desert in the centre of Mongolia is one of the world's largest deserts, and around it is a halo of slightly higher rainfall and sparse, scattered vegetation. Further again from the central core, the desert regions are circled by grassy steppe country, suitable mainly for grazing but with some possibilities of agriculture.

Little rainfall comes to Mongolia, for the plateau is surrounded on all sides by mountains and air from the oceans must climb the ridges. The monsoon winds from the China Sea have spent most of their moisture over the lands further south. To some extent, the basin has a water cycle of its own, for much of the rain that falls can be accounted for by local evaporation, and precipitation on the inner slopes of the surrounding mountains runs by a medley of seasonal rivers back to the centre of the plain to be lost in evaporation again or settled in shallow lakes. Little moisture enters the basin and scant surface water flows away.

The Gobi is not the world's driest desert, though rain averages less than eight inches a year overall. Precipitation is seasonal, and most falls between June and September, sometimes in localised showers, sometimes in an overwhelming downpour that washes away surface soil and ruins grazing lands and crops. Ulan Bator has an average annual rainfall of 8 inches, but has on one occasion received 5 inches in twenty-four hours. Temperatures are extreme, with shade readings in summer sometimes over 115°F, and minimum readings in winter 30 or 40 below zero. Icy polar continental winds out of Siberia bring a six months' cold season from September on, and temperature averages remain below freezing until February and March. In the dry climate, snowfalls are light and soon evaporate despite the lower temperatures, so the dry yellowish grass is available for grazing all through the winter. In summer, the air is equally dry, so much so that it is possible to see rain fall from the clouds and evaporate before it reaches the ground.

Despite the low rainfall and the dry climate, temperatures through the year are cool enough for precipitation to have greater effect than in a hot region such as the Sahara Desert. The great extremes of local temperature and barometric pressures, however, cause the wind to blow almost daily, with fierce sand-storms in summer and piercing cold blasts in winter. Worn by water and the wind, much of Mongolia is peneplain, with flat erosion surfaces broken by occasional monadnocks. The smooth surface of the Mongolian Peneplain is some 5,300 feet elevation in the south of Mongolia. The Gobi Peneplain averages 4,000 feet, and the Pang Kiang Erosion Surface, evidently the result of wind scour on soft beds, appears in undrained basins, sometimes 400 feet deep, sunk into the surface of the surrounding plain, with bad land dissection about the rim. In the desert, where grass has no chance to grow, the scouring of the wind over a very long time has left almost nothing but pebbles, gravel and sand-dunes. The lighter materials, those that can be raised or driven along by the wind, move steadily southwards towards the Ordos Desert and Loessland about the Hwang Ho.

South of the Gobi, most of China's Inner Mongolian Autonomous Region is in the fringe land of slightly higher rainfall and some

Plate 25 Beyond the limits of cultivation: shepherds of Inner Mongolia, on their short-legged ponies, use whips to control their flocks. *(China Pictorial)*

Plate 26 Mongol nomads: a man and his wife in front of their felt *yurt*. *(Courtesy: Gun Kessle and Jan Myrdal)*

vegetation. The grass of the steppe is seldom tall enough for harvest, though in seasons of higher-than-average rainfall it can reach seven or eight feet in height. If the great desert is barren and featureless, the steppe land is little better, and the traveller can move for days across almost unchanging scenery. Most of Inner Mongolia can be classified as steppe country rather than true desert, but the extremes of temperature, the limited moisture, and the immense variation of seasonal climate make living a constant struggle for survival.

The people of Mongolia, by force of circumstances, must be nomads, for they cannot rely on storage of fodder to keep their flocks in times of shortage. Each tribe moves within a recognised territory, from one grazing ground to another, driving before them their herds of cattle and their flocks of sheep and goats. For transport they have horses and two-humped Bactrian camels; for houses they have yurts, round dome tents of skin over a wicker framework, three to four feet high and twelve to fifteen feet across. Grass is their chief resource, flocks and herds are their wealth, and from their animals they have food, clothing, shelter, transport and warmth. Their staple foods are mutton, milk, cheese and butter; their clothing is made from sheepskin or woollen cloth; their fuel is dried cattle or camel dung.

Contest on the geographical frontier

Inner Mongolia, a great crescent from Manchuria to Kansu and Sinkiang, is a geographical frontier region between desert and steppe in the north and settled agriculture in the south. The Great Wall of China was built two thousand years ago in an attempt to define a vague, shifting boundary between climatic regions, and to hold apart two different peoples with conflicting ways of life.

To the Chinese, Mongols are utterly alien. Their language is in no way related, their butter and cheese are nauseous, and the freedom enjoyed by their women has appeared immoral to the civilised men of the south. Most important of all, they have been dangerous neighbours.

Over the centuries, the frontier of climate has fluctuated north and south. In the Ordos Region and in Mongolia Proper, scattered remains of walls and ruins of houses show the places where Chinese settlers in the past took advantage of rainy seasons to extend their fields into the steppe and to establish settled agriculture on former grazing lands. When dry years followed, fields and houses were left, abandoned among the dust-bowls, and the frontiers of Chinese civilisation retreated towards the south. For the nomads, a cycle of increased rainfall extended their pasture lands northward into the contracting desert, but in times of great drought, when the grass failed and the flocks died of starvation, they became a desperate people with few alternatives to banditry and plunder.

The cities and granaries of China were a constant temptation and an obvious source of supply to these tribesmen of the north, and it was not always desperation that brought them south to raid. The great advantage of nomad life is not so much that the herdsmen move constantly over great tracts of country, for tribal grazing circuits are carefully restricted by custom, but that they can move, suddenly and swiftly, great distances in little time. The same technique that under peaceful conditions can uproot a camp and move to new pastures almost overnight was equally suited to bringing an army of well-mounted men unexpectedly far into China. The Mongols are superb horsemen, who almost live in the saddle, and they often held the initiative over the static defences of the Chinese peasants and their rulers.

It was for this reason that the Great Wall was built and maintained. It supplied lodgings for garrisons, passes for supervision of travellers, and some control over the movement of imperial subjects into the unwanted freedom of the steppe, and, most important, it checked marauding armies or small raiding parties from the north. When enemy horsemen came to the wall, they had to storm one of the gateways or to climb across an undefended section and use winches, cranes or pulleys to bring their horses with them. Either method caused delay, so that Chinese scouts with beacon fires could send signals to the rear, bringing warning to the army groups stationed in reserve and giving Chinese defences plenty of time to prepare for the threat and to meet it in the field. As a static line of defence, the Great Wall was useless, but as a device to gain the initiative from free-riding raiders, it served its purpose well.

Such strategy, of course, has not always been sufficient to drive out the invaders. For several centuries over the last two thousand years, whether through changes of climate or through internal weakness and military failure, great parts of the north have fallen under alien rule, and dynasties have been set up by 'barbarians' with their capitals on Chinese soil. Of all these conquerors, the greatest were the Mongols, who ruled the whole of China from 1280 to 1360, and made the proud empire one province of a con-

Plate 27 The Great Wall of China, which runs a thousand miles from the north of Peking to the Kansu Corridor, placed a barrier between the nomads of the steppe and the settled peasants of China Proper. The original wall was completed by the first Emperor of Ch'in in the third century BC, but the main course of the present wall was established by the Ming dynasty five hundred years ago. *(Courtesy: Mrs P. Reichl)*

tinental realm that stretched from Muscovy to the Sea of Japan. The dynasty lasted less than a hundred years, but it left its mark on Chinese civilisation, and the memory of humiliation and disaster serves only to intensify a long enmity based on border warfare, raids of plunder, and punitive expeditions of revenge.

In the eighteenth century, Chinese armies under the Manchu emperors at last destroyed the military power of the Mongols, and the nomads were crushed between the advancing frontiers of China and Tsarist Russia. In the early days of the Republic, Outer Mongolia was torn from China by the intrigues of rival war-lords, and Soviet Russia seized the opportunity to establish the new People's Republic firmly under her own control. Inner Mongolia, however, now an Autonomous Region under the Communist Government, faces a new period of development, for the climate barrier between settled farmland and grazing steppe is being attacked by intensive agriculture, and the Chinese may conquer the grassland in the same fashion as they have already colonised Manchuria.

It is hard to tell, as yet, how successful this advance of cultivation will prove. Two thousand years of ruined settlements show where the men of the past pressed marginal agriculture too far towards the desert. In some regions, to give the soil time to store up moisture, wheat can only be planted once in three years, but near the capital, Huhehot, there are new fields and plantations, and at Paotow on the Hwang Ho there is steady growth of heavy industry.

The effect of this pressure on the nomad people will soon be serious. Already there are estimated to be twelve million people in Inner Mongolia, but only a tenth of that number are Mongols. Both populations are increasing, but the Mongols are now a minority in their own country, many of them look for work with the Chinese in the cities and towns, and their nomad herds are squeezed between an expanding area of more intensive agriculture and the blank waste of the Gobi. In theory, even the nomads are subject to Communist organisation, with co-operatives and communes; in practice, the tribes are left a fair degree of latitude and independent ownership. Meanwhile, however, economic progress and the inflow of new colonists brings settlement to Mongolia, and it seems that, though the Han Chinese may have lost many battles to the barbarians, they are now winning the last war against their ancient and traditional enemies.

The roads to Central Asia

The main road from Peking and the railway north from Tatung cross the Gobi Desert to Ulan Bator, but the long crescent of Inner Mongolia has few communications routes east and west. The caravan trains of travelling merchants follow the Great Mongolian Road west and north from Huhehot, but the greater part of its length runs through the People's Republic to the south of the Gobi Desert. Within the Autonomous Region, the Winding Road goes from Huhehot to Paotow on the Hwang Ho, then past the inland drainage system of the Edsin Gol and across the Black Gobi into Sinkiang. Two thousand years ago, the Edsin Gol region supported an important chain of Chinese military outposts in the north, and the dry climate has preserved great quantities of archives written on bamboo and wood, passports, lists of stores, and reports of patrols. Now the climate has changed and only ruins remain. The Black Gobi is the most forbidding of all the Mongolian deserts, a plateau of clay and sand with no wells and almost no rain.

The main road into Central Asia from China and Mongolia is the Imperial Highway through Lanchow and Yumen along the region known as the Kansu corridor. It is near Lanchow, as we have seen, that the road and a railway cross the Hwang Ho, and from Lanchow the routes run more than four hundred miles north and then north-east through Wuwei to the 'Jade Gates' of Yumen, traditional frontier city of the ancient Chinese empires. To the south of this road and railway lies the high ground of Tsinghai. To the north is the Great Wall, and beyond that Edsin Gol and the deserts, Ala Shan and Black Gobi. Between the two extremes of mountain and desert, the Kansu corridor is a fertile tract of ground suitable for intensive agriculture, chiefly of wheat. Irrigation is essential, for the annual average rainfall is less than 10 inches, and on the banks of every river there are waterwheels to feed canals in the country around. As in the Ordos Region about the northern loop of the Hwang Ho, more than four-fifths of the land is irrigated, a proportion matched elsewhere only in a few parts of the rice paddy regions of South China (map 17, page 34). Even so, though the land is fertile, river water is limited, and the spread of agriculture is firmly controlled by its supply.

There is a Chinese legend that 2,500 years ago and more, the great philosopher Lao-tzu abandoned his country and set off on a final pilgrimage to Central Asia. As he passed the border post at Yumen, a frontier guard begged him to leave some teaching behind him, and the sage set down the essential part of his thoughts in a work called *The Classic of the Way and Its Power*. This short book, concise, paradoxical and mystic, has been an inspiration for scholars, philosophers and men of religion in China. Some claim that Lao-tzu travelled to India and taught the Buddha, though disciples of Gautama deny it.

Beyond Yumen, the roads divide. From Ansi the Imperial Highway and the railway go north-west into Dzungaria. South-west is the Great Silk Road, so called after the trading caravans that have brought silk from China to the West since the classical times of

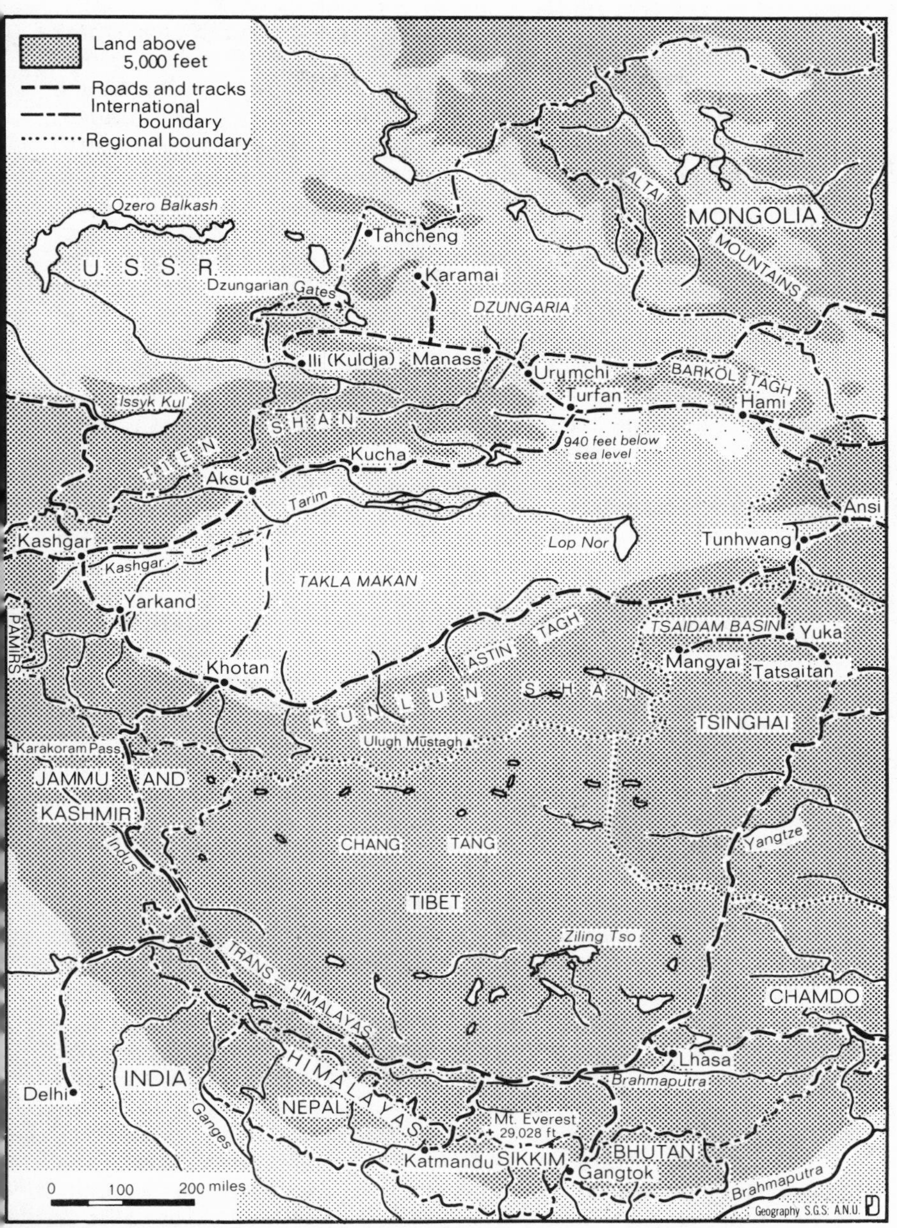

Map 23 Sinkiang and Tibet.
To be read in conjunction with Chapter 6.

Greece and Rome. The ancient road passes Tunhwang, where Buddhist cave-temples and monasteries have preserved the carvings and the manuscripts of twelve centuries past. It was along this route that Chinese priests and monks travelled to India in medieval times, and Marco Polo and other European travellers came through Central Asia to the court of the Great Mongol Khan.

Sinkiang

The Sinkiang Uighur Autonomous Region is divided into two unequal parts, north and south of the Tien Shan and their eastern extension. The southern part is dominated by the desert called Takla Makan, the northern part by the plain of Dzungaria. The Imperial Highway leads across desert country from Ansi to Hami, then follows the southern slopes of the Barköl Tagh to Turfan and crosses a low-lying pass over a break in the mountains to Urumchi, capital of the whole region.

The Turfan Depression, a remarkable fault trough reaching 940 feet below sea-level, is one of the lowest places of dry land on earth, and has recorded daytime shade temperatures of 130°F. North-west of Turfan and 9,000 feet above sea-level, the city of Urumchi, also known as Tihwa, has a population of varied races—Uighurs, Kazaks, Kirghiz, Mongols, Manchus, White Russians, and others. The mixture reflects past history, when this territory, also known as Chinese Turkestan, was disputed ground between rival empires, religions and tribes. In the far west, on the borders of Soviet Russia, the Dzungarian Gates and the upper Ili valley were pathways of conquest for the Mongol armies of Genghis Khan as the Golden Horde moved into Russia and the Arab empires of the Middle East.

Dzungaria

The Dzungarian Basin, roughly triangular in shape, and some fifty thousand square miles in extent, is enclosed on the north-east by the Altai Mountains of Mongolia, on the north-west by ranges of the Ala Tau and the Tarbdegatay Mountains on the borders of Soviet Kazakhstan, and on the south by the great range of the Tien Shan and the secondary ridges of Bogdol Ula and Barköl Tagh. All these mountains have peaks over 13,000 feet, but the surface of the plain is actually below sea-level in the far west. Sections in the east are more than 3,000 feet, but the greater part is less than 1,500 feet above sea-level.

Rainfall over the whole of Sinkiang is light, and no part of the Dzungarian Basin has more than 10 inches a year. The high grounds of Mongolia and Tibet and its great distance from them are an effective obstacle to any moist air. Its own mountain ranges, however, have 20 or even 30 inches precipitation a year, some of which must come from outside, possibly from as far away as the Atlantic Ocean, and the main source of water on the plain comes from the rivers which flow down the flanks of the ridges to end in shallow lakes, reedy marshes and sand-fields. Around Manass, in the foothills of the Tien Shan, government production and construction corps have organised water conservation works, reservoirs and canals; more than 125,000 acres have been put to agriculture, with mechanised farms growing cotton, rice, wheat and corn. Elsewhere, the land is too dry for anything more than light grazing, and Australian experience indicates that a rainfall of 10 inches a year will support no more than ten sheep to the square mile. The majority of the people, known by the ancient name of Uighurs, live in nomad tribes much like their Mongol neighbours to the east.

Plate 28 Cultivation in the marginal lands of Sinkiang: 'Displaying the spirit of the "Foolish Old Man" who removed the mountains . . . , members of the third production team of the Akzuz brigade of the "East is Red" People's Commune in Kungliu County work hard to transform the poor soil.' It is yet to be seen whether the final result of their work will be farmland or a dustbowl. *(China Pictorial)*

Besides the development of irrigation agriculture and the traditional pastoral economy, there is some lumber exploitation of mountain forests, in particular of the white birch which grows on the slopes below six thousand feet, and is valuable as a building material. Higher up, there are forests of Siberian larch, with some trees over a hundred feet tall, and all these upland regions are hunting grounds for fur-bearing animals—fox, wolf, sable, ermine and bear.

Most important to China, however, are the oilfields, first discovered in 1955 at Karamai in the north-west of the plain near the mountains of the Russian border. Six new oilfields have been discovered since that first success, there is now a pipeline from the fields to Yumen and Lanchow; and the Yumen Oil Administration, which controls all exploration and processing, announced a production target of 100,000 tons in 1959, and processing of 30,000 tons. Because of this new development, the capital city of Urumchi, formerly no more than a market town, has increased its population in the last fifteen years from 60,000 to more than 300,000. Coal-mines have been developed, oil refineries have been built, and there are new industrial plants for metals, chemicals, power, machine tools and construction work. Despite the immigration of Chinese technicians and settlers, the population is still essentially Uighur, the official language is Uighur, and the government has conscientiously embarked on a large-scale education campaign, with many colleges and schools, although there is still a severe shortage of suitable teachers. In the whole of Sinkiang, the population is now some six million, of whom an estimated four-fifths are Uighurs, another tenth are Kazaks or members of smaller nomad groups, and only some 5 to 7 per cent Han Chinese.

Southern Sinkiang

South of the Tien Shan divide, the greater part of Sinkiang is occupied by the Tarim Basin, roughly like a diamond in shape, about 800 miles from east to west and some 400 miles at its widest point north-south. In the east, the general level is some 2,000 feet above sea-level, and in the west it rises to 6,000 feet. All around are mountains—on the north the Tien Shan, whose highest peak, Khan Tengri, is 23,616 feet, on the south the Kunlun, frontier wall of Tibet, and its lower extensions north-east, the Astin Tagh and the Nan Shan, whose highest peaks are over 20,000 feet. In the west, the Pamius, a knot of mountains 18,000 feet and more, have high glacial valleys suitable for normal pasturage, and from the city of Kashgar two roads lead by passes north into Soviet Kirgiziya and west to Samarkand. Within the ring of mountains the Tarim River curves in an eastward course along the north of the Takla Makan

Desert to the marshy ground and inland lake of Lop Nor, and the desert lands extend north-east towards the Gobi of Mongolia.

Marco Polo came this way, from Samarkand to Kashgar, and he described the Desert of Lop:

> This desert is reported to be so long that it would take a year to go from end to end, and at the narrowest point it takes a month to cross it. It consists entirely of mountains and sand and valleys. There is nothing at all to eat. But I can tell you that after travelling a day and a night you find drinking water, not enough water to supply a large company, but enough for fifty or a hundred men and their beasts. And I can tell you that in three or four places you find the water bitter and brackish; but at all the other watering-places, that is, twenty-eight in all, the water is good. Beasts and birds there are none, because they find nothing to eat.*

If Yumen is the gateway between China and Central Asia, Kashgar controls the chief passage to the west. Travellers along the ancient trading routes must pass through these two cities, but they have a choice of roads. On the north, the highway leads from Ansi through Hami to Turfan, then forks south to follow the drainage area of the Tarim River through Kucha and Aksu to Kashgar. The second road goes past Tunhwang, south of Lop Nor and the Takla Makan, through Khotan and Yarkand. It was this latter route that Marco Polo followed, and he has described the oasis towns, with their cotton-fields, vineyards and orchards, in terms that still apply today.

The desert itself is, as the great traveller described it, an utter wilderness of sand-dunes and rock, waterless and lifeless. Rainfall here—1,200 miles across the barrier of Tibet to the nearest sea in the Bay of Bengal—is minimal. Annual precipitation is usually less than 5 inches, mostly in spring, but extremely variable, and Yarkand generally records only half an inch. Like Mongolia, the whole region is primarily an internal drainage system with a virtually closed water cycle, and the dry climate allows immense fluctuations of temperature. The monthly average of Kashgar, altitude 4000 feet, varies from 22°F in January to 82°F in July, but shade temperatures in summer reach 115° and minimum temperatures in winter can be −20°F. In some places, the temperature change between day and night in a single period of twenty-four hours can exceed 60°F.

---

*R. E. Latham (trans.) *The Travels of Marco Polo*, Penguin Books, p. 53. The translator tentatively identifies the city of Lop with modern Charklik, and the Desert of Lop as the Gobi. It seems most probable that the Desert of Lop refers both to the Gobi and also to the Takla Makan, for the desert country is continuous from Sinkiang into Mongolia.

It is from the mountains round about that the oasis towns receive their water. On the peaks are permanent snowfields and, as these snows melt, river waters flow down the slopes towards the desert floor. At high levels, around 10,000 or 15,000 feet, there are alpine meadows with rich grass for pasture. Below this region, the hill slopes are covered with loess, blown by the winds from the desert. The streams tear the light soil away, cutting out erosion gullies and gorges and returning the wind deposits to the surface of the plain. At the foot of the ranges, the streams disappear under beds of Piedmont gravel, formed from the detritus they have brought down from the upper slopes; the water is drained underground, emerging again at the end of this belt and continuing its journey into the dead heart of the plain. On the north of the desert, the Tarim River collects tributaries from the Tien Shan, and the Yarkand River and the Khotan contrive to join it from the south. All other streams from the southern mountains are lost in the desert.

The cities of this region are founded on the fans of alluvium at the base of the mountains. On the northern side of the Takla Makan, they are close to the mountain wall, but on the south the settlements are established at the desert edge of the Piedmont gravel, where the water emerges from underground before its last run into the wilderness. Farming is intensive. More than 80 per cent of the cultivated land is irrigated, both by normal surface canals and also by the *karez*, a technique invented in Persia and Central Asia which uses long underground tunnels to bring water from the mountain slopes to wells on the surface of the plain. It has been estimated that one crop of grain requires five acre-feet of water, the equivalent of 60 inches rainfall, which gives some indication of the evaporation rate in this thirsty climate. In their growing conditions, these oasis towns resemble Mildura and the Murray Irrigation Region of north-western Victoria. They have the same high temperatures, the same dependence on river waters, and the same problems of over-extended demand for water and resulting salinity. In the south of the Takla Makan, seventy miles and more from the present oases, there are ruins of cities which were established and occupied between A.D. 300 and 1200. Geographers dispute whether the successive extension and withdrawal of colonisation is evidence for cycles of climatic change or merely of excessive and conflicting demands on limited supplies of water. It seems most likely that there has been some variation in climate and that recent centuries have been drier than the past, but the network of underground drainage systems has often caused minor changes in part of a river system to have serious effects, resulting in the failure of water supplies at a considerable distance from the original disturbance.

In the northern oasis settlements of Turfan and Hami, irrigation fields are used largely for market-gardening; the melons of Hami and the raisins and other dried fruits of Turfan are famous in Asia. Elsewhere, wheat is the chief crop both in acreage and production, sown in winter in Dzungaria and in spring in the Tarim Basin. The main commercial crop is cotton, with local varieties which need comparatively little water grown largely in the south of the basin. As in Dzungaria, the government has paid great attention to expanding the agricultural base and to developing modern techniques of irrigation, conservation and agriculture. It is claimed that land under cultivation has more than doubled since 1949 and now exceeds three million acres. It remains to be seen, however, whether this new development actually represents an efficient use of formerly wasted water resources or a dangerous pressure on the margins of possible cultivation.

Apart from the line through Hami and Urumchi towards the Dzungarian Gates, Sinkiang has no railway communications, and the developing network of roads still follows the ancient tracks of trading caravans. The major industrial development in the Tarim Basin has been the atomic plant and testing ground at Lop Nor, now the centre for China's research into atomic energy and armaments for war. The desert provides a most suitable testing ground. There are known to be plants for the production of atomic material and for the assembly of nuclear weapons at Lanchow in Kansu.

Tsinghai and Tibet

From the ancient city of Tunhwang, a main road goes south into the mountains towards Lhasa in Tibet. The road crosses a spur of the Nan Shan, then descends into the Tsaidam Basin, 6,000 to 9,000 feet above sea-level, before recommencing the climb into the Kunlun Ranges. In the high country east of the road, between the Tsaidam Basin and the lowlands of Kansu, lies the Koko Nor, or Tsing Hai, 10,500 feet above sea-level. From this great salt lake the whole province gets its name.

Chapter 3 described the mountain country about the headwaters of the Hwang Ho. The Koko Nor is separated from that river by only a single range of mountains. Sining, the capital of Tsinghai, is in the lowlands west of Lanchow in Kansu and the Sining River is a tributary of the Hwang Ho. A main road leads from Lanchow through Sining then across the mountains along the south of the Koko Nor into the Tsaidam Basin.

In earlier Chinese history, the tribesmen of this region, south of the Kansu corridor and west of Loessland, were among the most consistent enemies of the empire. Almost inaccessible to armies from China, their raids were a constant threat to travellers into the western regions, and on occasion the attacks reached even the imperial capital. The mountain slopes have areas of excellent grass, and there is fair pasturage in the steppe country over much of the Tsaidam Basin. Sining wool is famous, long, coarse and strong, and widely used for rug-making. Since ancient times the Tsinghai Region has been noted for the quality of its horses. The grasslands are still used for breeding and raising horses, and their population is estimated at three or four thousand head.

It is the Tsaidam Basin, however, in the east of the province, that is the scene of major modern development, for geological surveys have discovered important reserves of coal and oil. The chief oilfield is at Mangyai in the far north-west, with secondary fields about Tatsaitan and coal near Yuka, both towns in the centre of the basin. Iron ore has been found in the Nan Shan ranges; and in the far east, at Chaka, there are plans to develop chemical plants in order to process the rich sodium chloride deposits of the neighbouring lakes.

The Tsinghai Region is a lower extension of the Tibetan highlands, and the Nan Shan are an outlying ridge of the Kunlun Shan. The greater part of Tibet, some 230,000 square miles in extent, lies south of the Kunlun and north of the Himalayas. In the west, the two great ranges curve together, and the Karakoram, an extension of

Plate 29 Herdsmen near Sining in Tsinghai, where life is supported by sheep herds, horses and yaks. Yak dung, piled behind the house, is used for fuel. The houses are built of rammed earth and brushwood, and the bundles stacked along the wall of the yard will be used later as roofing material. *(Courtesy: The Geographical Magazine)*

Plate 30 Soldiers of the Chinese People's Liberation Army surveying on the frontier between Tibet and Nepal, near the foothills of Chomolungma, Mount Everest. *(China Pictorial)*

the Kunlun Massif, stretches across the north of Kashmir. In the east, south of Tsinghai, the broad line of mountain ridges swings towards the south. Here, in a series of great valleys, lie the head-waters of the Salween River of Burma, the Mekong of Thailand and Indochina, and the Yangtze Kiang and Hwang Ho of China. Over all Tibet the general altitude is sixteen thousand feet above sea-level, and Mount Everest, called Chomolungma in Tibetan, is 29,028 feet high.

Temperatures are generally low, firstly on account of the high altitudes, and secondly, in the north, because of the increasing high latitudes. In the south, the Himalayas rise in a series of ridges steeply from the plains of India to a crest line 20,000 feet high, and the monsoon brings heavy precipitation, either of snow or of rain. Lhasa, in a valley north of the Himalayas at an altitude of 12,000 feet, has summer maximum temperatures of 80°F, a winter average at freezing point, and an annual precipitation of some 60 inches, almost all between May and September. In the Himalayas and in the southern mountains of Chamdo and Yunnan, the snow line is some 13,500 feet, but on the Kunlun Shan and its secondary ridges facing Sinkiang the declining precipitation reverses the effect of the cold northern air, and the snow line is 18,000 feet and higher.

In the northern part of Tibet, south of the Kunlun and west of the main road north from Lhasa, the Chang Tang, the Plateau of Tibet, is a windswept waste of salt lakes and swamps, barren mountains, wide, cold, desolate valleys, and a treeless alpine desert, with elevation seldom less than 17,000 feet and an average temperature above freezing point in only two months of the year. The region has few people, is seldom visited, and is almost completely uninhabitable.

From the north, where Ulūgh Mustagh, on the border of Sinkiang, rises 25,327 feet high, the Chang Tang slopes generally south and south-east, over almost half the geographical region, to the Nyenchentanglha ranges, or Trans-Himalayas. South of this more broken country, whose highest peaks are still more than 20,000 feet, a long east-west trough, known to the Tibetans as Po, contains the headwaters of two great rivers, Brahmaputra and Indus.

In the far west, the Indus flows northwards and soon enters Kashmir, but the Brahmaputra, known in Tibet as the Tsangpo, runs 800 miles from west to east between the two great ridges of the Himalayas and the Trans-Himalayas. Here there are deep valleys, some of them less than 5,000 feet above sea-level, and temperatures a good deal warmer than on the plateau above. There is grass for grazing and some agriculture, increasingly developed after the Communist Chinese took over the government of the Dalai Lama in 1951. Unlike the rest of Tibet, the Po region has considerable forest growth, and there has been some attempt to develop light industry from local products—timber, leather, woollen textiles and clothing. Quite naturally, there are major plans for the use of hydroelectric power.

Lhasa, the capital of Tibet, with a population of 70,000 in 1953, is 12,000 feet above sea-level, in the valley of a tributary to the Brahmaputra. The city is set in a green valley, with houses and gardens across the river plain, and monastery buildings on the slopes and cliffs of the mountains which rise 6,000 feet above the valley floor. Dominating the whole city is the massive palace, monastery and shrine of the Potala, with roofs of gold and walls of white and sacred red, built on a rock and towering almost 1,000 feet above the city street level. Lamaism is a form of Buddhism, and the Dalai Lama was recognised by his people both as a spiritual leader and as the temporal ruler of Tibet. For almost twelve years now, he has been an exile in India, while the government of the country has been run by Chinese officials and controlled by Chinese armies.

The main part of the Tibetan population, rather more than a million people, live in the south-east near Lhasa, but settlement is peripheral to the region as a whole. The people of one valley are largely isolated from those of another, and communications in this cold rugged desert are so limited and slow that Tibet is not likely to gain economic coherence. The main beast of burden, the ubiquitous yak, moves at a speed of two and a half miles per hour.

Four motor-roads, however, meet near Lhasa. The main route from Tsinghai in the north crosses the Brahmaputra and continues south over a pass through the Himalayas to Sikkim, India and East Pakistan. Along the Po trough a strategic motor-road from Khotan in Sinkiang across the Karakoram Pass joins the Upper Indus valley near the Ladakh ranges in Kashmir with the area about Lhasa, and then leads eastwards across the great mountain ridges of the Chamdo Region to Szechwan in West China. A new road to the south now links Tibet with Katmandu, the capital of Nepal.

Plate 31 The Potala at Lhasa, palace and traditional home of the Dalai Lama, now in exile in India. *(Wen-wu Publishing Company, Peking)*

Conflict of empires

It may at first seem surprising to describe the Communist state of the People's Republic of China as imperialist, for such a term is generally used only for the remnants of European empires in Asia and Africa, and occasionally for the international policy of the United States of America. If the words empire and imperialist, however, are to remain anything but meaningless insults, they must surely be applied to territories occupied by one people and governed by another with a different cultural, economic and social background. On these terms, the lands of Outer China comprise one of the greatest empires in Asia, or indeed in the world, and Chinese imperialism takes second place only to the Russian dominions of Soviet Siberia and western Asia.

In Mongolia, Sinkiang and Tibet, the central government at Peking has gained control of peoples who differ from the Han Chinese in race, language and culture. In Mongolia, as we have seen, the nomads of the steppe are under increasing pressure of colonisation by new settlers from the south. In Sinkiang, the Uighurs, of Turkish origin and Moslem faith, are similarly subject to Chinese rule. Their lands, wherever possible, are put to Chinese-style settled agriculture, and the resources of oil and atomic industry are turned

Plate 32 Commanders and fighters of the Sixth Transport Company of a certain unit under the General Logistics Department of the Chinese People's Liberation Army take a break from their communications and convoy duties on the road between Tsinghai and Lhasa to study the works of Chairman Mao. ***(China Pictorial)***

to the advantage of the whole Chinese Republic. Above all, in Tibet, an accepted government has been overthrown, and reports of rebellion and bitter fighting still come at intervals from beyond the Himalayas to encourage the propagandists of anti-Communism and keep alive their fear of China.

From the Chinese viewpoint, there are strong arguments and justifiable claims to this empire. Mongolia has long been connected politically with China, whether by war or by conquest. The hill tribes of the west have been equally involved with the Chinese world, and in the days of power of the great Chinese dynasties in the past, the Dalai Lama and all his people were regularly compelled to recognise their vassalage to the Son of Heaven. It was, moreover, in response to the threat from barbarians to their north and west that the Chinese first developed an interest in Central Asia and established control of the oasis kingdoms in the desert.

Curiously, while the steppes of Mongolia and the high plateau of Tibet have always been an effective barrier against Chinese-style occupation, the cities of Central Asia, scattered along the caravan routes of the forbidding desert, have generally been amenable to Chinese dominance. Despite the great differences in area, there is little change in technique between the agricultural methods of north China and the water control and irrigation of the oasis farmlands. As a result, since the days of the Han Empire when the first Chinese generals and administrators were sent to the western regions to establish a defensive salient against the barbarians of the north and of the west, China has maintained an effective interest in Central Asia. Though present Chinese control in Sinkiang dates from the great campaigns of the Ch'ing general Tso Tsung-tang in 1877, the Chinese can show a history of involvement two thousand years old.

Besides the problems of nationalist rebellion, of which the most notable example has been Tibet, the frontiers of these outlying territories are a constant potential source of dispute with China's neighbours. In dealing with India, Soviet Russia and Outer Mongolia, the Peking government claims alternatively, and sometimes simultaneously, firstly that the present frontiers were forced upon China in the past by 'unequal' and therefore unjust treaties, and secondly that, even if the treaties are recognised, the border lines they describe have been misinterpreted to China's disadvantage.

On the south of Tibet, China has made claims against India to redraw the border, in particular to India's north-east, where the Chinese line runs at the base of the Himalayas rather than at the crest, and in the Ladakh area of Kashmir, where the Chinese motor-road crosses Indian-claimed territory. In 1962, this dispute developed into a short war. The Chinese army inflicted a sharp defeat on the Indians, and then returned behind the disputed boundary. So far the quarrel has only been with India. China has at present good relations with Pakistan, and Chinese pressure on Nepal, Sikkim and Bhutan, the small states on the southern slopes of the Himalayas, has been little more than neighbourly and rather less oppressive than that exercised by India. In the south-east, however, the Burmese government has reported infiltration, the stirring of rebellion, and occasional battles with Chinese troops from Yunnan.

In the argument with India, China can claim that the MacMahon Line was a device of British imperialism, and that the present government has no right to accept it. The same accusation can also be levelled at the Soviet Union, for large tracts of land from Dzungaria in the west to Manchuria in the east were occupied by Tsarist Russia in the nineteenth century only after considerable military threat and pressure against the weakened Manchu dynasty. By the same token, the very existence of the People's Republic of Mongolia is regarded by China as an infringement of a traditional sphere of influence and a relic of Russian opportunism in the early difficult years of the Republic. These larger claims are sometimes made, but seldom pressed. On the other hand, the Chinese have shown violent excitement over ostensible Russian advances on the Ussuri and the Amur Rivers on the borders of Manchuria, and it is still disputed whether the boundary between Dzungaria and Outer Mongolia should follow the crest or the foot of the Altai Mountains.

Manchuria, with its great investment in heavy industry, is naturally a sensitive region for the Chinese government, and Sinkiang, because of its new oilfields and atomic power, is becoming nearly as important. All through history, the Inner Asian frontiers of China have been lands of nomad migration where caravans of merchants and travellers journey among the isolated oasis towns. There has always been conflict and a moving pendulum of empire, but a strong China will expect to maintain its ground. It is worth noting that maps of China prepared by the Nationalist government in Taiwan include Outer Mongolia as a matter of course, and extend the border against India at least as far as do their rivals in Peking.

7 The Basin of the Yangtze — 1: Tibet to the Gorges

South China

Chapter 2 discussed the essential physical divisions between west and east, Outer China and China Proper, and within China Proper outlined the contrast between north China and south China. For north China, Chapters 3 and 4 have traced the course of the Hwang Ho and described the delta lands of the North China Plain. In considering the lands of south China, it seems equally appropriate to discuss them in terms of river basins and valleys, for the drainage area of the Yangtze is some 750,000 square miles, a fifth of the whole country, and more than 200,000,000 people, a third of the population, live within that region. Except for the provinces of the far south and the south-east coast, all south China is in the basin area of the Yangtze.

Two major physical features distinguish the lands of the Yangtze from those of the Hwang Ho in the north. Firstly, the great dividing range of the Central Mountain Belt, which largely separates the tropical maritime air and the monsoon climate of south China from the polar continental air and the dry climate of north China. Secondly, the nature of the two great rivers: while the Hwang Ho scours its way through Loessland and deposits silt across the plain, the Yangtze Kiang still cuts through deep gorges for much of its length, and its delta formation is of comparatively recent origin.

In comparing south China with north China, George B. Cressey prepared a table of contrasts, summarised in Table 3, page 130. This may give an effective impression of the difference between the two territories.

In history and culture too, the people of south China have differed from those in the north. Chinese civilisation arose and developed in Loessland and the North China Plain, but it found its area of greatest expansion in the fertile valleys of the Yangtze Basin and the south. While the steppe peoples were alien to the Chinese and while nomad life could never be compatible with Chinese settled agriculture, the pattern of peasant farming and communal irrigation work already established in the Hwang Ho Basin was readily transferred

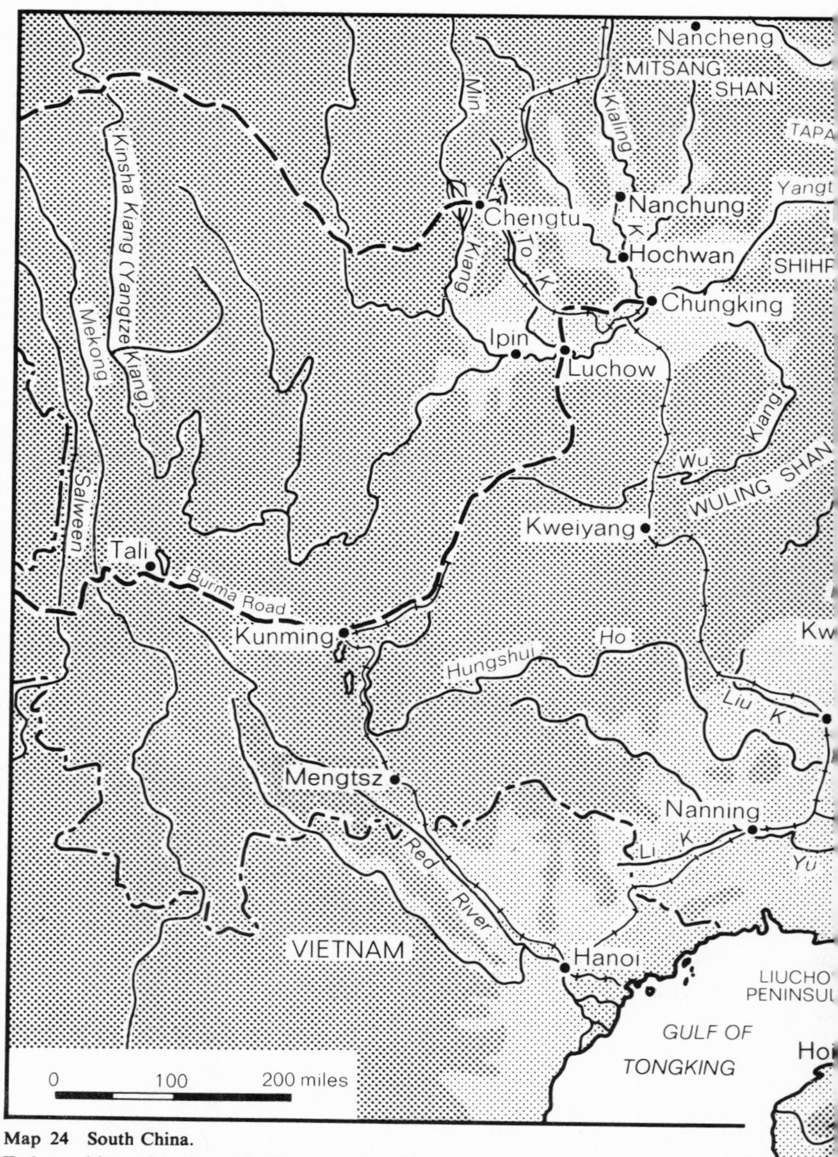

Map 24 South China.
To be read in conjunction with Chapters 7, 8 and 9.

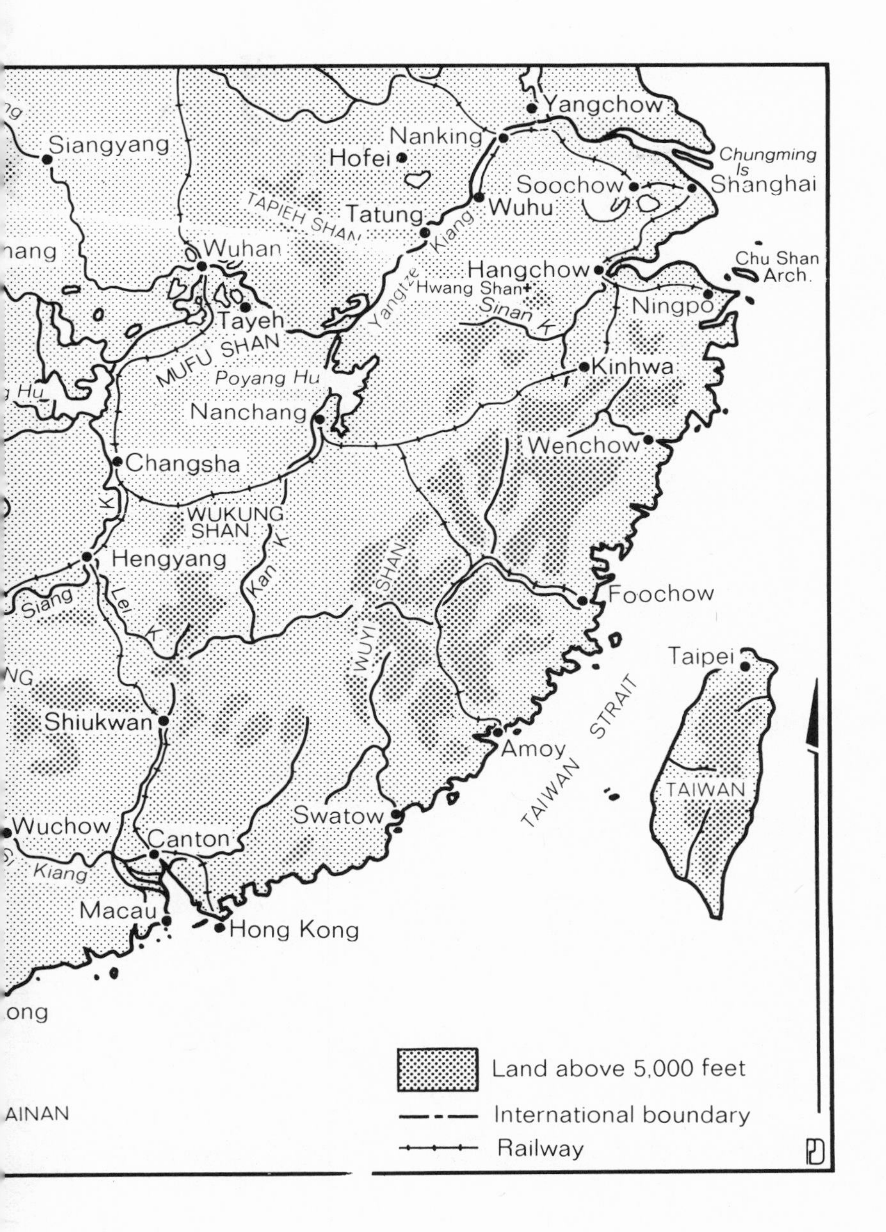

Yangchow
Nanking
Hofei
Chungming Is
Siangyang
Soochow
Shanghai
TAPIEH SHAN
Tatung
Wuhu
Wuhan
Yangtze Kiang
Hangchow
Chu Shan Arch.
Hwang Shan
Sinan K
Ningpo
Tayeh
MUFU SHAN
Poyang Hu
Kinhwa
Nanchang
Wenchow
Changsha
WUKUNG SHAN
Hengyang
Kan K
WUYI SHAN
Foochow
Siang
Lei K
Taipei
TAIWAN STRAIT
Shiukwan
Amoy
TAIWAN
Swatow
Wuchow
Canton
Kiang
Macau
Hong Kong
Land above 5,000 feet
International boundary
Railway

to the lands of the south. In the north, the techniques of hydraulic engineering were used to hold rivers within their banks and to bring additional water to thirsty fields; in the south, the same tools were used to drain marshes and to maintain the regular cycles of flood through terraced paddy-fields.

Table 3

North China	*South China*
Large areas of level land, with hills	Extensive mountains, with scattered plains
Limited and variable rainfall, 15 to 25 inches	Abundant and dependable rainfall, 40 to 80 inches
Disastrous droughts and floods	Water readily available for irrigation
Cold winters, hot summers, occasional snow	Cool winters, hot humid summers, frost uncommon
Brown and dust-blown in winter	Green landscape at all seasons
Forests rare	Abundant vegetation, bamboo
Unleached calcareous soils	Leached non-calcareous soils
Four to six months growing season, one or two crops	Nine to twelve months frost-free, two or three crops
Wheat, millet, kaoliang, dry agriculture	Rice, tea, silk, wet farming

Adapted from George B. Cressey, *Land of the 500 Million*, McGraw-Hill, 1955, p. 248.

On the other hand, Chinese civilisation, which can be traced back almost 4,000 years in the heartland of north China, is comparatively recent in the south. There was considerable colonisation during the first centuries A.D., but it was not until the T'ang and Sung dynasties, around A.D. 1000, that the region of the Yangtze was firmly within the control of the Imperial government, and to this day, in the more distant and inaccessible regions, non-Chinese tribesmen still maintain their traditional way of life with some degree of autonomy.

Chinese settlement, naturally enough, followed the lines of the river valleys: the villages and farmlands were established on level ground suitable for irrigation, and those non-Chinese people who would not accept the new ways of life were steadily driven into the hills. The natural barriers and the succeeding, distinct waves of colonisation, however, have also produced a diversity of dialects and some variety of race. In north China the national language, Mandarin, is in common use and there is little difference in pronunciation from one district to another. In south China, the divisions of hills and mountains have produced differences of dialect—so much so that the speech of a man from Canton is quite unintelligible to a man from Shanghai, and the non-phonetic characters with which the Chinese language is written can provide the only point of contact (map 4, page 16).

As with language, physical appearance varies from north to south China. In the north, the basic Chinese stock has received some admixture from Mongol and other northern invaders, but overall the physical appearance of the people is similar. In south China, intermarriage and absorption with the peoples of different regional tribes have produced a generally lighter, shorter physical type, but there is considerable variation from one province to the next. It is claimed that the southerners are more radical and restless than the classical and conservative north, and in Imperial times, by and large, the north held the predominance of political power, while the south tended to produce the greater wealth and the more imaginative statesmen. In the present century, the Chinese revolution under Sun Yat-sen received its greatest impetus and embarked upon its victorious struggle from the southern city of Canton. Chiang Kai-shek comes from Shanghai District and, although the Communists won the civil war from a northern base at Yenan, their first government was established in Kiangsi and Mao Tse-tung is a man from Hunan.

Chamdo, Yunnan and Kweichow

Geology and landform

In the eastern part of the Tibetan Highlands and south of Tsinghai, the administrative region of Chamdo contains the headwaters of the great rivers Salween, Mekong and Yangtze (map 23, page 113). Here the mountain ridges of the Kunlun and allied ranges swing from their east-west alignment to run almost north and south. A single motor-road, from Lhasa to Chengtu in Szechwan, crosses the region, but otherwise the territory is very largely unexplored and is inhabited only by a few aboriginal tribespeople.

South of Chamdo, the mountain ridges fall away to the high

plateau of Yunnan, with a general level 6,000 to 7,000 feet above sea-level in the west and several peaks more than 15,000 feet. The great rivers and their secondary streams gain their water from melting snow. They flow through a land of tall forests and great chasms, where the torrents at the valley bottom may lie 5,000 feet down a sheer wall of rock, with the crests of the ridges on either side no more than quarter of a mile apart. Often the only way across is by a swaying bridge of bamboo, although many of the tracks wind down precipitous mountain-sides and up the opposing face. Through the centuries these tremendous obstacles of topography, and the malaria that infests the deep valleys, have formed a barrier on the route from China to India and Burma. Since early times, trading parties have made their way across the dangerous ridges, and in World War II the famous Burma Road from Szechwan through Kunming to the west provided a life-line from the Western Allies to the government of Chiang Kai-shek at Chungking; but the route is impossible against a firm defence, and it was in this region that the armies of the Emperor Kublai Khan invading Burma met their only defeat on land. The border of China with Burma is still not defined, and the native tribesmen of the hills are potential trouble to either government.

The main stream of the Yangtze, known also in these upper reaches as the Kinsha Kiang (Gold Sand River), rises in the slopes of the Ulan Ula ranges in the south-east of Tsinghai at an altitude of some 18,000 feet, and flows south through Chamdo in valleys parallel with its great neighbours the Salween and the Mekong. These latter continue south by deep-cut valleys through western Yunnan into Burma, Laos and Vietnam, but the Yangtze, in a series of sharp bends, turns east along the northern face of the plateau. At Ipin in Szechwan, where the river emerges on the south-west of the Szechwan Basin, it has travelled some 1,600 miles from its source and has descended 16,000 feet. It is now only 1,000 feet above sea-level.

With the steep gradient, the unevenness of the drop, and the frequent breaks in its long profile, the Upper Yangtze shows all the features of a typical mountain river, and geologists have suggested that the abrupt change of course in northern Yunnan is of comparatively recent date. It is very possible that in earlier times the Upper Yangtze continued south across the plateau along the present course of the Red River. Later, regressive erosion by streams flowing from the south-west into the Szechwan Basin captured the Upper Yangtze and swung it north and east away from its original course.

Geological evidence also suggests that the massif of Tibet is still rising, and this frontier region between the ancient shield and the lower ground of China Proper is subject to earthquakes in a belt from Kansu in the north to western Yunnan and the Burmese border. In 1925, a major tremor around Lake Tali killed one out of eighteen people in the affected area and destroyed the homes and fields of 100,000 others. (In a land of rice paddy cultivation, even a small disturbance can do immense damage, breaking the bunds that hold water in the fields, cracking the mud film at the bottom so the water drains away, or even altering the slope of the ground and rendering existing terracing useless. Such sudden damage may take months to repair before crops can be sown again.)

From the high ground of western Yunnan, drained by the river systems of the Mekong and the Salween, a central ridge runs eastwards towards Kweichow. On the north of this watershed, the land is drained by short tributaries of the Yangtze, and on the south lie the headwaters of the Red River and other smaller streams flowing south-east through Hanoi and Haiphong to the Gulf of Tongking. Further east are the upper reaches of the Si Kiang which runs through Kwangsi to Canton. Eastwards the plateau declines in height, with a general level of 3,000 feet above sea-level in the south and east of Kweichow.

The reduced elevation is largely a reflection of increasing karst development, for this region of south-west China is formed of Devonian limestone, thoroughly dissected by water. Limestone is permeable, and in many places rain sinks straight into the rocks with no run-off and none of the normal erosional development. Instead, streams and rivers flow underground through great parts of their courses, among intricate caverns and natural tunnels with sink-holes from the surface to the ground water-level.

There are many Chinese landscape paintings that show incredible mountains, vertical slopes and overhanging cliffs, wreathed in clouds and looming as if without support in the misty air. Westerners sometimes consider these as figments of the artists' imagination, but Kweichow has mountains just as fantastic as any dream or nightmare could devise. The vertical erosion of rain-water through the joints in the limestone first creates sink-holes and then, when these reach ground water-level, the deep holes widen to valleys and the streams continue to undercut the soluble rock. Supporting pillars are cut away, caverns collapse, till a new surface has been formed and the old surface is represented only by the tops of a few overhanging peaks and cliff-faces not yet fallen. Where the rock-beds lie horizontal, the hill-tops may be rounded, but elsewhere the strata stand vertical, and the hills can rear upwards like a row of balanced blocks, with crags projecting above the valleys.

The solution sequence is evolutionary from west to east: central Yunnan is a high plateau well over 5,000 feet, with a few deep sink-holes, which increase in number and size towards the east.

Plate 33 Karst limestone formations at Wind Cave Hill near Kweilin in Kwangsi. The vertical walls are the result of advanced solution by underground water, and caverns in the cliffs mark former ground water levels. *(Courtesy: Camera Press)*

In Kweichow, the upper plateau surface has almost disappeared, and the lower level of the solution valleys is predominant. Here are the most spectacular landscapes, with isolated rocky peaks and level land between them seldom more than half a mile across. There are few surface streams, for most water is carried away below the ground. In Kwangsi, at the final stage of the cycle, the process of solution is almost complete; a few great towers of rock remain, but a new plain surface has been established at the lower level. In all this region, including Kweichow Province, western Kwangsi and western Hunan, no more than 4 or 5 per cent of all the land can be classed as even approximately level.

Climate

In climate, the plateau of Yunnan has been well described by Cressey as an island of moderate temperatures and clear skies surrounded on three sides by hot, humid lowlands. Indochina on the south, Kwangsi and Kweichow to the east, and Szechwan to the north are all to various degrees affected by the tropical air of the South China Sea, but Yunnan, more than a mile high, has a temperate climate. In summer, there may be thunderstorms from May to July, and July and August are warm, but the season is not oppressive, and maximum temperatures at Kunming, the capital of Yunnan Province, are seldom above 90°F. In winter, from November to May, the weather is clear, with snow on the mountains and some light falls on the plain in February, but few day-time frosts. Minimum temperatures at Kunming are about 20°F in December and January, whereas the monthly averages are almost 50°F. Precipitation varies with exposure to the humid air masses from the south: southern slopes may register 120 inches a year while sheltered northern faces have as little as 30 inches. Kunming has an annual precipitation of some 42 inches, with the highest monthly average almost 10 inches in July. See maps 11-14, pages 26-7.

Kweichow, on lower ground, has no such advantages; it is often cloudy and humid, oppressive, with higher temperatures in summer, and a more even rainfall through the year. The capital, Kweiyang, has 46 inches annual precipitation, an average temperature of 37°F in January and 77°F in August. Both the Yunnan Plateau and the hill country of Kweichow, free from frost for at least ten months of the year, have a long growing period. The mountain forests are superb, with rhododendrons, azaleas and poplars, but the soils (map 8, page 23), mountain red earth heavily eroded and leached, and mountain yellow podzolic strongly acid, are poor for agriculture. Kweichow, in particular, with small areas of level ground, is one of the weakest agricultural provinces of China.

Resources and communications

The chief summer harvest is rice, with some double cropping in Yunnan, but the grain is too expensive a food for many of the people and they content themselves with maize, sweet potatoes and other vegetables. There is good quality tea, some tobacco and, until recent times opium, harvested just before the rice planting in spring, was the most valuable cash crop of all. It has now been banned. In Yunnan, fruits include peaches, pears, oranges and lemons, and there are also walnuts and chestnuts. However, only about a twentieth of the area of the two provinces can be put under cultivation, and the people have a constant struggle to feed themselves.

Yunnan Province, some 168,000 square miles in area, has more than 20,000,000 people, and the population of Kweichow, 67,000 square miles, approaches that figure. The two capitals, Kunming and Kweiyang, each with half a million people, have no rivals in size, and the only other cities of note are Mengtsz in southern Yunnan, on the railroad from Kunming to Hanoi in Vietnam, and Tali in the north, near the lake of the same name, by the road to Burma. In former times, Tali was an important staging post for travellers on the old trade route across the mountains, and the region is famous throughout China for the decorative patterning and the quality of the marble which is mined in the surrounding hills.

There are no major deposits of iron in either Kweichow or Yunnan, but there are reserves of coal available for local industry near Kunming, at Kaiyuan north of Mengtsz, and at Anshun near Kweiyang. In non-ferrous metals there is copper and zinc, important reserves of bauxite and large deposits of tin; until World War II, Yunnan was responsible for 6 or 7 per cent of the world's tin production. Any real development, however, must wait on improved communications, for the links are still tenuous and the rugged country makes transport difficult and expensive. Kunming is connected by rail to Hanoi in Vietnam (a narrow-gauge rail relic of French expansion at the beginning of this century), but there is no line yet between Kunming and Kweiyang. In the last few years, a line has been built to cross the Yangtze at Chungking in Szechwan, then pass through Kweiyang and Nanning in Kwangsi on the supply route to North Vietnam, but any rail or road construction in the mountain country of the south-west requires great effort and skilled engineering. The main form of transport is often by coolie carriage,

Plate 34 **Mangshih, a village in Yunnan near the border with Burma, with essentially non-Chinese population.** *(Courtesy: Gun Kessle and Jan Myrdal)*

human porters following narrow paths, paved at best with stone, through wooded ravines and up steep cliffs from one valley to the next.

Not surprisingly, this hill country of the south-west, so far from the heartland of China Proper, with broken terrain and difficult communications, still contains a great number of unassimilated aboriginal tribespeople. In Kweichow there can be found more than eighty non-Chinese groups, and in Yunnan less than half the population regard themselves as true Chinese. The hill people of neighbouring countries mingle either side of the official borders and, while their farming interests are much the same as the settled people of the lowlands, central and provincial governments are compelled to recognise their separatism and cultural differences. Under Communist rule, local administrators have done their best to limit friction between the Chinese and the minority peoples, and in Yunnan, Kweichow and western Hunan fully half the area has been divided into Autonomous Districts, with special rights for the non-Chinese people under supervision by the central government.

East from Kweichow, the high ground continues along the ridge of the Nan Ling, dividing the middle basin of the Yangtze from the far south of China. In the north, the mountains enclose the Szechwan Basin, and the ranges link across the Yangtze Gorges with the Tapa Shan of the Central Mountain Belt. From all the northern slopes there flow tributaries of the Yangtze.

Szechwan

Szechwan means 'Four Rivers' and the modern province gets its name from four great streams which join the Yangtze there. Though there is some disagreement, they are generally identified as the Min Kiang, the To Kiang, the Kialing Kiang and the Wu Kiang. As a measure of their contribution, the mean annual discharge of the Upper Yangtze is some 185,000 cubic feet per second, but by the time the river reaches the Ichang Gorges it has increased to more than 500,000 cubic feet per second. The Min Kiang, in particular, which flows from the Min Shan on the north-west of the Szechwan Basin, past the ancient city of Chengtu, and joins the Yangtze at Ipin, was long regarded as the upper course of the Yangtze itself, and it was not until the seventeenth century that Chinese explorers identified the Upper Yangtze as the main stream.

The Yangtze flows north-east along the south of the Szechwan Basin, near the base of the mountains which rise into Yunnan and Kweichow. The Min, To and Kialing join the Yangtze from the north; the Wu comes from Kweichow to join the river from the south shortly before it enters the gorges. On the east, the basin is separated from Hunan south of the gorges by the Shihpao Shan, and on the north-east the Tapa and Mitsang Shan divide it from the upper reaches of the Han Kiang and the provinces Hupeh and Shensi. This eastern ridge has peaks 8,000 feet high, and on the west the high ground rises in great steps to the ridges of Chamdo and the massif of Tibet.

Within this ring of mountains, the province of Szechwan is 75,000 square miles in area, with a population of 60,000,000 or 70,000,000. The general elevation of the basin itself slopes from about 3,000 feet in the north to 1,000 or 500 feet in the south, and the city of Chungking, on the junction of the Yangtze with the Kialing Kiang, is 700 feet above sea-level. Only about 5 per cent of the land is level ground, but much of the rest is hill country with local contours of a few hundred feet, so the slopes are comparatively easy to terrace. The rainfall is sufficient to allow rice cultivation even without the aid of additional irrigation.

This, indeed, is the remarkable feature of the Szechwan Basin. Surrounded on all sides by mountains, those on the south are yet not so high as to hold back the maritime air flowing inland in summer, and rainfall over the region is an average of 40 inches a year. During the summer, a dry föhn-type wind from Tibet gives Chengtu in the north-west clearer skies and less rainfall than Chungking, but the mountain barriers on the north tend to hold the humid air and keep the season warm, wet and sticky. In winter the rainfall is less, but the successive ridges of the Chin Ling Shan and the Mitsang Shan protect the basin from the full effect of the cold continental air masses of Mongolia and, though there may be snow on the mountains around, freezing conditions are rare, and the growing period extends for eleven months of the year. The climate is equable. Average temperatures for Chengtu in January and July are 44°F and 78°F, and during both winter and summer a steady cloud cover prevents much evaporation and increases the effectiveness of the rain. While excellent for agriculture, however, it is not an attractive climate to live in. Travellers across the mountains from the north remark on the brown winter of Loessland and the lush green of the basin, but from the plateau of Yunnan, well named 'South of the Clouds', the skies above Szechwan appear grey among the mountains. See maps 11-14, pages 26-7.

The fertile soil and the favourable climate have attracted one of the most densely settled populations of China, though in recent years efficient techniques and intensive farming have maintained production of food ahead of the population increase and in general Szechwan Province is still a net exporter of grain. More than two-thirds of the land is double-cropped and some three-quarters has the benefit of extra irrigation. Crop failure is uncommon, and unlike the lower basin of the Yangtze there is comparatively little danger of

Plate 35 A small commune in a hill valley in Szechwan. Banks for an irrigation channel are being constructed with the earth carried in baskets. Materially, the construction of the houses and the electricity poles appears superior to the scene at Mangshih in plate 34. ***(Courtesy: The Geographical Magazine)***

flooding. The main summer crop is rice, with wheat in winter (map 16, page 32), and it has been fairly said that anything grown anywhere in China can certainly be grown in Szechwan. The whole region is like a garden, developed everywhere as fully as possible, and beside the two staple grains there are also grown corn, rape-seed, kaoliang, soybeans, tea and a great variety of fruit. Sugar-cane, grown in the south-west, is a major cash crop and there is a considerable silk trade centred around Chungking. Estimates claim there are some 16,000,000 pigs in Szechwan, and the province is a major producer of hog bristles. In former times this region was well-known for its opium, and the hills round about still produce other medicines and herbs important to the Chinese pharmacopoeia. Oil from the tung-tree is used throughout China for various manufactures such as lighting fluid, waterproofing and caulking, and paint.

The hill country of Szechwan is famous for the variety of its natural vegetation. Most of the lower slopes around the basin have been cleared for agriculture, but on the higher ground broad-leafed, evergreen forest shades into deciduous, and above 6,000 feet the growth is mainly coniferous, with shrubs and flowers, including the famous rhododendrons and azaleas growing wild. At the highest points, there are alpine pastures, meadow and bamboo groves. Around the margin of the basin there are outcrops of coal, with considerable deposits in the east and the centre. The reserves are slight compared to those of Shensi and Shansi, some 300,000,000 tons of anthracite and 3,500,000,000 tons of bituminous coal, with anthracite in the west near Chengtu on the Min Kiang. More recent exploration has discovered reserves of natural gas and oil near Nanchung in the centre of the basin on the Kialing Kiang. If these can be developed effectively, they will be of immense importance, supplying modern fuel to a region of established population. There are no major known deposits of other minerals, though there are some small reserves of iron in the south-west. Before the discovery of oil, Szechwan Province had been designated as a region of light industrial development only. One of the main industries, still maintained, is the traditional extraction of salt from brine wells.

One road from Szechwan leads west across the Chamdo Region to Lhasa in Tibet and the Burma Road goes south through Luchow, but communications by land are difficult in all directions. During

Plate 36 A traditional rope and bamboo bridge near Chengtu in Szechwan, decorated with the hammer and sickle of the Communist Party. *(Wen-wu Publishing Company, Peking)*

the Han dynasty, 2,000 years ago, the imperial highway from present-day Sian on the Wei Ho came south across the Chin Ling Shan and the Mitsang Shan to Chengtu, and for much of its length through the ridges and valleys it was supported only by wooden trestles, built out and perched on the mountain-side in a remarkable feat of early engineering. Only a little less striking in design, the electrified railway north from Chengtu now follows the same route, entering the mountains by the valley of the Kialing Kiang and joining the Lanchow-Sian line at Paoki. A motor-road accompanies it, another leads east through the mountains along the Wu Kiang and then to the Lower Yangtze, and a main south route with a newly built bridge across the Yangtze links Chungking to Kweichow and Yunnan.

If communications out of the province are difficult and few, those within the basin are not particularly easy. The rivers and streams have eroded their beds of soft red sandstone so travel cross-country is difficult, and most of the waterways other than the Yangtze and the lower reaches of the main tributaries are either unsuitable for transport or take only small craft. The people live chiefly in villages and small towns, and in 1950 Chungking was the only city with more than 1,000,000 inhabitants, though the population of the province was then more than 50,000,000. During World War II the Nationalist Government built a number of motor-roads, admittedly with poor surfaces, and the Communists have since improved them.

Chengtu, second-largest city and the capital of the province, is situated in a remarkable drainage and agricultural region of its own, on the alluvial fan formed by the Min Kiang where it leaves the hill country and spreads sediment across an open plain. On a smaller scale, the debris brought down by the Min Kiang posed the same problems of silt and flood as the Hwang Ho in the north, but 2,000 years ago the great engineer Li Ping established a system of canals and, when he died, left instructions that the channels should be cleared of silt every winter, so that the dykes need not be raised excessively. There is a monument and temple to him at the head of the plain. The canals are still maintained, $7\frac{1}{2}$ acre-feet of water is supplied over 500,000 acres, and the work of the earliest Chinese settlers of the Ch'in and Han empires is continued by the peasant farmers of modern communes. More than 5,000,000 people live on the 1,750 square miles of the Chengtu Plain.

The largest of the four main rivers in Szechwan is the Kialing Kiang, with its two great secondary streams, the Fow Kiang and the Chu Kiang. The Kialing Kiang is over 600 miles long, more than half its length being in the Szechwan Basin, and the combined catchment area of the three-river system is 90,000 square miles.

Plate 37 The wharves at Chungking on the Yangtze, with river steamers, floating docks, barges, lighters and sampans. *(Courtesy: The Geographical Magazine)*

Between them they drain the north and centre of the basin and at Hochwan, fifty miles from Chungking, they combine into a single stream. For some distance up from Chungking both the Yangtze and the Kialing Kiang are navigable by small river steamers, but sand-bars, rapids and gorges make such transport difficult, and most carriage by water must be maintained in smaller boats.

Chungking, built on a spit of land at the junction of the Kialing Kiang and the Yangtze, is the major city of the province, and during World War II it became the capital of the Nationalist government. By its situation, it is a terminal port for the largest river steamers which connect Szechwan with the provinces of the Lower Yangtze and the east. The city itself lies on a high spur above the two rivers, with an inclined railway to bring heavy supplies from the docks below. Land is so limited that the airport was built on a sand-bar in the river, flooded and therefore closed at high water.

At Chungking, the Yangtze is no more than 300 yards wide, in a deep-cut channel with a seasonal rise and fall of seventy feet each year. Potentially, there are tremendous resources for hydroelectric power, and some small plants were built by the Nationalist government along the Kialing Kiang and its tributaries. The most suitable terrain and the most impressive projects, however, are those on the Yangtze, and the present government has plans to dam the river at Chungking and at Ipin in the south-west.

The Gorges

From Chungking to Fengkieh, the Yangtze flows through an increasingly narrow valley, and at Fengkieh the river enters the great gorges. In the 400 miles between Chungking and Ichang, there are twenty-five rapids which are dangerous to ships. Below Fengkieh the stream which was 300 yards wide at Chungking is narrowed to 150 or 200 yards, while great cliffs 1,000 or 2,000 feet high tower above the water. There are a dozen famous gorges, and in the fifty miles just above Ichang, three in succession, called the Sanhsia, follow close, one after another.

The Yangtze Gorges provide some of the most spectacular river scenery in the world, and they have been famous resorts for poets, scholars and hermits. Temples and pagodas are perched on hills and cliffs above the stream, and legends and stories tell how great armies

Plate 38 The Sanhsia, Three Gorges, on the Yangtze above Ichang. ***(China Pictorial)***

fought and were destroyed in the narrow road which leads across China from west to east. From Chungking it is possible to sail by special river steamer 1,400 miles to Shanghai on the sea-coast and, in the days when European nations forced their will upon China, gunboats used this means to bring reminders of their power into the very heart of the country. However, to this day transport along the Yangtze Gorges is still usually carried by junk, sailing at frightening speed downstream among rocks, and powered on the return journey by teams of men, a hundred strong, hauling the boats with great cables of split and woven bamboo. The most powerful engines are needed to hold river steamers and make headway against the rapids, while the journey by junk upstream from Ichang to Chungking regularly takes one or two months.

At Ichang, the river is 300 feet above sea-level, and the mean annual discharge is over 500,000 cubic feet per second. There are great seasonal variations, with summer flow in the narrow gorges 200 feet above winter level, and records of the water rising fifty feet in a single day. Navigation is more difficult when the summer flow increases the force of the current, though there is some compensation as the water also covers the most dangerous rocks. Floods can drop as quickly as they come, and there is a story of one river steamer which was stranded on a projecting rock 120 feet above the low-water level. For reserves of hydroelectric power, estimated at more than 10,000,000 kilowatts, the Sanhsia have no equal in China, and there are plans to dam the Yangtze near Patung at the head of the gorges, where a wall 400 feet high would hold back a lake reaching almost to Chungking.

It seems most likely that the gorge link of the Yangtze is an example of back erosion and capture similar to that already described between the Upper Yangtze and the Szechwan Basin. Structurally, fault lines are continuous from the Tapa Shan south across the gorges, and the rapids of the river and the narrowing of the cliffs are commonly related to the anticlinal ridges of hard limestone, less subject to erosion by water. In all probability, Szechwan was originally the centre of a limited river system with no direct access to the sea, and the Yangtze itself began from these hills. Backward erosion of the rock first broke the mountain barrier to give an outlet from Szechwan to central China, then the Upper Yangtze was captured in the same way.

Through Chinese history, Szechwan behind its mountain walls has often played a separate political role at times when the empire has been divided. At the end of the great Han dynasty, the state of Shu in Szechwan was one of the famous Three Kingdoms and the general Kuan Yü, God of War in the Chinese pantheon, served that state, and met his end when he was trapped by enemies among the gorges. So the path to the east along the Yangtze and the road to the north across the Han Kiang and the Chin Ling Shan have supported frontier posts as often as they have received imperial highways. It was at the Yangtze Gorges that the armies of Japan turned aside to the south, and during the war the Nationalists held Szechwan while the Communists dominated Loessland. The independence of the people in this fertile and almost isolated basin has often been maintained by war-lords and has sometimes swung the balance of power in China. It is interesting to note, if one must search for separatist tendencies in the Communist state, that Szechwan now appears one of the difficult provinces, sometimes reluctant to share its prosperity and surplus of grain with the central government and the other regions of China.

8 The Basin of the Yangtze — 2: Wuhan to the Sea

When it emerges from the gorges into central China, the Yangtze has no more than half its final volume of water. At Ichang, as we saw in Chapter 7, the average flow is 500,000 cubic feet a second, but at Tatung in Anhwei, where it enters the delta plain about Nanking, the river discharges almost 1,100,000 cubic feet a second. A quarter of the basin is in the mountain country about the Upper Yangtze and a slightly smaller territory is drained by the rivers of Szechwan, but half the basin area and more than half the run-off comes below the Yangtze Gorges. The middle reaches of the Yangtze, through Hupeh, Hunan and Kiangsi provinces, receive water from several rivers and lakes, and in particular from its greatest tributary, the Han.

The Han Kiang and the Central Mountain Belt

The Han Kiang, almost 1,000 miles long, with a basin area nearly 70,000 square miles, is the fourth river of China Proper, slightly smaller than the Si Kiang of Kwangtung and Kwangsi, but longer than the Hwai. In many respects it is a smaller version of the Yangtze, with a similar series of mountain valleys and open plains separated by narrow gorges.

The Han rises on the slopes of the Chin Ling Shan, about 5,000 feet above sea-level, and flows first through a broad alluvial valley between the Chin Ling Shan and the Mitsang Shan, by the ancient city of Nancheng, formerly known as Hanchung. The soil is soft red sandstone, easily eroded or terraced, and rice cultivation is maintained on the lower slopes and the valley floor in the same fashion as in Szechwan. North of the Han and south of the Wei Ho lies China's great climatic barrier, the Chin Ling Shan. The brown semi-arid scenery of Loessland stops on its steep northern face, and the hills and mountains on the southern side are humid and green.

The Han valley cuts deep into the surrounding hills, and the steep slopes of the watershed retain little of the rain that falls on them. As a result, by the time the river breaks through the limestone ridges north of the Tapa Shan, in a series of canyons and rapids like those of the Yangtze, it has travelled only half its course but has received three-quarters of its run-off. In the upper Han valley, where the mountains drain almost the last moisture from the maritime air which moves north in summer, the water pours from the slopes into the main channel; and at Siangyang, near the head of the lower course of the Han, the seasonal precipitation is reflected very quickly by great variations in flood. The mean annual discharge there is some 42,000 cubic feet per second, but the spate can rise to 1.25 million cubic feet per second, and the water level may vary by sixty feet. Dams are planned which should control the flooding along these middle reaches, but the effect of the swift run-off is still dangerous to the people of the Han valley, and a constant threat to the great cities near its junction with the Yangtze.

The land around Siangyang, like the higher ground about Nancheng, is transitional between wheat and rice regions. Wheat, millet and barley are heavily cropped, but rice cultivation is maintained even at the margin of favourable climate. See map 16, page 32. The middle basin of the Han is enclosed by mountains north, west and east, with a slighter range of hills north-east towards the North China Plain, and a narrow opening south towards the Yangtze. As the river flows south, it divides the main range of the Central Mountain Belt from the eastern extension, the Tapieh Shan, and where the Han nears the Yangtze, the valley opens out, the stream divides and there are natural lakes and marshes.

In the high ground to the west, as we have seen, the upper Han valley is a basin among the towering peaks of the Chin Ling Shan, two or three miles high and a firm barrier against climate and communications from north to south. East of the narrow valley which the Han cuts south of Siangyang, the Tapieh Shan, though seldom more than 3,000 feet high, have formed in the past a similar obstacle to movement north and south between the North China Plain and the lands of the middle Yangtze. In modern times, the Tapieh Shan have been colonised and settled, but it is only in comparatively recent dynasties that this process has taken place. The main south railway from Peking to Wuhan now runs through a saddle in the hills and the main motor-road follows the Lower Han valley south between the mountains along the ancient path of immigration and war. Since earliest times, this region has been a battleground between north and south, and records from A.D. 200 tell the story of how the famous general Kuan Yü of Shu, aided by a sudden flood along the Han, destroyed his enemies of the north.

> In the eighth month there were great rains, the Han Kiang flooded, and the level ground was several score feet under water. All seven armies under Yü Chin and his fellow generals were flooded out, Chin and his officers climbed high ground

to avoid the water, and Kuan Yü's soldiers sailed in great ships to attack them. Chin and the others were completely exhausted, and they surrendered. P'ang Te, however, was on an embankment, carrying armour and holding a bow, and he hit his mark with every shot. From morning till the sun had passed midday, he continued the battle. Kuan Yü attacked more and more fiercely, Te's arrows were finished, and he continued the struggle hand to hand. He fought on, quite unafraid, but the water rose higher and his officers and soldiers all surrendered. Te took a small boat to make his escape, but the boat was swamped and overturned, he lost all his weapons and held on alone to the upturned boat in the water. He was captured by Kuan Yü.*

The hills and rivers south of the Yangtze

When the earliest Chinese settlers came to the barbarian lands of the south, they tended to avoid the marshland and lakes about the main stream of the Yangtze and followed the valleys of the rivers which flow through the southern mountains, making their earliest settlements in such places as Changsha on the Siang Kiang or Kweilin high in the Nan Ling ranges. The first patterns of settlement were on lines of communication for exotic trade through the ports of the far south coast. It was not until later that Chinese immigrants started to farm land in the more difficult regions of the hill slopes and the marshes.

Physically, China south of the Yangtze is dominated by the Nan Ling ranges, which extend east from the plateau and high ground of Yunnan and Kweichow, and the Wuyi Shan which swing north-east as a rocky backbone to the coastline of Fukien. The main ridge of the Nan Ling is 3,000 feet high and the Wuyi Shan, separating Kiangsi from Fukien and Chekiang provinces, has many peaks over 4,000 feet. On the west, the Wuling Shan extend to the Yangtze Gorges and form part of the mountain wall about Szechwan, and a main central ridge, the Wukung and the Mufu Shan, with elevations above 3,000 feet, divides the central basin of the Yangtze. On either side of this ridge two great lakes receive the waters of a series of rivers flowing north from the watershed of the Nan Ling and its secondary ranges. On the west, close to the place where the Yangtze emerges from the gorges, the Tungting Hu has the major tributaries Yuan and Siang. On the east, the main stream into the Poyang Hu is the Kan, but both rivers and lakes have a multitude of secondary streams in the watercourses and narrow valleys of the southern hills.

On a clear day to the south of the Yangtze, you are never out of

*From *Tzu-chih t'ung-chien*, 1956 Edition, Peking, p. 2161.

sight of the hills. The river plains at their widest are no more than ten or fifteen miles across, and often not so much as a mile. Farming is intensive on the valley floors, and terracing is extended as far as possible up the hillsides. Outside the territory of the major ridges, elevations are seldom more than 2,000 feet, and while some 15 per cent of the region may be classed as approximately level, more than 20 per cent is under cultivation. Over the whole area of 155,000 square miles, estimates suggest a population of more than 80,000,000 people: a ratio of 500 to the square mile, or 2,500 to the square mile of cultivated ground, or one person to every one-third of an acre of farmland—figures which certainly encourage intensive cultivation.

This region is in the heart of south China, to some extent sheltered by the Nan Ling from the full effect of tropical air, but generally humid and cloudy over a green landscape, with a reliable and heavy annual rainfall between 50 and 70 inches, and frost-free weather for ten months of the year. In January there is some influence from the cool continental conditions of the north, and the weather through the winter is often clear, mild and pleasant. In summer, July may have two or three weeks with temperature maximums over 100°F and humidity in the 90s. See maps 11-14, pages 26-7. This period called *mei-yü*, or 'Plum Rain', is gloomy, depressing and utterly enervating for men, but it is excellent for their crops and in particular for rice cultivation.

Land use and agriculture

The rice crop in China needs intensive labour, adequate water supply to keep the paddy-fields flooded, and a temperature of 70°F or more during the four months of the growing period. Early in the year, the main fields are put into repair, the baulks and dams along their sides are rendered waterproof, and at the same time the separate seedbeds are sown broadcast and thick. After about a month, the seedlings are ten inches or a foot high. When the rains come the fields are puddled with heavy rakes dragged backwards and forwards until water and soil are churned together into a thick muddy porridge. The seedlings are plucked in bundles from the seedbeds, and are transplanted by hand into the slurry of the main fields, four or five together in regular lines. In many areas, two crops are gained in one season by planting two sets of seedlings in alternate rows, one a couple of weeks after the first. For three months after the transplanting, the fields must be kept covered with four or five inches of water. Where paddy-fields are built on the slopes above a valley floor, small dams and reservoirs are constructed higher in the hills to maintain a regular supply of water. Often, the same flooded fields are used as ponds for rearing fish, with a further side benefit that the fish eat mosquito larvae; though there is very little, unfortunately, that discourages the ubiquitous leeches. As the crops develop, they are weeded two or three times. Harvesting, generally, is done by hand, and threshing in the fields separates the grain from the straw used for fuel or for animal fodder.

Rice can be grown as a dry crop, but in China this is seldom done. On higher ground, where rainfall is insufficient to keep the fields flooded and extra water cannot be found by irrigation, barley, rape-seed, soybeans, sweet potatoes and some winter wheat are grown; but rice occupies half the cultivated land, almost all the level ground, and in some regions nothing else is sown. Of all other crops in this region tea is the most important, for some two-thirds of the country's tea-growing area lies in these southern hills and central Hunan is the largest producer of tea in China. The warm, wet climate, with high humidity, overcast skies and frequent foggy weather, is very suitable, as is the soil, neutral towards the north of the Yangtze basin but developing increasing acidity further south.

To an outsider, the Chinese seem to pay the same attention to tea, its different varieties and their distinctive flavours, as the connoisseurs of Europe do to their wine. Wine in China, incidentally, is more like the Japanese *sake*, made usually from fermented rice or other grain and valued rather for its alcoholic content than for its bouquet and savour, though the wine from Shaohing on the south of Hangchow Bay is praised throughout the Chinese world. Tea is a subject of more refined interest.

Tea grows as a bush, trimmed short so that the leaves may easily be reached for picking. The picking is done in April before the spring rains, in May, and again in August or September. The same leaves may be used for green tea, which is dried by firing; for black tea, which is allowed to wither and ferment before the final firing; and for oolong tea, for which the leaves are only semi-fermented. Besides being sold as loose leaves, the form in which it is generally used in the West, tea is often compressed into 'bricks', about five inches square and half an inch thick, for export to Tibet, Central Asia and Russia. Special blends may be prepared by adding petals of flowers, and in the same shop the price of tea can vary greatly.

If one remembers the stories of the great tea races—how the clipper ships waited impatiently while coolies loaded their holds in the ports of the Yangtze delta and along the coast of Fukien, and then raced ninety days and more across the Pacific, round the Horn and up the Atlantic to dock with the incoming tide in the Port of London—it is hard to realise that China tea is no longer one of the world's great trading commodities. Until 1880, with exports of 300,000,000 pounds annually, China held a monopoly of the international market, but during the next ten years the plantations of India and Ceylon almost entirely usurped her position. China has never recovered. While a considerable quantity of Chinese tea still finds its way to the Western countries, the greater part of the export trade is to the overseas communities of Chinese in South-East Asia. In part, this failure to meet the competition of India and Ceylon may be explained by China's inferior processing and less efficient organisation, but the China teas, black or green, are mild in taste, sometimes too bland for the European palate. While the English and Australians normally add milk and sugar to strong tea, the Chinese preserve their dislike for dairy foods, too reminiscent of barbarian nomads, even to the teacup. One side effect of the national habit of boiling water for the staple drink may be noted: China's medical history does not include the plague of cholera.

The great forests which formerly covered the lands about the Yangtze are being steadily cleared away. Those of the plains and the accessible valleys went long ago, and increasing pressure of population, with slash-and-burn agriculture preceding settlement, has brought tremendous devastation in the last two centuries. Cutting is still heavy, even in the wilderness areas of the mountains towards Szechwan and Kweichow and in southern Hunan, for the wood is very fine. The trees are taken for their timber and great rafts of pine, bamboo, maple and camphor are floated on the Yangtze down to Wuhan and the river ports still further to the west.

Industry and communications

East of the Poyang Hu, near Kingtehchen in Kiangsi, clay called kaolin, from the Chinese term meaning 'high ridge', is mined from the upper slopes of the Paitsi Shan. Kaolin is an ingredient of fine porcelain ware, and the products of the great imperial potteries at Kingtehchen have been famous for centuries throughout the world.

As might be expected, the major lines of communications and the large cities and towns of the south Yangtze hill country are found along the valleys of the major rivers. Though travellers since the earliest times have followed the rivers, and though there was a canal built across the watershed south from Kweilin two hundred years B.C., the streams for most of their length are too turbulent for large craft, and on the upper reaches there are only small junks and shallow rafts. South of the Yangtze the main railway line from Wuhan through Changsha to Canton follows the valley of the Siang Kiang and its tributary the Lei, with another line branching at Hengyang across the Nan Ling through Kweilin into Kwangsi, and onwards south-west to Hanoi in North Vietnam. Two roads and a railway lead across lower ground in the central ridge of the Wukung and Mufu Shan from Changsha to Nanchang, capital of Kiangsi Province, near the Poyang Hu. Further east there are railway links to Hangchow in Chekiang and Foochow on the Fukien coast.

Besides these major routes, however, communications in the hill country are never very easy, and none of the cities has more than 500,000 people. Though Changsha and Hengyang have plants for agricultural and mining equipment, with railway workshops also at Nanchang in Kiangsi, the region as a whole is dominated industrially by the great complex of Wuhan on the Yangtze.

The lakes of the middle Yangtze

When the Yangtze Kiang leaves the gorges, it ceases its deep incutting along its bed and enters an alluvial plain, sometimes widening into lakes and marshes, sometimes narrowing between hills and cliffs, on its way eastwards to the delta country and the sea. The Yangtze Plain was originally a series of deep lakes, but the sediment brought down from Szechwan and the upper reaches of the other rivers has largely filled the lakes and left them shallow, and much of the land has been drained by canals and reclaimed behind dykes.

As Cressey has remarked, the geography of the Yangtze Plain is better described as hydrography, for water is the key to the landscape, and the people of Hunan describe their province as three parts mountain (mostly in the hill country to the south), six parts water, and one part plain. It is only during the last thousand years or so that this region of low land close to the river has been controlled and settled, and the process is not yet complete: there are occasions when reclamation projects press too hard against the river, and disastrous floods can still occur. Ultimately, however, unlike the Hwang Ho on the North China Plain, the Yangtze can be controlled by man.

The major difference between the Hwang Ho and the Yangtze is that, even on the plain, the bed of the Yangtze is adequate in normal times to carry the water and the sedimentary material on to the sea. After the narrow gorges, the river widens out to a full mile at Wuhan, the river terraces are clearly developed, and the bed is more than forty feet deep. At Nanking, near the beginning of the delta, the average depth is 130 feet. Even so, all along the length of the river there are dykes and levees, from twenty to more than fifty feet high, to hold back the flood waters from cities and farmland over an area of a 100,000 square miles. While the river may normally run within recognised banks and does not constantly seek to change its main course to the sea, the extent of its basin, north, west and south, brings a tremendous flow of water through the plain, with immense potential for seasonal variation.

At Wuhan in winter, the channel of the Yangtze is sometimes barely six feet deep, but the increase in the summer may be forty-five feet. When the water from the main stream through the gorges combines with the Han and southern tributaries, the flow can be astronomical, and both in 1931 and in 1954 the river at Wuhan was measured at more than 2,500,000 cubic feet per second, with a depth of over fifty feet above low-water level. No dykes could hold such a mass of water. In 1931 some 34,000 square miles of normally dry land was flooded, the whole city of Wuhan was under water to a depth between four and eight feet, 140,000 people were drowned, and 25,000,000 were driven from their homes. This flood, the worst recorded anywhere in the world, affected people numbering twice the population of Australia, and devastated an area slightly larger than the whole of Tasmania. In 1954 the flooding was equally extensive, but the loss of life was far less, due largely to the efficiency of government relief measures. On this occasion, Wuhan escaped, for though the river rose 58 feet 4 inches above low-water level, the dykes had been raised to 59 feet 4 inches, and they held.

In both these disaster years, flooding on the Yangtze was accompanied by flooding on the Hwai Ho in the south of the North China Plain, and rainfall over the wide area drained by tributary streams was generally more effective in bringing on the crisis than immediate precipitation over the narrow Yangtze Plain. Rainfall at Wuhan averages 50 inches a year, the greater part between April and July, while the average monthly temperature varies from 40°F in January to 85°F in July and August. Wuhan, then, is comparable to the other cities of the hill country to the south. However, all this central basin is affected by temperate cyclones, or depressions, which move east down the line of the Yangtze and force precipitation from the humid air coming inland from the south. This pattern of climate has been discussed in Chapter 2 (maps 9 and 10, page 24), and it was the influence of seven of these depressions one after another that brought 24 inches of rain to the region about the middle Yangtze Basin in July 1931. A similar pattern developed to cause the great flood in 1954.

In times of more moderate flow, the Yangtze is controlled naturally by the two great lakes, Tungting and Poyang, and artificially by flood basins. The middle section of the Yangtze is divided into two considerable flood plains, separated by a narrows where the high ground of the Mufu Shan on the south approaches the Tapieh Shan north of the river. Tungting Hu and the lower course of the Han lie to the west; Poyang Hu, in the centre of the circle of hills which is Kiangsi Province, is on the east.

The course of the Yangtze by-passes both the great lakes, though they are connected to the river by several channels. When the main stream is low in winter time, water from the southern tributaries flows through the lakes to join it on its way to the sea. In summer,

Plate 39 A trestle bridge in the lake country of Kiangsi Province. *(China Pictorial)*

however, when the flow through the gorges and from the Han increases, the current can flow the other way and the lakes expand rapidly as they receive water from both their regular tributaries and also from the swollen Yangtze. The lakes are shallow and subject to great variations in area between high and low-water, but they can be controlled within dykes and in most years they give essential respite to the flood defences along the main course of the river. In flood stage, the Tungting Hu covers 1,450 square miles, and the Poyang Hu 1,075 square miles.

Flood control and land reclamation along the Yangtze, as for the more difficult problem of the Hwang Ho, is based on a system of lakes and reservoirs to absorb excess flow of water. Besides the two great natural lakes there are a number of artificial basins, notably the Kingkiang Reservoir at Shasi below Ichang and north of the Tungting Hu, built in 1954 with an area of 355 square miles, and the Tachiatai Flood Basin west of Wuhan between the Yangtze and the Han. The reservoir at Shasi provides a good example of what organisation can do with large numbers of men and primitive equipment. It was built in no more than two and a half months, with 300,000 workers, but very little machinery.

Behind the dykes and levees, the alluvial soil of the river plain is one of the most fertile in China, and the middle Yangtze Basin is one of the most productive regions in the country. As in the southern hills, rice is the major crop, grown with particular success in the lake regions about Tungting and Poyang, and Hunan is known as the 'rice-bowl' of China. In winter there is barley and wheat, while cotton is a major crop for summer harvesting, particularly in the middle and lower valley of the Han where the climate is favourable. The textile-manufacturing centre of Wuhan is close by. Hemp, jute and rami, a grass from which Chinese linen is made, are also grown in the plain and hills about the Yangtze for processing at Wuhan.

In the middle Yangtze Basin, high-grade iron ores are mined near Tayeh in Hupeh, south of the Yangtze below Wuhan. Coking coals are found at Puchi on the Yangtze in Hupeh and at Pingsiang in Kiangsi on the railway line across the saddle of the Mufu and Wukung Shan. At Shihhuiyao near Tayeh, a river port has been developed to supplement the railway connection with Wuhan, while local coal and fine-grade limestone provide the raw material for some local smelting and also for an important cement works. Like Changsha, Nanchang and the other cities of the South Yangtze Hills, however, all these local centres are subordinate to the main industrial and communications network focused on Wuhan.

Wuhan

For the middle Yangtze and indeed for central China, Wuhan is an obvious centre for communications, and early in the Communist regime Wuhan was chosen, with Paotow on the far Ordos loop of the Hwang Ho, as a future base for the development of heavy industry. The choice was a natural one, for some reserves of coal and iron in the district were already known, and Wuhan had established connections by river, road and rail up and down the Yangtze, along the valley of the Han, across the Tapieh Shan to the North China Plain, and through the southern river systems by the Tungting and Poyang lakes. With technical assistance from Russian engineers, the Han Kiang was bridged in 1955 and the Yangtze in 1957. The bridge across the Yangtze is more than a mile long and the span over the river itself 1,250 yards. It is high enough to allow 10,000 ton ships to pass even at high water in summer. There are two decks, the lower carrying a double-track railway, the upper a six-lane motor-road. This north-south link-up of land routes, until very recently the only such connection between north and south China, set the seal on Wuhan's major importance for modern industrial development.

The metropolitan area of Wuhan in fact comprises three cities:

Hankow on the north of the Han, Hanyang on the strip of land between the Han and the Yangtze, and Wuchang to the south of the Yangtze. The combined population of the three is now in the region of 2,000,000, of which the majority live in Hankow, while Wuchang, the provincial capital of Hupeh, is the administrative and education centre. In the nineteenth century, under the administration of the modernising Viceroy Chang Chih-tung, the Hanyang Iron and Steel Works was one of the first major industrial plants established in China and No. 1 Cotton Mill at Wuchang was started early in this century. Now, however, Hanyang is chiefly concerned with textiles, and the Wuhan Iron and Steel Corporation has built its fully integrated plant at Wukang on the Yangtze east of Hankow. It has almost four square miles of workshops, with automatic blast furnaces, open hearth ovens and rolling mills capable of handling seven-ton and fifteen-ton steel ingots. Annual output of steel is claimed to be 3,000,000 tons.

Wuhan has been a Chinese settlement at least since the time of the Han dynasty 2,000 years ago, though like most other cities of the Yangtze Plain it owed its importance rather to strategic, political and commercial interest than to major industry. With the great variation in water-levels between winter and summer, it is impractical to use docks and wharves on the river banks, and goods and passengers are landed onto moored hulks and rafts connected

Plate 40 **The road and railway bridge across the Yangtze at Wuhan, first to link north and south China.** *(Foreign Languages Press, Peking)*

to the shore by pontoon bridges. In many of the smaller river ports, loading and unloading is carried out by ferries and lighters while the ship is at anchor in midstream.

In the summer flood, ocean-going ships of 10,000 to 15,000 tons can sail upstream as far as Wuhan. In the days of European imperialism, when Britain controlled the Yangtze as a special sphere of influence, Wuhan, 630 miles from the sea, was recognised as a treaty port with full rights for foreigners to trade.* The river is now closed to all but Chinese ships. In summer slightly smaller craft, still capable of deep-sea sailing, can travel up river as far as the mouth of the gorges at Ichang, and besides these there are special river steamers, no more than six-feet draught, which can negotiate the shallows in winter as well as the full spate of summer. And in and among all these vessels are hordes of junks and sampans, large and small, different in build for the lakes, marshes and rivers, varying in power from oars through sail to small motors, with special flags to indicate the cargo they carry from one port to another, housing aboard them whole families of boatmen who spend their lives on the water. Of all the rivers and waterways in the world, the Yangtze is probably the busiest.

The Yangtze delta

Soon after the Yangtze passes Kiukiang and the mouth of the Poyang Hu, its course turns north-east through a narrowing of the plain between the Tapieh Shan and the ridges about Hwang Shan in southern Anhwei. Near the river port of Anking it emerges again onto a wide flood plain, and the effect of the ocean tides is first noticed at Wuhu, still two hundred miles from the sea. Here is the beginning of the Yangtze delta.

It is recorded in the histories that not much more than 2,000 years ago the Yangtze came to the sea by three or four separate streams, all branching from the region of Wuhu. The southernmost course curved south into Hangchow Bay, one or more others went due east into the area of marshland about Tai Hu and then to the sea either at Hangchow Bay or near present-day Shanghai. In time, these alternative routes were silted up, and the northern course is now the Yangtze's sole outlet to the sea.

For volume of water, the Yangtze is the largest river in Asia, with a mean discharge at the mouth of 1,150,000 cubic feet per second,

*In the last stages of the civil war before the Communist takeover, the British *Amethyst* made her escape from the Yangtze under the guns of a Chinese army. Shortly afterwards, a British motion picture retold the adventurous story of fine seamanship; but the fact remains that *Amethyst* was one of the last gunboats to invade and patrol China's inland waters.

or half a cubic mile of water every day. Estimates have suggested that each year the river carries more than 5,000,000,000,000 cubic feet of solid material—rocks, gravel and soil—past Wuhan, and the swift flow of water takes the greater part of this alluvium all the way to the sea. Chungming Island, in the mouth of the river, has grown steadily during the last centuries, and the sea currents carry the Yangtze's silt around the coastline into Hangchow Bay and the Chu Shan Archipelago off its southern point. Between Hangchow Bay and the Shantung Peninsula, because of silt brought down by both the Yangtze and the Hwai, the coastal waters are shallow and the land has been extended steadily on a broad front guarded by dykes.

To the south of Hangchow Bay, the hills of southern Chekiang are an extension of the Wuyi Shan of Fukien and form a backbone to the northern part of the rocky south-eastern coast. A railway line to the former treaty port of Ningpo follows the coastal plain south of the bay, and another runs south through Kinhwa to Kiangsi Province. North of the valley of the Sinan Kiang, the massif about Hwangshan, 4,600 feet, closes off the Yangtze delta from the east and south. Roads now run through this hill country, but it was not settled until comparatively late, and it does not support a large population.

North of the Yangtze, the great divide which reaches from the Tibetan Highlands through the Chin Ling Shan and Tapa Shan to the Tapieh Shan peters out in central Anhwei north of Nanking, at a range of low hills which form the watershed between the Yangtze and the Hwai. Elevations are nowhere more than about 1,000 feet, and the railway from Nanking to the north runs through the middle of the region, but the main lines of communication in the past have gone through the city of Hofei, capital of Anhwei Province, on the west of the hill country, or along the line of the Grand Canal on the east (map 20, page 70). The slight elevations are no real barrier to seasonal air movements, and the climate of the Yangtze delta merges gradually with the more temperate and increasingly cooler conditions of the Hwai valley and the North China Plain to the north. Summer is tropical, with the same hot, damp, enervating atmosphere as the middle Yangtze Basin further inland. Winter, with continental air from the north, is short but cold, and the average January temperature in Shanghai is 38°F, two degrees lower than Wuhan. Since some of the air from the north passes over the Yellow Sea, the winter climate is less dry than that of the North China Plain and precipitation is rather less variable through the year than it is in the north. See maps 11-14, pages 26-7. The borderland of climate, however, between continental winters and tropical summers, can once every few years produce the curious phenomenon of light snowfalls on palm-trees.

Land use and agriculture

In the delta land, the water table lies close to the surface of the ground, canals are everywhere, rice cultivation is intensive and production is almost as high as in Hunan Province in the middle Yangtze Basin. Wheat and barley are the winter crops, and in summer corn and soybeans are also sown (map 16, page 32). In the areas near the coast, behind the salt-pans and the dykes, there are important plantations of cotton, for that crop is comparatively resistant to salinity in the soil and good yields can be obtained from land where other plants would not survive.

This region of the Yangtze is also one of China's major silk-producing districts. Mulberry trees are planted in rows along the dykes, with groves of them across the open countryside. Two-thirds of China's production now comes from this region, with some from Shantung in the north and the balance from Szechwan and Kwang-tung provinces. The mulberry trees are pruned down to bush size, and the leaves are fed to silkworms four to six times a day for the thirty days of their life in that stage of metamorphosis. At the end

Plate 41 The Yangtze Plain, at Chitung on the north of the estuary. The chequer-board fields, divided by irrigation channels, have varied crops of rice, vegetables and cotton. Close linear settlements indicate the density of the population and the intensive nature of cultivation. *(China Pictorial)*

Plate 42 Cotton and rice grow side by side on a commune near Soochow, the fields separated by a narrow bund. Man-power still carries most of China's products along such tracks as these in the first stages of transport to factories and further processing. *(China Pictorial)*

of this period, the worm spins its cocoon in one or two days, changes into a chrysalis, and emerges as a moth some two weeks later. The moth lives only three or four days before it lays its eggs and dies, and the cycle begins again. The cocoons are unravelled for their silk. It is estimated that silkworms consume 150 pounds of mulberry leaves to produce one pound of silk and that mulberry trees yield some 70,000 pounds of leaves to the acre. For a long time, silk was one of China's great exports, and some scholars of economic history attribute the decline of ancient Rome to the drain of gold eastwards along the Great Silk Road through Central Asia to buy silk and other luxury goods from China. In the disturbed period before World War II, however, under the influence of civil disorder, foreign invasion and the depression of 1929, together with some outdated techniques of manufacture and distribution, China lost her place as chief world silk exporter to the Japanese. Though methods have improved since the war, artificial materials such as rayon and nylon now compete with silk and have rendered it less valuable as an export. As a cash crop, cotton is more important.

The cities of the delta

The delta of the Yangtze is heavily populated: Kiangsu Province, apart from the two great cities of Nanking and Shanghai, has a population approaching 45,000,000 spread over an area of 41,500 square miles. A large part of the reclaimed ground near the sea is fairly lightly populated so this would indicate an average density in crop-land of some 15,000 people to the square mile. This is the highest ratio for any province of mainland China; although most of the province would be classed as rural and agricultural, twenty-five people to the acre is comparable with modern suburban housing in several parts of Australia. Moreover, in this region agriculture is essential as there are no great mineral resources for industry.

In Imperial times, Kiangsu and Chekiang provinces were famous for their cities and for their culture. In the official examination system for entry into the Imperial civil service, the scholars of this region regularly filled the highest places, and the provincial libraries and private collections rivalled those of Peking and the Imperial Palace itself. The prosperity brought by government influence and culture was encouraged and maintained by commercial success. Some towns were famous for their products, as Shaohing in Chekiang for rice-wine and Soochow in Kiangsu for the beauty of its women, while others, such as Chinkiang and Wuhu on the Yangtze, Yangchow on the Grand Canal and Ningpo by the sea, were important primarily as trading centres. Of the older historic cities, however, Nanking and Hangchow, both former capitals of the empire, are the greatest and most important.

Hangchow, provincial capital of Chekiang, with a population now of some 750,000, lying at the head of the great bay of the same name, was the seat of the southern Sung emperors till their overthrow by the Mongols in the thirteenth century. Marco Polo, who saw the city after that conquest, described it as still the greatest in the world. Its prosperity and importance have continued; it is famous for the beauty of its gardens, bridges and canals; and tourists come every year to wander about and sail upon the West Lake, and to stand on the sea wall and watch the Hangchow Bore, a solid wave of water, sometimes eight feet high, which is formed by the spring tides twice a month as they sweep along the shallow bay into the narrowing estuary.

Nanking on the Yangtze, with a population approaching 2,000,000, was for a short time the capital of the Ming dynasty, and is still recognised as the capital by the Nationalist Taiwan government. From the third century A.D., it has been the chosen capital of great independent states during times of division and, until the last century, it was famous for its magnificent buildings and for its antiquities. In 1853, however, the city was captured by the army of the Taiping rebels and served as capital to their ephemeral empire until it was sacked and destroyed by the Imperial armies of the Manchus in 1864. In that civil war, which brought wholesale destruction and devastated most of the Yangtze Plain, the monuments which had been the glory of Nanking were almost all destroyed. Little remains of the past but the great city wall, twenty-two miles long, and the tomb of Sun Yat-sen, founder of the Chinese Republic, who was buried on Purple Mountain outside the city in 1925.

More recently, in 1968, a great bridge across the Yangtze, to match the first at Wuhan, was completed at Nanking. The river is now crossed by both road and rail, and the lines continue east to Shanghai and south into Chekiang. In many ways this is an even more spectacular triumph for the present government than was the bridge at Wuhan for, besides the difficulty of the task, this work was carried out and completed without the aid of Russian technicians, who were withdrawn from China in the early sixties.

Figure 8 Shanghai.

The sketch map shows the development of a treaty port, and provides a contrast to the plan of Peking (figure 7, page 82). Shanghai was originally a fishing settlement, but the old town is now dwarfed by the development which has taken place since the city was opened to international trade and settlement by the treaty of 1843. The period of the foreign concessions in the nineteenth and early twentieth centuries saw immense expansion of population, drawn by the wealth of trade, and irregular spread of settlement, notably along the waterfront and on the major roads leading to the hinterland.

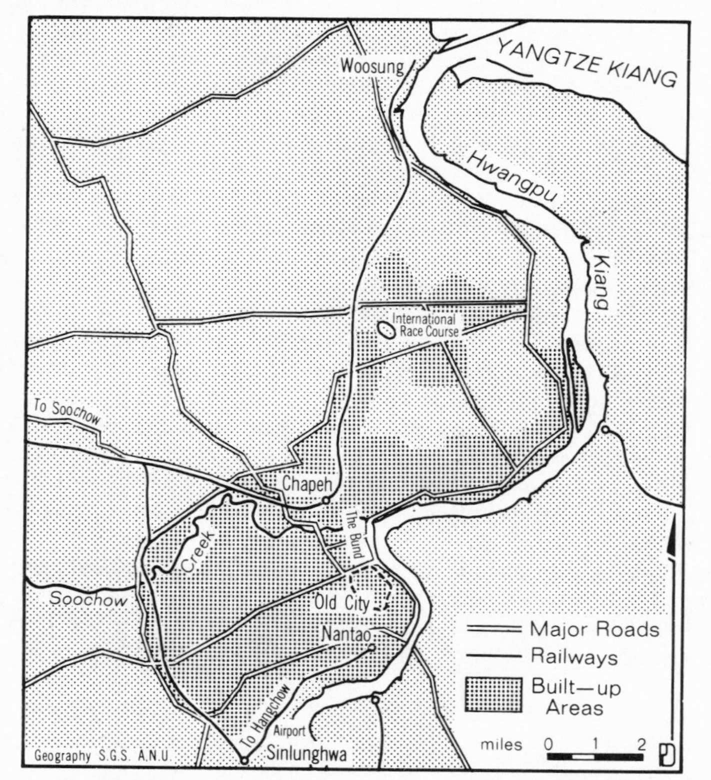

Plate 43 **The waterfront at Shanghai. Formerly one of the busiest harbours in the world, the port is now almost empty of ships. Nevertheless, though overseas trade has declined, other uses have been found for the great merchant offices, and Shanghai is still one of the major industrial centres of China.** ***(Courtesy: The Globe and Mail, Toronto)***

In the Treaty of Nanking, which concluded the First Opium War between Britain and China, it was agreed that certain ports should be opened to foreign trade, and the British chose an area of ground outside the small walled town of Shanghai at the mouth of the Yangtze for a territorial concession. This later became an International Settlement, with a French Concession beside it, and over this area Chinese law was no longer effective and foreign jurisdiction, criminal and civil, took its place. In time of troubles within China, Shanghai was a haven for refugees, and in time of prosperity it was the major port for overseas trade and one of the busiest harbours in the world. For commerce, Western law was generally more practical for both foreigners and Chinese, and the great business and trading houses were chartered with headquarters in Shanghai. As a bridgehead for trade between two alien cultures and two totally different systems of law, extra-territoriality and foreign concessions served some useful purpose, but to any patriotic Chinese the arrangement was an imperialist insult. It was constantly subject to abuse and in 1931 and 1937, when the Japanese were preparing to attack China, they ferried their troops into Shanghai and camped there in security till they were ready to launch an invasion across the boundary line of the International Settlement. At the end of World War II, the foreign

Plate 44 The Shanghai Heavy Machine Tool Works: a giant deep-boring machine for open-end holes, capable of processing a work-piece fifteen yards long weighing twenty tons. *(China Pictorial)*

powers renounced their privileges and, after the Communist victory in 1949, Shanghai's international position was completely changed.

The city and port of Shanghai is some fifty miles from the open sea, on the Hwangpu Kiang, a tributary of the Yangtze estuary. It is not a remarkably good site for a great harbour, for it is barely above sea-level and the ground is soft mud. The centre of the city is some fourteen miles up the tidal creek of the Hwangpu, and the famous Bund, the sea defence wall, is near the junction of Soochow Creek, which runs inland to the city of that name on Tai Hu (fig. 8). The main channel has been deepened and widened but it still requires constant dredging, and large vessels can enter the Yangtze estuary only at high tide when the depth of water across the bar at the mouth increases from twenty to thirty-five feet. In spite of all this, Shanghai is the greatest city in China, with a population of 6,000,000 people in 1954 and at least 7,000,000 now.

The port rose to prosperity on trade with the West—trade which was in many ways an exploitation of China as a whole—and when the Communists came to power it was generally expected that Shanghai would be left to wither and die, while new industries were developed further inland in the heart of China. In fact, this did not happen, for the resources of machinery and technical ability preserved in Shanghai were too important to be ignored by realistic planners and, in 1963, after the failure of the Great Leap Forward, there was even a campaign for all industrial cities to 'emulate Shanghai'. Centre of a wide transportation network, with facilities for storage and handling and with a highly sophisticated workforce, Shanghai has not only held its place as a centre for light industry and processing, leading the country in output of cotton, silk and woollen goods, but it has also received government investment for heavy industry. Culturally, at least until the advent of the Red Guards, Shanghai was less pious, puritanical and restrictive than Peking and the cities of the north. Its position as a sea port and the memory of its cosmopolitan past have kept the people rather more receptive to ideas from outside, and often more enterprising in their commercial dealings. Even under the Communist regime, most of the black market and illegal private enterprise has been centred and organised with efficiency from Shanghai.

With a hinterland comprising the whole Yangtze basin and the greater part of the North China Plain, Shanghai is China's major port and still one of the busiest in the world, though, with changed patterns of trade, industry in China is often centred on available man-power rather than on any particularly favourable distribution of natural resources. Perhaps most important of all, because of China's limited long-range communications, Shanghai and the other great provincial centres may always become economic and political rivals to the central government at Peking. Faced with the twin dangers of potential under-employment and political frustration, such mass movements as the Cultural Revolution may be seen as attempts by the central government to encourage national unity, and it is not surprising that in recent years the rulers of China have become increasingly concerned with projects to encourage city-dwellers on the eastern seaboard to migrate inland and use their labour for more productive agricultural projects, far from their former homes.

Plate 45 (pages 166-71) shows the processes of rice cultivation in the eighteenth century and today. The original engravings were executed about 1760 by a London engraver, John June, from a redrawing of Chinese works believed to have been brought back from Canton by an East India trader, and these were probably prepared originally as part of a farmer's manual. The set of twenty-four prints is now in the possession of the Victoria and Albert Museum, London. In present-day China, rice cultivation is still labour-intensive, and mechanisation is on a modest scale. Rice-growing sites, on valley bottoms between steep hills, are the same, while clothing, tools and organisation have often changed very little. ***(Courtesy: Victoria and Albert Museum, London*** **(i);** ***China Pictorial*** **(ii)*)***

45a (i) and (ii) Preparing to transplant and ploughing the paddy field.

45b (i) and (ii) Planting the young rice.

45c (i) and (ii) Raising water to the field.

(ii)

45d (i) and (ii) Reaping.

(i)

45e (i) and (ii) Threshing.

(ii)

45f (i) and (ii) Breaking the husks.

(ii)

9 Tropical China

South of the hills about the Yangtze Basin, the backbone ridge of Wuyi Shan and the east-west divide of the Nan Ling, there are no barriers to the full effect of the tropical maritime air from the southern and eastern seas. The Tropic of Cancer, where the mid-summer sun comes directly overhead, runs just north of Canton and directly through the Bay of Swatow in Kwangtung. Further north, however, the island of Taiwan and the whole coast of Fukien receive the same humid air in summer and are equally protected by the northern mountains from the cold continental air flow in winter, so they too may be fairly counted as regions of the tropics.

In this area there are few places where rainfall is less than 50 inches each year, and the natural vegetation, still surviving on the more inaccessible slopes of the mountains, is a dense tropical rain forest. Minimum temperatures are seldom lower than 40°F, and snow is seen only on the highest peaks. Summer is humid and oppressive, with temperatures often over 100°F, and a season from May through June is called accurately, but depressingly, the 'Mouldy Period' (see maps 11-14, page 26-7). On the other hand, the few months from the end of the monsoon in October to the beginning of the winter chill and damp in January can be very pleasant, with soft clear weather; and, as in the Lower Yangtze Basin, the climate generally so unattractive to men is admirable for their crops. The growing season in the lowlands continues the full twelve months, and in much of the south two separate plantings of rice can be harvested every year (map 16, page 32).

Chinese armies and settlers from the north first came to this region in the third century B.C., and territory was conquered as far south as Vietnam. It was a long time, however, before colonisation was fully established, and the region remained of little interest to the people of the north, noted only for the exotic tribute—birds, flowers and precious stones—that were brought to the court for the amusement of the emperor. To this day, in Yunnan, Kweichow and Kwangsi in the south-west, and in Fukien and Taiwan in the south-east, there are large numbers of indigenous non-Chinese people still preserving their minority customs and largely unassimilated into the social and cultural patterns of the country as a whole.

Even among the Chinese, there are distinctions between the descendents of people who came to settle at different times. Many of the men of the south trace their ancestry on their present soil to the T'ang or Sung dynasties, and they sometimes speak of themselves as men of T'ang to differentiate themselves from the Han Chinese of the north. The Hakka (the name is taken from a phrase meaning 'guest people') are a separate group of Chinese descended from a different migration, with considerable intermixture of indigenous stock. T'ang men and Hakka live side-by-side in neighbouring villages, the Hakkas generally on the poorer ground, and though both speak Chinese their dialects are different.

From the mangroves of the seashore and the palms of Hainan Island to the conifers and bamboo of the upland slopes in the northern hill country, the far south is a territory of natural tropical or sub-tropical forest, with orchids and camphor trees among tall canopies of green and the great climbing lianas. Almost everywhere, however, the peasant farmers have cut away the natural cover to make room for their fields, and once destroyed the forest seldom returns. As a result, over much of the open country there is valueless scrub and fields of broad-leaved grasses. The small-scale plots of Chinese peasant farmers encouraged this destruction and much of the land was left waste. It is only in recent years, under a system of common ownership, that any large-scale programme of re-afforestation has been established. In the meantime, with hillslopes and wasteland, only about 15 per cent of the total area of Kwangtung and Kwangsi is cultivated.

The yellow-red soils of the Si Kiang Basin and eastern Kwangtung reflect the leaching caused by heavy rain making the soil strongly acidic (map 8, page 23). Frequent liming is needed and heavy fertilisation is essential for good yields. Water-buffalo are used for draught work in the paddy-fields, pigs, ducks and poultry are common, especially in the neighbourhood of Canton, but the main source for additional manure is human. With hard work, an efficient farmer in these southern regions can use the year-long growing season to combine harvests of two different varieties of rice, reaped in June-July and October-November, with a catch crop of vegetables or winter wheat at the end of each year (map 16, page 32). Rice is by far the most common crop, generally grown in fresh-water paddy, but with some dry cultivation on the hillslopes inland and some brackish-water paddy along reclaimed areas of the seaboard. Other crops include sweet potatoes, sugar-cane, groundnuts and tea, while barley is an important grain in eastern Kwangsi, maize in the far west, and a few isolated valleys may still support fields of illegal opium.

Of resources for industry, there are the iron-ore deposits on Hainan Island and another field on the Upper Han, a river which flows in to the sea near Swatow in eastern Kwangtung. Coal, however, is lacking, and the region as a whole is scheduled for only light industrial development, at least until the rivers can be controlled for hydroelectric power. There is manganese in the area of the Liuchow Peninsula in the far south-west of Kwangtung and there is tungsten in the hills near the Kiangsi border, but the region's development has naturally taken place at the communications centre in the delta about Canton.

Kwangsi and the Si Kiang

In Chapter 7, when considering the karst limestone of the Yunnan and Kweichow Region, page 131, we noted that the last stage of its development is to be found in western Kwangsi, south and east of the Yunnan Plateau. The Kwangsi Chuang Autonomous Region, east and west of the Si Kiang is severely broken by hills and mountain ridges, with high ground up to 4,000 feet and river valleys little above sea-level. Among the mountains, in deep eroded beds with many gorges, a whole system of rivers, the most important being the Hungshui Ho, Liu Kiang and Kwei Kiang from the north, and the Li and Yü Kiang from the south, join finally at the Si Kiang, or West River, at Wuchow on the border of Kwangtung, six feet above sea-level. From there their waters flow together to the sea in the Pearl River estuary at Canton.

The Si Kiang, measured from the upper reaches of the Hungshui Ho in Yunnan is 1,650 miles, the third longest in China Proper, and its drainage area, on the southern slopes of Yunnan and Kweichow and among the rugged country of Kwangsi, receives heavy monsoonal rain on steep slopes with a high run-off. Its narrow deep-cut bed enables flood levels to rise safely far above low water, and at Wuchow, where the river is half a mile wide, the variation between summer and winter is seventy or eighty feet, with a high-volume reading in time of flood of over 2,000,000 cubic feet a second, greater than anything recorded on the Hwang Ho. Annual rainfall at Wuchow is 50 inches, with a monthly average of some 5 inches between April and August, and high monthly readings of up to 15 inches through the same period, a reflection of heavy precipitation in the typhoon season. Temperatures are never below freezing and seldom above 100°F, and monthly averages vary from about 60° in February to 80° in July and August.

Like Yunnan and Kweichow to its north, Kwangsi has a large non-Chinese population: of an estimated 20,000,000 total inhabitants, some 10,000,000 belong to the tribes of the Chuang people, 3,000,000 are Yao, and 1,000,000 are Miao. Formerly, Kwangsi was considered a regular province of the empire, but under the People's Republic, to safeguard the non-Chinese communities, the whole territory has been designated Kwangsi Chuang Autonomous Region, administered like the Autonomous Districts in Yunnan and Kweichow but on a larger scale, with the regional capital at Nanning.

The rivers in Kwangsi, navigable far inland, form important communication links that are now supported by railways running north and south. The main line from the north runs through Hengyang in Hunan to Hanoi in Vietnam, and it is joined at Liuchow in Kwangsi by the line from Kweiyang that has recently been extended to Chungking in Szechwan. In contrast to the improvement in north-south communications, there is still no rail connection between Nanning and Canton, and the Si Kiang, which carries great quantities of goods east and west, has no road or railway along its course below Wuchow. Kwangsi is separated from the seacoast and the Liuchow Peninsula by a ridge of mountains, but the coast road is of less importance for communications than the road and railway north from Tsamkong towards Nanning.

From Wuchow on the border of Kwangtung and Kwangsi, the Si Kiang flows 230 miles to the Pearl River estuary near Canton. Here, in 3,000 square miles of delta, three rivers, the names indicating the compass points from which they flow, come to the sea: the Si Kiang, (West River) the Pei Kiang (North River), and the Tung Kiang (East River). The total basin area is almost 400,000 square miles. Even in the alluvial plain of the delta, the level ground is interrupted by individual hill peaks, while transport among the river flats is complicated by a maze of shifting channels, most of them now man-made, which guide the waters to the sea and drain the fertile land. The Pearl River, after which the estuary, and sometimes the whole river system, takes its name, is actually a comparatively short stream confined to the delta region, which receives as tributaries the Pei Kiang and the Tung. The Si Kiang has a separate channel to the estuary. On a boat sailing across the mouth of the bay from Hong Kong to Macau, a passenger can see where, far out from the shore, blue water gives place to a well-defined channel of yellow and red, coloured with soil washed out to sea by the combined flow of the rivers.

With three great streams coming at one point to the sea, and with great variation in rain all through the typhoon season, flooding along the rivers is possible in any year. On occasion the flow of the Si Kiang even in the open delta region has raised the water thirty feet above low level. The channels, however, as on the Yangtze, are protected by dykes lined with trees, and the present government has added to the river defences. Like Kwangsi, communications in Kwangtung are often maintained by water: river steamers can travel up the Si Kiang as far as Wuchow and reach sixty miles on the lower course of the Pei Kiang, but the Tung Kiang, smallest of the three rivers, takes steamers for only a few miles on its lower course during the season of summer flood. Further upstream, launches are used.

Communications by road follow a number of passes north and east across the 3,000 foot ridge of the Nan Ling to Hunan, Kiangsi and Fukien, but the main railway line lies close to the course of the Pei Kiang going through the pass at Shiukwan on its way to Hengyang in Hunan. Two roads lead south-west towards the coast near Hainan Island and another goes north-west to Kweilin in Kwangsi. The ancient canal across the watershed of the Nan Ling at Kweilin connects the upper reaches of the Siang Kiang and the Kwei and saves cross-country portage, but it is now seldom used.

Canton, Hong Kong and Macau

Canton, the capital of Kwangtung Province, with a population around 1,500,000, is linked by railway, road and river transport systems to every part of the province, and dominates the region of some 50,000,000 people to an extent unequalled by any other city in China. Early in this century it was the largest city in the country and, although it has since been overtaken and passed by Shanghai, Peking, Shenyang and some other industrial centres of the north, it is still of major importance both in economics and politics. It was near Canton that the mid-nineteenth century Taiping rebels established their earliest bases, from here the Nationalists began the Northern March of 1926 which re-established the unity of China, and the Canton Commune of the Communist Party of China was first established in 1927. One of the chief tourist attractions of the city is a memorial to the martyrs of an abortive rebellion which was led by Sun Yat-sen shortly before the final overthrow of the Manchu dynasty.

Canton has been a centre for trade in the southern seas since its earliest Chinese settlement, more than two thousand years ago. It was to Canton that Arab and other Muslim traders came from the west, centuries before the Europeans, and race trouble and riots against foreigners in Canton have been recorded as early as the seventh and eighth centuries. When the Europeans arrived they were given small welcome, and it was felt that they were privileged in even being allowed to trade. They were restricted to their trading posts, known as 'factories', for a limited season, and were compelled to quit Chinese soil each year. The First Opium War, which broke out in 1840, was primarily motivated on the British side by merchants anxious to maintain an immoral trade against Chinese official opposition, but the British government became more anxious to support them when it learned how its subjects were treated with contempt by the Chinese authorities, and how the envoys of the greatest maritime power in the world had been insulted by the servants of the Chinese emperor.

The 3,000 square miles of delta region about Canton, varying between hill country and level ground, with a 1,500-mile network of constantly changing canals and river channels, contain several cities, a total population well over 12,000,000, and a density of some 4,000 to the square mile. A shortage of coal in the hinterland prevents any great development of heavy industry but there is dock and harbour work and small-scale local industry. Kwangtung Province is the third highest producer of Chinese silk after Szechwan and Kiangsu, and there are manufacturing and weaving centres at Canton and the neighbouring delta cities of Shuntak and Fatshan. Sugar is also a major export of the region, with processing plants for sugar-cane at Shuntak and Tungkun. Canton itself is a mixture of modern buildings and narrow crowded streets, with a mile of waterfront lined by buildings five or six stories high and an open park on the sand-bar island called Shameen, the former site of the foreign concessions. But the city is no longer such an important centre of trade as it was in earlier years. The Pearl River at Canton has a low-water depth of only six feet, and its course lies over bedrock which makes dredging and deep cutting difficult. The harbour was generally adequate for merchant vessels of the nineteenth century, it is still used by great numbers of small craft, coastal and river vessels, fishing junks and rafts, and twelve miles downstream at Whampoa there are new dock facilities which can take vessels up to 10,000 tons. Even so, both as a port and as a commercial centre, Canton's dominant role in the south has been pre-empted by the British colony of Hong Kong.

In 1841, at the end of the First Opium War, the British obtained possession of the island of Hong Kong, eighty miles south-east of Canton. In 1861, the city of Kowloon on the mainland was also ceded by China, and in 1898 British control was extended north over the Kowloon Peninsula through a ninety-nine year lease of the so-called New Territories. The area of the island is thirty-two square miles, Kowloon is four square miles, and the leasehold of the New Territories is 360 square miles, ten times more than the other two sections of the colony combined. In 1861, the colony of Hong Kong contained less than 10,000 people; in 1941, there were almost 1,500,000; and at the present day there are 4,000,000, who live and work in what is now one of the busiest seaports of the world and also a major centre of light industry.

Plate 46 Hong Kong: intense settlement with tall buildings and land reclamation on the harbour shore. Shanty towns, often without water supply, spread up the hill-slopes too steep for modern constructions. The breakwaters in the harbour give protection to small craft in time of typhoon. *(Courtesy: Hong Kong Government Information Services)*

The great natural asset of Hong Kong is its harbour, an S-shaped strait of deep water between the island and Kowloon, guarded at either end by smaller islands and deep enough to hold the largest ships in safety. Even before World War II, the harbour and its advantageous site, close to Canton and sharing with it the hinterland of Kwangtung Province, was sufficient to make the colony one of the major ports of East Asia, but it was long overshadowed by Shanghai to the north. With the ending of foreign concessions and the Communist takeover soon after the war, Hong Kong was left as the only entrepot to China which offered reasonable security to investment capital. When Great Britain recognised the Communist government, the funds the Bank of China held in Hong Kong were transferred as a matter of course from Nationalist to Communist control, and since that time it has proved convenient for the Peking government to allow the continued existence of the British colony as a link between China and the outside world.

Almost an anachronism in post-war Asia, Hong Kong has faced some difficult problems and periods of adjustment. The colony is a haven not only for foreign capital but also for native Chinese, fleeing for one reason or another from the present government. Since 1949, when the first great wave of refugees fled before the advancing Communist armies, there has been an average intake of some 2,000 illegal immigrants each month, despite control measures along the border, particularly strict on the British side, for there is a limit to the numbers of people that the colony can absorb. The continual growth of population, partly by natural increase but largely by immigration, has put an immense strain on public services and great housing settlements have had to be established north of Kowloon in the New Territories. For commercial reasons the tax revenue is low, the economic structure of the colony is an almost perfect example of *laissez-faire* capitalism, and there is a wide gap between rich and poor.

Hong Kong's growing importance as a gateway to trade with China was hard hit by the American boycott of goods originating from mainland China, which was imposed at the time of the Korean War in the early 1950s. The boycott is now being lifted but it forced Hong Kong to diversify so that it has become not only a trading port, but also a major manufacturing centre for such light industries as toys, plastics, clothing and materials. There are some mineral reserves: lead, wolfram, silver and tin, kaolin clay for pottery, and reserves of iron ore under concession to a Japanese company. Besides these, there are enormous profits from tourism and the hidden assets accruing to a great free-port in finance, trade and transport.

Through this development, the government of Hong Kong has established a remarkable history of achievement, juggling difficult problems of politics, finance and population for a territory which must buy most of its food and water from Communist China, across the border. Militarily Hong Kong cannot be defended and Chinese armies could re-occupy the territory any day, but so far, despite some internal troubles and some arguments, the colony has survived and prospered. Twenty-eight years from now the lease on the New Territories expires and they should return to China. Without them Hong Kong will no longer be viable, but things may change by then and the treaty may yet be re-negotiated.

Near the western point of the Pearl River estuary, forty miles across from Hong Kong, lies the small territory of Macau, a peninsula of eleven square miles granted to the Portuguese by the emperors of the Ming dynasty in 1557. Macau's population, now also swelled by refugees, approaches 500,000 including 3,000 Europeans, but it is neither so prosperous nor so secure as Hong Kong, and disturbances within the colony and pressures from the mainland have compelled the government in recent years to accept considerable control from the Communists. The main industry of Macau is tourism, with gambling in the official casinos, and the visitor on the hydrofoil or ferry from Hong Kong, as he comes up the narrow harbour channel, may admire the fishing boats of Macau and China on either side of the waterway; where Communist flags fly next door to storage tanks emblazoned by the flying horse of an American oil company.

Hainan and the south coast

Around the delta and the Bay of Canton, circling ridges of high ground extend from the mountains of the north, with isolated outcrops about the Pearl River estuary and a barrier ridge separating land-locked Kwangsi from the littoral strip of south-west Kwangtung, the Liuchow Peninsula and the island of Hainan. The mainland coast and the peninsula have open plains covered with useless savanna grass. Hainan, 13,124 square miles in area, almost as big as Taiwan and fifteen miles from the mainland across the narrow Kiungchow Strait, is open country at the north which rises to the several peaks of the southern Wuchih (Five Fingers) Mountains, with elevations over 6,000 feet. Like neighbouring Kwangsi, the population of Hainan has a high proportion of non-Chinese tribesmen and, as in other parts of the south, the Chinese settlers occupy the flatter and more productive country, particularly around the northern port city of Hoihow. The tribesmen, who are Miao or Lu by race, live in the more rugged country to the south. The non-Chinese, comprising one-third of the island's population of more than 3,000,000, still practise primitive slash-and-burn shifting agriculture, and Chinese and non-Chinese alike suffer from weakening tropical diseases such as malaria and hookworm. Hainan is one of the poorest regions of China, but it is also one of the areas with great possibilities for expansion. There is still room for many more people, the climate would support coconut palms and rubber plantations, and there are large known deposits of high-grade iron ore in the north-east, as yet undeveloped.

On all the southern sea-board, naturally enough, fishing is important, though it does not take such a predominant place in the economy as in Fukien further to the north, and the deep-sea fleets of China have to compete with long-distance Japanese expeditions, more highly mechanised and better equipped. Close inshore, the Pearl River estuary and other waters have been so intensively fished by trawlers, drifters and long-liners that some areas are almost fished out. In the delta region, fresh-water fish farming is becoming an important industry, and fish fry from the Pearl River is exported all over South-East Asia.

Along the coast, in Kwangtung and Fukien Provinces, great numbers of people live their lives entirely on boats and junks, gathering fish from the sea and carrying freight and passengers through the harbours or along the coast. They have their own markets and often keep chickens or other livestock aboard, and bamboo is tied to the children's backs to keep them up if they fall overboard. To some extent, this floating existence may be a result of the pressure on available land, but many of the boat-people appear alien to the settled Chinese, they are treated with some discrimination, and it is likely that they are of aboriginal descent or

Plate 47 Typhoon damage in Hong Kong: metal bends and breaks like thin wood and sheets of tin, moving down the street at fifty miles an hour, can cut a man in half. ***(Courtesy: Hong Kong Government Information Services)***

Plate 48 After the typhoon: an ocean-going ship turned over and sunk at dockside. *(Courtesy: Hong Kong Government Information Services)*

migrants from the south seas. Their communities can be found in every port and harbour of the coast, and one of the better known is at Aberdeen, on the south-west of Hong Kong Island, where tourists come to eat fish kept alive for them in cages below the floating restaurants and to admire the picturesque but crowded romance of the village of boats that surrounds them.

From Canton and Hong Kong, north-west up the coast of China as far as Japan, it is typhoon territory. Typhoon is Chinese for 'great wind', and typhoons are tropical cyclones very similar to the hurricanes of the West Indies and the southern United States, and, though much larger in scale, to the willy-willies of north-west

Australia and the cyclones of Queensland. The typhoon develops as an intense depression surrounded by winds of great strength circling anti-clockwise. The central depression, the 'eye' of the storm, perhaps twenty miles across, is often comparatively calm, but the winds around reach more than seventy-five miles an hour and the whole complex may be one or two hundred miles in diameter. A typhoon travels at an average speed of ten to fifteen miles an hour. Like other great tropical cyclones, typhoons are formed in warm waters among the islands on the west of a great ocean, where tropical currents supply great quantities of water vapour. It is believed that the initial pocket of low atmospheric pressure develops through differential heating of land and sea. The Philippines, south-east of China, are often hit first by typhoons, but the storms then move northwards and from July through September a series of them attack the Chinese coast, Taiwan and the nearby seas, each rather further north than the last, till those at the end of the season strike against Japan.

Modern ships at sea are in comparatively little danger from a typhoon and are well equipped to ride them out, but on land typhoons are terrifying and violently destructive. Few things can be more disconcerting than to sit on a chair in a ten-storey building and to feel the whole structure quivering beneath you. Nor, indeed, is it much more pleasant to look out the window and see metal lamp-posts bent like string and sheets of roofing-iron blown like scythes down the street. Steel-framed buildings are safer than ordinary brick, for the wind is strong enough to flatten anything that is not well-founded and solidly built. With the typhoon there comes rain, enough to flood the streets and cellars and often to cause land-slides which sweep away houses and bury people alive. Even in the protection of Hong Kong harbour, the sea has washed large ships among the rocks far above high-water level, and at Swatow in 1922 a typhoon and a tidal wave flooded and destroyed three-quarters of the city and killed 50,000 people. Fortunately, the typhoon pattern is a sea-borne one and, though Canton may be affected, the great winds do not penetrate far inland from the coast.

The south-east coast

The contrast between the open plain of the Hwang Ho in the north and the mountains about the Yangtze in the south is maintained along the eastern coast of China. From Hong Kong to Hangchow Bay, the shore-line is rugged and deep water lies close in. Further to the north, the former courses of the Hwang Ho and the mouths of the Hwai and the Yangtze have brought down solid matter to extend the coastline into a shallow sea, with tidal flats. The islands of the Chu Shan Archipelago east of Hangchow Bay precipitate most of the silt as it drifts south, and the mountain backbone of southern Chekiang and Fukien is reflected in the tight bays and small islands of the jagged coastline which runs 600 miles south to the Bay of Canton.

The border of Fukien Province runs along the high ridge of the Wuyi Shan, which encloses Kiangsi Province and the basin of the Poyang Hu on the east and south. Fukien and southern Chekiang are largely mountainous, the level ground restricted to a narrow coastal strip, the small deltas of the many rivers that flow direct to the sea and inland flood plains. More than nine-tenths of the region is covered by mountains, with some elevations rising to 4,500 feet. The whole coast has a largely tropical climate. Foochow, the capital of Fukien, has an annual precipitation of 56 inches, with monthly averages, allowing for the usual increase in summer rains, fairly evenly distributed over the year, but with great variations from one year to the next. Expected September rain is some 7 inches, but the recorded maximum is 25 inches, brought by autumn typhoons. Temperatures are fairly even, with few days of frost

Plate 49 The medley of islands, shoals and straits about Macau is typical of the broken coastline of south and south-east China. The buildings in the foreground are on the peninsula of Macau, the land on the right is the People's Republic of China. *(Dragonfly Books, Hong Kong)*

Plate 50 Fishing off the coast of Fukien. *(China Pictorial)*

and summer temperatures seldom exceeding 100°F, but the summer humidity is high and oppressive. See maps 11-14, pages 26-7.

The aboriginal people of this region, known by the generic Chinese name of 'Yüeh', for a long time remained sheltered by the mountain barriers and undisturbed by colonisation from the north. It was not until the T'ang dynasty, little more than 1,000 years ago, that Chinese settlers in considerable numbers broke over the land frontier into the river valleys of the south-eastern slopes, and in Fukien like the other provinces of the far south there is still a considerable difference between the original inhabitants and the later settlers. The name 'Yüeh', describing the people who lived in the coastal lands of the south, is a geographical rather than a racial term and, as may be imagined, trade and travel along the coast produced some sense of community among them before ever the Chinese arrived. There have been in history a number of southern coastal states with the name 'Yüeh', and the present name 'Vietnam' represents a southern pronunciation for the two Chinese characters meaning South Yüeh.

The population of Fukien Province may be estimated now at some 18,000,000, and the coastal plain is as densely populated as the region of the Yangtze delta or the area about Canton. The soil is acid and not very fertile, but the growing season is long enough for two successive harvests of rice (map 16, page 32), with major secondary crops of sweet potatoes, vegetables, citrus fruit and peaches, and considerable plantations of sugar-cane, though Fukien is still a net importer of rice, wheat and sugar. The most important cash crop is tea, for the tea-growing country south of the Yangtze extends into the hills of western Fukien. Bohea tea, so called from another name for the Wuyi Shan, was one of the most famous Chinese exports in the great days of the tea-clippers.

The pressure of population and the excellent harbours and anchorages along the indented coastline have encouraged the people through the centuries to seek a living from the sea, either as boat-builders using timber from the hillsides, as fishermen or as sailors. During the Ming dynasty, great imperial ships built in Fukien sailed the Indian Ocean and discovered Africa before ever the Portuguese had rounded the Cape of Good Hope. Though Chinese government interest since that time has seldom been so concerned with the sea, men from Fukien have manned ships of every nationality trading in Asia. In the nineteenth and early twentieth centuries, whether for gold, for trading or as indentured coolie-labourers, great numbers of Fukienese left China to settle in every country of South-East Asia and the Pacific, their numbers rivalling those from the southern province of Kwangtung. The present Chinese government finds it valuable to maintain facilities for the Overseas Chinese to send back money to their relatives and their homeland. The official Overseas Chinese Investment Company promises to invest money sent back in this way in industrial development, particularly in Fukien Province; it pays an annual interest of 8 per cent, and undertakes not to nationalise the plants involved.

The ship-building yards of Fukien and southern Chekiang construct large motorised junks for the coastal and Yangtze river trade and for the fishing fleets. Much of the hill country is still covered by natural forest varying with elevation, but the timber industry maintains a systematic re-afforestation programme which supplies good quantities of fir and pine, and considerable areas of bamboo. Timber is exported in junks as far north as Tientsin (map 20, page 70). Close inshore there are oyster beds and purse-seine fishing, and deep-sea fleets operate out of the major ports. Apart from the sea-lanes, communications are poor. One railway goes inland from Foochow and Amoy across the mountains into Kiangsi and there is a road south from Ningpo linking the cities on the coast, but the mountain ridges running down to the sea make coastwise travel difficult, and the streams of the rivers are generally too steep and turbulent for anything more than light craft and rafts in their upper reaches. The effect of these divisions is shown in the dialects of the people. Over all the hill country of south China, the people of one valley tend to have some difference in speech from those of another, but in Fukien the local variations, not only in speech but also in custom and even in the traditional rig of sailing craft, are particularly strong.

The major cities are all on the coast, from Ningpo, Haimen and Wenchow in Chekiang, to Foochow, Chuanchow and Amoy in Fukien, and Swatow in Kwangtung. Foochow, the largest, has a

Plate 51 The landscape of tropical China: paddy fields at harvest time and terraced hills growing tea; a student brigade taking part in constructive labour and learning through the practice of production. *(China Pictorial)*

The teachers and students of the tea-growing school
both study and take part in productive labour.

population of some 750,000 and is famous for its laquer-ware. Swatow, with rather less than 500,000, dominates the eastern part of Kwangtung Province and is well known for a special manufacture of embroidered grass linen. Until recent years these coastal cities were significant ports for overseas trade, but since World War II and the Communist victory most international shipping has moved through Shanghai and the Canton-Hong Kong region.

Offshore from the Fukien coast are two groups of islands held by the Nationalist enemies of the mainland government: Matsu outside the Bay of Foochow, and the larger Quemoy across the entrance to the harbour of Amoy, a mile and a half from the mainland. There are larger islands, closer to Taiwan, that are held by the Peking government, but through the chance of war these two groups remained in Nationalist hands when the cease-fire became effective in 1949. They are little more than a minor nuisance to the Communist government though a point of prestige for Taiwan and, while a crisis has occasionally been stirred up by shelling from the mainland, there has been no serious attempt in recent years to take them. In twenty years' occupation, the Nationalist garrison has constructed such a defence network of gun emplacements, tunnels and bunkers, that the chief of the American military advisory group on Taiwan has told newsmen: 'The Nationalists are so well dug in on Quemoy, and they have so many supplies stored up, that there is no way the Chinese Communists can take it'. He added: 'In fact, I doubt if we [the US Army] could take it.'* For the time being, however, so long as the United States Seventh Fleet continues to patrol the Taiwan Strait, it is unlikely this stalemate will be broken.

---

*Major General Richard C. Ciccolella, quoted by *The New York Times Weekly Review*, 26 October 1969, in an article on Quemoy.

10 Taiwan

One hundred miles from the Chinese mainland, Taiwan is a major unit in the string of islands which border the western Pacific from the north of Japan to the Philippines, New Guinea and Melanesia. Taiwan itself lies between latitudes 25°37′53″ and 21°45′25″ north and longitudes 119°18′3″ and 122°6′25″ east, and the Tropic of Cancer passes almost exactly over the centre of the island. Seventy-five miles to the east is the nearest land of the Ryukyu Archipelago and some sixty miles to the south are the closest of the Philippines. Further afield, the mainland port of Shanghai is 400 miles to the north, the nearest of the large Japanese islands, Kyushu, is 600 miles north-east; Luzon in the Philippines is 200 miles south, and the city of Hong Kong is 400 miles west. At the present time, Taiwan, with the offshore islands of Quemoy and Matsu and the small archipelago of the Pescadores, is politically separated from the mainland and held by the rival government of the Kuomintang or Nationalist Party.

The history of colonisation

Because of its position, though Taiwan is temptingly close to the mainland of China, there are strong natural links with the outside world of the Pacific and, although the island is now with reason regarded as Chinese, the periods of its history when it has been firmly controlled by the central government of the empire have been few and short. In the pattern of the past, there is nothing unusual in the present separation of Taiwan, under General Chiang Kai-shek, from the Communist government at Peking.

Early Chinese records contain several references to islands in the eastern seas, and some of these references have been identified with Taiwan, but there is no definite evidence of contact before the early seventh century, and there was no major settlement by Chinese colonists before the fourteenth and fifteenth centuries. When they arrived, the new settlers found the island occupied by earlier immigrants of Malay race, who had arrived in force towards the end of the sixth century and had driven the more peaceful aborigines into

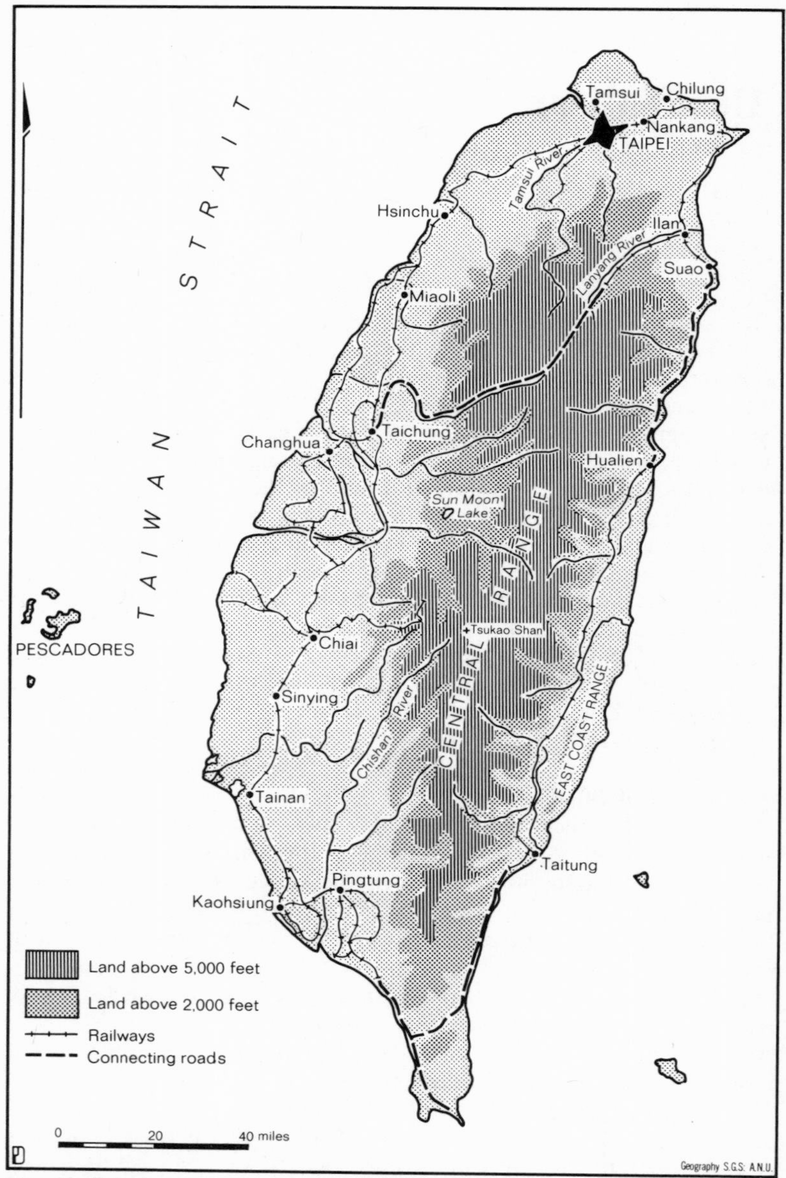

Map 25 Taiwan.
To be read in conjunction with Chapter 10.

the hills. By pressure of numbers in spite of varying resistance the Chinese established themselves in the fertile plains on the west of the island, and those tribesmen who would not submit to their culture were compelled in their turn to move away into the mountains of the east.

Such a pattern of Chinese settlement was already well-established on the mainland, south of the Yangtze Kiang, where 'peaceful penetration', maintained with many petty skirmishes but seldom with full-scale war, had spread the boundaries of the Chinese world steadily to the south and west. Expansion was almost inevitable, for the military power of the Imperial court was available to support the settlers on the frontier, and nowhere on the mainland did the new colonists find a culture that could rival their own in the arts of civilisation or of war. By conquest, intermarriage and assimilation, the Chinese dominated and absorbed the indigenous people that they met, and drove the remnants of resistance into the hills; as in Yunnan, in the far south-west of Mainland China, the process which was started 3,000 years ago in the valley of the Yangtze is now reaching its last stages on the eastern coast of Taiwan.

However, this pattern of expansion, so successful in south China was impossible to maintain in mainland South-East Asia or in the islands of Indonesia and the Pacific. As the Chinese emigrants moved further from their homeland, into Malaysia, Sumatra, the Philippines or Hawaii, they found established and well-organised societies. Throughout South-East Asia there are great numbers of 'Overseas Chinese' and Chinese communities often hold a dominant economic position, yet this position has been gained under the protection of Western imperial governments, and the Chinese themselves have wielded small political power. Outside the natural boundaries of the Chinese homeland, with the exception of the city-state of Singapore, Taiwan is the only territory that is settled, controlled and governed by immigrants from China.

Chinese control of the island was obviously facilitated by its proximity to the mainland and by the political and military weakness of the aboriginal peoples whom the first Chinese settlers encountered. Even so, it was a long time before Taiwan was accepted by the central government as a part of the Chinese empire, for Chinese rulers were often reluctant for overseas conquests. In the fourteenth century colonists in the Pescadores Islands near Taiwan were actually repatriated to the mainland. By the seventeenth century the island had some 30,000 Chinese settlers, but was effectively disowned by the Chinese emperor and was a base of operations for Japanese and Chinese pirates. There were, moreover, other interested nations. In 1590 Portuguese sailors gave it the name 'Formosa' or 'beautiful island', and in 1624 the Dutch, from their headquarters in the East

Indies, established a fortified base in the south at Tainan. In 1626 the Spaniards from the Philippines attempted to occupy the north, but they were driven out by the Dutch in 1641. In 1661 the Chinese pirate Cheng Cheng-kung, known in the West as Coxinga, seized Taiwan from the Dutch and proclaimed an independent government.

On the mainland at this time, the middle years of the seventeenth century had seen the decline of the Chinese Ming dynasty and their conquest by the Manchu Ch'ing. To give his rule a semblance of legitimacy, Coxinga proclaimed his loyalty to the fading house of Ming, and he attracted to his cause great numbers of refugees who came to settle on the island. In 1683, after Coxinga's death, his successors surrendered to the Manchus and Taiwan, which now contained a majority of people of Chinese descent, was governed for 200 years as part of Fukien Province.

At this outer fringe of the empire, the sway of Chinese government was weak and, although there was no major interruption to its rule, control was often lax. Immigration continued, chiefly from Fukien and Kwangtung provinces, but by 1886, when Taiwan was raised to the status of a province with a population of 2,500,000, the weakness of the Manchu government had made other countries greedy for concessions. In a series of diplomatic and military skirmishes, the Japanese government established first its interest in and then predominance over the island, and in 1895, at the end of the Sino-Japanese war, Taiwan was ceded to Japan.

Fifty years of Japanese rule gave Taiwan a firm colonial government, certainly stronger and more competent than any that ruled in Mainland China. The island was regarded as a source of agricultural produce—mainly rice, sugar and tea—and the base of the population, despite some attempts to introduce Japanese colonists, remained Chinese. The Japanese came as officials, business or professional men, but few of them struck deep roots. On the eve of World War II, the population of Taiwan was about 6,000,000 of whom some 400,000 were Japanese. When Japan surrendered in 1945 the island was restored to the Chinese government, and by 1954 all Japanese had been returned to their own country.

Government and people

The repatriation of almost 500,000 Japanese during the nine years after a Chinese government regained control of Taiwan is only a sample of the massive movements of people that marked Taiwan's history in the first years after the end of Japanese rule. Chiang Kai-shek, as the leader of the government officially recognised by the allies against Japan, received the surrender of the island in October 1945, but the victory against Japan was only a prelude to the full eruption of civil war against the Communists under Mao

Tse-tung, and by the end of 1949 the armies of Chiang Kai-shek's Nationalist Party had been driven from the mainland. In the aftermath of the defeat, some 2,000,000 refugees and 500,000 soldiers came to Taiwan in flight from the victorious Communists. In June of 1950, on the outbreak of the Korean War, President Truman of the United States called a halt to the civil war in China and guaranteed the security of Taiwan by sending the US Seventh Fleet to guard the straits between the island and the mainland.

The exiled government and the new refugees were not altogether welcome. Fifty years of separation from China had left the Taiwanese with little real interest in the problems of the home government, and during the first years of restoration, inspired partly by Japanese sympathisers but primarily by a real sense of local patriotism, there were several moves of rebellion against Nationalist rule. In 1947, a major revolt was put down with the loss of some ten thousand Taiwanese lives, including many leaders of the community. To the native Taiwan Chinese, there may have seemed little difference between the departing Japanese and the new regime of Chiang Kai-shek.

Twenty years later, this division of people still affects the island's politics and economics. In much the same fashion as the Japanese colonists, the Nationalist refugees from the mainland have dominated the government services, the army, the provincial administration and the universities, while the Taiwanese have maintained their traditional hold over the minor civil administration and the economic system. Time has lessened the sense of grievance and will naturally continue to do so, while the government itself, after the disasters of defeat on the mainland, has shown both energy and authority in guiding the fortunes of the one province that it still controls.

With the help of 1,500,000,000,000 dollars of economic aid from the United States between 1951 and 1965, the Nationalist government has managed the economy with imagination and skill, and the people themselves have made full use of their opportunities. By the middle of 1965 Taiwan was judged to be at economic 'take-off point', and economic aid, no longer necessary, was formally discontinued. Few other 'developing' countries have shown such progress, and the history of Taiwan's economic 'miracle' in the last twenty years appears now as a triumph for American generosity and a revitalised Nationalist government.

Physical geography

The area of Taiwan is 13,807 square miles, measuring some 250 miles from north to south and about ninety miles at the widest points from east to west. The island is regular in shape, with a slight curve in the north-south axis similar to the neighbouring mainland coast. The north-eastern section of the axis curves towards the arc of the Ryukyu Archipelago, and the southern extension can be traced through the northern islands of the Philippines toward Luzon. In geomorphological terms, Taiwan is a tilted fault block, with a steep scarp on the eastern side facing the Pacific, and more gradual slopes leading to alluvial plains on the west coast. Geologically, the fault block is still active and there are more than 300 earthquake shocks a year, although the majority of these are fortunately slight. The fault block is evidently still rising, there has been some volcanic activity, and there are numbers of hot springs and fumaroles both north and south of the island.

The main topographical feature of Taiwan is the range of high mountains running east of centre from north to south. Almost half the island is occupied by the Central Range, with thirty peaks over 10,000 feet, and the highest, Tsukao Shan, also known as Yu Shan, reaching 12,956 feet. On the east, the massif descends steeply towards the sea, with a narrow fault valley and a secondary ridge parallel to the coast between Hualien and Taitung. North-east, the Lanyang River has cut a deep valley and formed an alluvial plain north of Suao. The main slopes east of the Central Range can reach a gradient of almost one in eight, and therefore road construction and all transport are extremely difficult. Within the range itself, tropical rainfall has scored and eroded gorges and steep valleys, and heavy growth of forest renders the mountains almost impenetrable. Only two roads lead across the northern part of the Central Range, and communication routes along the east coast have required great engineering skill and are always subject to interruption from bad weather, floods or landslides. In some compensation, the scenery is remarkably beautiful, and the highway between Suao and Hualien is a major tourist attraction.

Separated from the Central Range by the north-south valley between Hualien and Taitung, the East Coast Range is formed by a group of volcanic peaks some of which rise as high as 3,000 feet. Elsewhere, north and west of the Central Range, the massif descends in foothills and tablelands towards the alluvial plain. Here the slopes are more gentle and the altitude varies down to a few hundred feet above sea-level. The terrain is broken, with few continuous ridges or recognisable ranges of hills, and the rivers, variable in flood and steep in gradient, scour the valleys in every direction. High in the hills at the centre of the island, a secondary fault has formed the basin for Sun Moon Lake, more than 2,000 feet above sea-level and the site of an important hydroelectric power station, which was first built by the Japanese before World War II and is one of the most powerful in Asia.

A series of terraced tablelands, thick deposits of rounded sandstone, form a last belt of high ground between the mountains and the broad coastal plain on the west. Both the tablelands and the plain have been formed, at different times, by eroded material from the hills. Shallow waters off the coast have enabled deposits brought down by the swift-flowing streams of the mountains to build up swiftly and extend the cultivable land. As the rivers emerge from the mountains and the foothills, they meander to the sea with average gradient no more than one in 2,000. The larger streams divide into a number of channels to form alluvial deltas, and all along the coasts are wide tidal flats, swampy ground, sand-bars and lagoons.

Because of the steep escarpment on the eastern side, the shallow waters of the west, and the simple shape of the island's shore-line there are few good harbours giving real protection for shipping. Only in the extreme north, at Chilung (or Keelung), and in the south, at Kaohsiung, are there safe anchorages for ocean-going ships. Other places afford havens for small craft and fishing vessels, but most are exposed and those on the west coast steadily silt up.

Over all Taiwan, land which is approximately flat is only 15 per cent of the total area. A fifth of the island lies above 3,000 feet, and almost two-thirds of it is classified as mountainous. As a result, it is not surprising to find that only about a quarter of the total land area of the island is actually under cultivation, and this area includes a considerable proportion of terraced slopes, often marginal in return and always liable to heavy soil losses in time of rain. With heavy subtropical and monsoon rainfall on steep hill-slopes and mountains, erosion is one of Taiwan's major problems.

Climate

As an island bathed by the warm waters of the Japan Current, Taiwan's climate is essentially maritime, but it is strongly influenced by the neighbouring mass of Asia and largely governed by the seasonal monsoons.

Each winter, from late October to late March, the northern monsoon brings cold air from the north of the Asian continent parallel with the mainland coast south-west towards the warmer regions of the Pacific Ocean. In Taipei, on the north of the island, the cold air masses keep the mean temperature around 60°F from December through March, while the moisture gathered by the monsoon in its passage over the East China Sea is sufficient to maintain an average monthly rainfall of 4 inches. In the southern part of the island, on the leeward side of the central mountain barrier the temperatures are much the same as the north, but there is far less chance of rain and many years suffer from two or even three months of drought.

Winter temperatures are comparatively mild, with occasional

snow on the mountain peaks but very few lowland frosts. The summers, however, are long and hot, lasting from May to November with mean monthly temperatures rising between June and September to 80°F and with an extremely high humidity. The season is dominated by the arrival of the south-west monsoon, which blows from May to September and carries warm moist tropical air from the ocean towards the heated land-mass of the continent. As it meets the mountains of Taiwan, this warm air rises and cools, bringing heavy rain to all parts of the island. The southern and central districts receive more rain in these conditions than does the north, but even in Taipei the monthly rainfall, averaging 10 inches, is greater than that received in winter.

Summer is also the season of thunderstorms and typhoons. In the typhoon season, mainly August and September, violent storms striking from the south-east can bring general damage to crops and particular disruption to communications on the east coast. One or two cross the island each year. They may precipitate 10 or 20 inches of rain at a time, and on some windward mountain slopes there are records of almost 40 inches in a period of twenty-four hours.

Rainfall, then, is abundant. The major cities, Taipei, Taichung and Tainan, all have rainfall of 70 or 80 inches a year. Some mountain stations have recorded annual rainfalls of 200 inches a year, and even the driest parts of the coast receive no less than 40 inches. Such great precipitation, however, though it serves to encourage natural growth, is not always a blessing. The steep mountain-sides and deep gullies of the rivers cause frequent floods and wide variations in flow, and because of the seasonal monsoon, only the north of the island has adequate rainfall throughout the year. Further south, because of the long winter droughts and the naturally high evaporation rate, irrigation is essential to farming. For many reasons, water control is a major task for Taiwan, to lessen the effects of flood and hillside erosion, and to supply moisture to cultivated lands in time of drought.

Population and communications

The population of Taiwan, now over 13,000,000, has more than doubled since the restoration of the island to China in 1945, and is still growing at the rate of some 3 per cent each year. Over the whole island, the density is one of the highest in the world, more than 900 people to the square mile. When it is remembered that only about a quarter of the land is suitable for cultivation, it is not surprising that in parts of the western plain, particularly of course in the area of the major cities, the density can rise as high as 3,000 to the square mile.

Such striking gains in population are common to many other developing countries in Asia and caused mainly by the impact of modern medical science. In 1905, after the first decade of Japanese occupation, the population was a little over three million, the crude birth-rate was 41.7 per thousand and the death-rate was 33.4. By 1965, the birth-rate was 32.7 per thousand, but the death-rate had declined to a remarkable 5.5.

The foundation for this rapid growth of population was laid in the early years of the Japanese occupation, when public health measures, rigid police and quarantine precautions, and compulsory vaccination ended the major threats of cholera, plague and smallpox. Malaria, the most serious disease remaining, was kept under control, until the breakdown of administration during World War II, when it again became common throughout the island. The Nationalist government has intensified the campaign against malaria, using modern insecticides and careful checking for new cases. At the end of 1964 the World Health Organisation declared the island malaria-free.

The distribution of population, even among the Chinese sections, is still controlled to some extent by the period during which each group arrived on the island. The non-Chinese tribes, largely of Malay origin, are to be found mostly in the hills and mountains, or along the rugged and less accessible region of the east coast. Descendants of the earliest Chinese settlers, the Hakkas from Kwangtung Province, who generally arrived before the middle of the eighteenth century, are mostly settled in the foothills and tablelands above the western plain. The major part of the plain itself is occupied by descendants of Hoklo emigrants from Fukien, who came and settled as peasant farmers in the eighteenth and nineteenth centuries. The people who fled to Taiwan from the mainland after the Communist victory came from every part of China, though mainly from Shanghai, Canton or Fukien provinces. Most of these refugees, businessmen and administrators, have settled in the cities.

The provincial administration of Taiwan is divided into sixteen counties (*hsien*), five cities (*shih*), and one administrative area around the park and museum at Yangmingshan near Taipei. The largest city is Taipei, present capital of the Republic of China, with a population in 1965 of 1,135,000 in the city itself, and 1,061,552 in the surrounding county. Chilung, the port for Taipei, has more than a quarter of a million inhabitants, and Kaohsiung, the chief harbour in the south of the island and now a major manufacturing centre, has more than 600,000. The two other cities, Taichung in the centre of the western plain and Tainan slightly north of Kaohsiung, both have populations around 400,000.

Taipei, which was also the centre of the Japanese administration, has almost trebled its population from half a million in 1950, and the other cities, though not quite so rapid in growth, have developed at considerable speed. Naturally this has put immense strains on the civic offices of the cities and Taipei, in particular, suffers seriously from shanty-town development, bad drainage, elementary sewerage and difficult communications. Originally laid out by the Japanese before World War II, the city was planned for little more than 200,000, and the growth of population in the thirty years since then has made an orderly development almost impossible. The centre of the city is dominated by unimaginative and ugly Japanese colonial architecture: stone and concrete blocks two or three stories high, with colonnaded sidewalks along straight narrow streets. Further out, wide boulevards with varying surfaces lead into bumpy roads to the outer suburbs, and pleasant houses behind high stone walls are set among grimy shops and huts and paddy-fields. Many of the houses built before the war are in Japanese style with sliding doors and smooth-polished floors, but there is much new building, both houses and flats in small home units. Shadowed by superb green hills,

Plate 52 Taipei, crowded, energetic, hot and generally overcast with cloud. Japanese commercial interest is evident from the large signs on the buildings in the city, and from the cars on the road. The majority of vehicles are for public transport: buses or taxis. On the left of the picture, there are ten cars in one lane coming off the bridge; every one is a taxi, and all are the same Japanese make of small car. Private transport is generally either by pedal cycle or light motorcycle. *(Courtesy: Government of the Republic of China)*

stretched over a hot, humid, river plain, Taipei leaves an impression of energy and confusion.

As the capital of the island and the home of the Nationalist government, it was considered important that the city should contain examples of the culture, art and scholarship of China. At the same time, and equally important, the economic and commercial development of the province has been centred largely on Taipei and its port of Chilung. This has led to some incongruities, notably at Nankang, a village some miles east of the city, where the central research institute of China, Academia Sinica, was re-established from the rump of its members who had chosen to leave the mainland after the Communist victory. The site is most attractive, with soft hills and impressive buildings; but a seam of coal was also found there and Nankang is now a mining village. A man-powered railway with trucks of coal runs past the main gate of the institute.

Despite such incongruities, Taipei is naturally the centre of the island's tourist industry, which is important both for prestige and for foreign exchange. Since 1956, visitors to Taiwan have increased in number from 15,000 to 150,000 per year, and earnings from this source have risen from one to thirteen million American dollars. In recent years, some of the increase has been due to US servicemen on rest and recreation leave from Vietnam, but a considerable proportion of foreign visitors are scholars with interests and specialties in the field of Chinese studies. The great numbers of private tourists from Japan and from the Chinese communities of South-East Asia help the Nationalist government maintain acceptance and recognition overseas.

To help such public relations, the government has encouraged the building of several large hotels in Taipei and other places of interest, and the National Palace Museum at Yangmingshan, which houses and displays the collection of art treasures brought across in the retreat from the mainland, was opened in November 1965. With the largest collection of Chinese art objects anywhere in the world, the museum is a centre for research and a source of immense prestige for the government.

Communications on the island, as might be expected, are easy and efficient on the western plain, but awkward and sometimes tenuous across the mountains to the east. The main rail system, the West Line, has some six hundred miles of track, with a main trunk line between Chilung on the north coast and Kaohsiung on the south, a distance of 250 miles. There is a loop line into the mountain area east of Taichung and a branch line from Chilung to Suao along the north-east coast. The East Line, through the fault valley between Hualien and Taitung, is a narrow-gauge track unconnected with the rest of the system. It is sheltered to some extent by the secondary ridge on

Plate 53 The National Palace Museum at Yangmingshan, just outside Taipei, houses one of the finest art collections in the world. The museum and the area around it are maintained as a state park with a special administration. ***(Courtesy: Government of the Republic of China)***

the seaward side, but is still frequently interrupted by floods or landslides.

Motor-roads, like the railways, are most effective on the western coastal plain, but road-building programmes have improved communications in the hill country in recent years, and on the east coast they form vital links between the separated railheads. The highway between Suao and Hualien, famous for its scenic beauty, joins the East Line rail system to the west, and further south the road round the end of the mountains from Taitung to Kaohsiung completes the circuit of the island. From the area of Taichung, a road leads across the mountain ranges to the east coast near Hualien, and since 1966 a new North Cross-Island Highway gives a direct route over the mountains between Taipei and the Ilan Plain. Most road freight transport is in private hands, but the government-run Taiwan Highway Bureau has the major part of the passenger traffic, and their 'Golden Horse' coaches, despite the generally unsealed roads, maintain a fair net of communications.

Silted on the west and rocky on the east, Taiwan has few harbours suitable for a coastal shipping trade, and sea transport is used mainly for communications with the island dependencies—the

Pescadores, Quemoy and Matsu—or for trade with the outside world. For these purposes, Kaohsiung and Chilung are the main ports, both being continuously developed and improved, while Hualien on the east coast handles some overseas trade and Suao harbour is being rebuilt to serve as an auxiliary to Chilung. There is regular overseas trade between Taiwan and Japan, the United States, Hong Kong and South-East Asia. Other vessels operate as far afield as Europe and various tramp steamers between the neighbouring Philippines, the Ryukyus and Korea.

The difficult terrain and the comparative isolation of many centres of population have encouraged considerable development of air transport. The weather can occasionally hinder flying, but there are regular scheduled flights between Taipei, Hualien, Taitung, Kaohsiung, Taichung and Makung, the chief town of the Pescadores Islands, and the island has more than twenty airports. Most of the flights are run by China Air Lines (CAL) and Civil Air Transport (CAT), both of which are 51 per cent government owned, though some schedule and charter flights are in the hands of private companies. CAT, as well as its domestic interests, operates flights overseas from Taipei International Airport through Hong Kong, Manila and Tokyo, and Taipei is a scheduled stop for a number of international companies on the route from Tokyo to Hong Kong.

Agriculture and fisheries

As in most Asian countries, agriculture is the basis on which Taiwan's economy rests, and her future prosperity, even her economic survival, will largely depend on the efficiency of her agriculture. The 3 per cent annual rise in population, which has so far shown small sign of abating, poses a constant threat, whose effects will be felt first on the island's capacity to feed itself.

The soils of Taiwan are not naturally very fertile. Many have been leached by centuries of heavy rainfall or intensive irrigation, and others, particularly in the alluvial plains, have poor drainage. The pressure of population and the small percentage of level ground on the island have compelled farmers to cultivate land which should never have been deprived of its natural cover and, in some areas, cultivation has extended onto slopes of 45° gradient. Although there is a short-term advantage in this increase of farmland, the heavy rainfall soon destroys the primitive terracing and washes away the topsoil into the valleys and plains below. Not only are the hills denuded of cover, but the streams become choked with worthless debris and good farmland further down may be lost under a covering of silt, sand and gravel. Because of its steep slopes and heavy rainfall the island is naturally liable to erosion, but overcultivation by the farmers and lack of proper maintenance, even in established areas of capability, have aggravated the situation. At the present time, areas lost by erosion are at least equal to any new fields that may be brought under cultivation, and it is clear that Taiwan has reached the limit of its available farmland.

The solution, then, is to make the best possible use of the land now available, and in this respect the climate is of some assistance. With the aid of irrigation, two crops can be harvested each year from a considerable part of the cultivated area and some regions even produce three crops. Some districts need drainage rather than irrigation, but everywhere the thin soils require heavy applications of fertiliser. On a small scale, individual farms use compost, manure and night-soil, but government programmes have organised agricultural development on an island-wide basis since the early years of this century. Under the Japanese, there were massive imports of chemical fertilisers and of beancake from Manchuria and successful experiments with high-yield varieties of grain. Rice production, designed to relieve Japan's food deficit at home, almost doubled between 1915 and 1939. Since World War II the Nationalist and United States governments, through the agency of the Sino-American Joint Commission on Rural Reconstruction (JCRR), have given technical and financial aid to some 7,000 government and public projects. Up to 1966, the JCRR had spent more than 7,000,000 dollars of American currency and the equivalent of 110,000,000 American dollars in Taiwanese money.

The JCRR programme was designed to give advice and assistance for practical solutions to rural problems, and at first it was chiefly concerned with improved crop production and irrigation. From this base the agency has extended its interests and, besides the improvement of seeds, the introduction of better fertilisers, insect sprays and extensive irrigation and flood control, its successful projects include livestock production mainly of pigs, reafforestation, rat control, and the general improvement of agricultural administration, home education and rural health. From practical experiments in projects of this kind, productivity has improved in almost every field of agriculture. Technicians come from overseas to study methods in Taiwan and Chinese aid teams are sent overseas to advise countries with similar problems in Asia, Africa and Latin America.

Rice is the main crop, with two harvests, summer and winter, and some conception of Taiwan's agricultural progress may be gained from the figures of annual rice production, which has doubled in the twenty years of Nationalist rule and now stands at some 2,500,000 metric tons. Because of the terrain the area of production has been extended very little and this development is almost entirely due to improved varieties of seed-grain, better techniques of cultivation, and increased use of fertilisers and chemical pest-control. For the time being at least, the increased yield of the rice crop has maintained the island's self-sufficiency in its basic food and still left a surplus for export.

Besides rice, secondary food crops are raised both for human consumption and for animal feeds. Sweet potato, with an annual production over three million metric tons in 1964 and 1965, is the next most important crop and is the staple food for the poorer people who cannot afford rice. Large quantities are also used for cattle fodder. Wheat, peanuts, soybeans and corn are also important but are produced in smaller quantities. Although some of these crops are exported, the main volume is retained for local consumption.

Among the crops grown primarily for export, sugar-cane has long been the most important, and under the Japanese administration

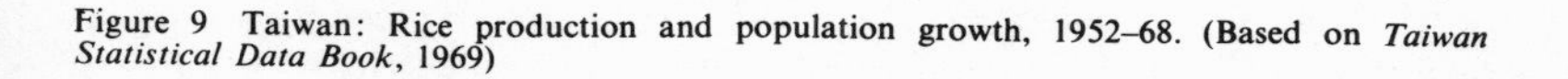

Figure 9 Taiwan: Rice production and population growth, 1952–68. (Based on *Taiwan Statistical Data Book*, 1969)

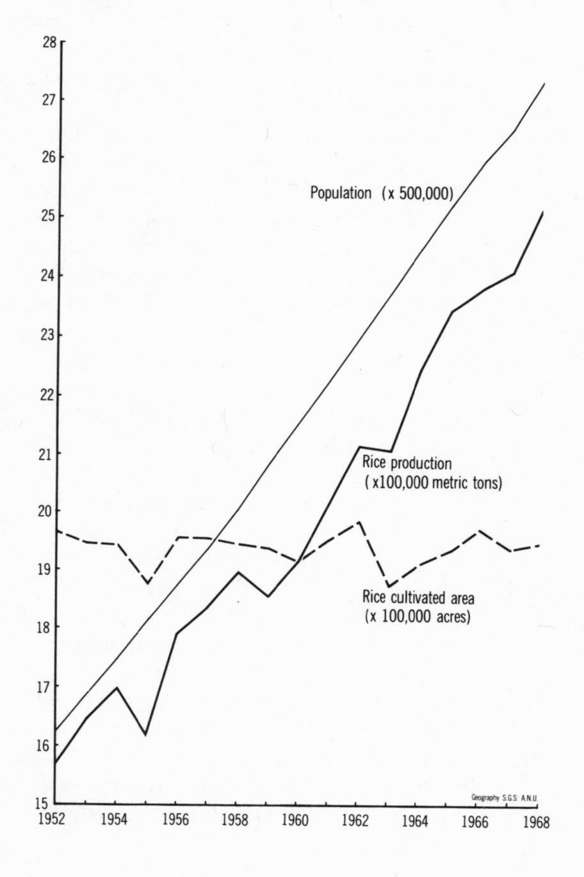

the shipments of sugar to the homeland represented half of the island's total export. Since then, fluctuations and quotas on the world market and the development of other crops have lessened its importance, though it still gains almost 10 per cent of overseas earnings. Bananas are shipped regularly to Japan in special air-conditioned ships, while cans of mushrooms, pineapple and asparagus are worth another 10 per cent of export value.

Formosan tea is grown chiefly on hillsides in the north of the island, both for domestic consumption and for export. Green tea is prepared by fast drying and black tea is produced when the leaves are left to oxidise and ferment; some black tea is flavoured with flowers such as jasmine or gardenia. In recent years, due largely to improved techniques of cultivation, production has been at the level of 45,000,000 pounds per annum, twice that of the early 1950s. Although Formosan tea is generally regarded by connoisseurs as inferior to that of the mainland, it has now gained a world-wide market.

Fishing in Taiwan, like agriculture, has benefited from mechanisation and capital development. With deep water on the east of the island, a shallow shelf along the Taiwan Straits, and warm currents on either side, there are good fishing grounds close to home. In these waters, fish are caught from unpowered craft such as sampans and rafts by every means at hand, and tidal pools and inland ponds are used for the cultivation of milkfish, shrimps and oysters. 'Inshore' fishermen with powered vessels troll or line for tuna, bream, sardines and mackerel, while further afield Taiwan has deep-sea fleets in most of the seas about Mainland China and South-East Asia and far into the Pacific and Indian Oceans. Since 1952, powered fishing vessels have increased more than five times in number and almost six times in tonnage, while the use of non-powered boats is declining. The effect is shown in production: coastal production has actually declined, pond fishery which is susceptible to technical improvement has developed steadily, inshore production has increased almost five times, and deep-sea production more than eight times. Harbours have had to be constructed along the coasts, for the smooth shoreline gives little natural shelter. The return on capital investment can be seen through Taiwan's overseas trade: during the early 1950s import of marine products was 300 times the value of exports; by 1961 the ratio was almost even, and since 1962, with the establishment of a deep-sea tuna fishing fleet, the favourable balance of trade rose to nearly 2,000,000 US dollars a year.

Agriculture is still dominant in Taiwan's economy, employing 53 per cent of the labour force in comparison with the next sector, industry which has 12 per cent. During the early 1950s, the percentage in agriculture was over 60, so there has been a gradual shift towards industry, commerce, transport and the administrative and service occupations, but it is likely that peasant farming will retain its importance for all the foreseeable future. In this field, a major development over the last fifteen years has been the implementation of the government's policy of land reform, firstly by reducing farm rent to 37.5 per cent of the annual main crop yield, then by sale of public farmland, and finally by compulsory purchase of tenanted land in private hands and the sale of land by easy payments to the tiller. Almost unique in its success, the land-reform programme has raised the number of owner-farmers or part owner-farmers from 61 per cent in 1949 to 87 per cent in 1965, and field checks on beneficiaries under the programme have shown a remarkable improvement in farming techniques and the use of equipment. To a very great extent, the development of Taiwan's agricultural potential reflects the economic and political activities of a strong and competent government.

Table 4

Taiwan: Population Distribution by Employment (age 12 and over) 1952 and 1966

		1952	1966
Agriculture		61.0	53.0
Industry		9.3	12.3
Commerce		8.5	9.0
Transportation		2.2	3.3
Personal services		7.7	9.0
Professions		2.5	4.1
Government services		6.0	8.1
Others		2.8	1.2
	Total	100.0 (2,936,000)	100.0 (3,870,000)

From *Taiwan Statistical Data Book*, 1969.

Minerals, power and industry

Taiwan is not well supplied with minerals, and far the most important are coal and natural gas. The workable coal reserves, estimated at some 260,000,000 metric tons, are found in the northern end of the island, but the coal is powdery and sub-bituminous, and little of it is of coking quality. Even so, with an output of more than 5,000,000 metric tons a year, more than double that of the early fifties, coal accounts for three-fifths of mineral production value. Gold and copper are also mined in the north, near Juifang in Taipei Prefecture, but the ore is neither rich nor very plentiful. Other major mineral resources include sulphur and pyrite, and large reserves of

Plate 54 On the flat west coast of Taiwan, sea salt is collected from great evaporation pans both for domestic consumption and for export. *(Courtesy: China Publishing Company, Taipei)*

marble, dolomite and talc in eastern Taiwan. On the south-west coast there are salt fields for the evaporation of sea water, with an annual production of some 400,000 metric tons.

Before World War II, some reserves of petroleum had been discovered in the foothills at the centre of the island, but prospects were poor and the known reserves are not great. In 1959, however, a rich reserve of natural gas was found in Miaoli County, between Taipei and Taichung, and production has been steadily developed. The reserves are estimated at 27,000,000,000,000 cubic metres, the daily production is now more than 2,000,000 cubic metres, and a north-south pipeline to carry gas the length of the island was completed in 1966. In the south, at Kaohsiung, a large oil refinery established by the Japanese to handle imported crude oil has now been taken over by the Chinese Petroleum Corporation: its production has been extended and a lubricants plant, with an overseas market for the finished product, was opened in 1965. Nevertheless, because of the overall shortage of minerals, Taiwan's industrial trade must depend largely on the processing and re-export of imported raw materials, and in the year 1968, agricultural and industrial raw materials were 57 per cent of the value of imports.

With steep slopes and high rainfall, Taiwan would seem suitable for the development of hydroelectric power. The rivers, however, are short and steep, and the silt that they carry tends to choke small storage reservoirs with sediment. Taiwan Power Company now has an installed capacity of 1,500,000 kilowatts, of which almost half is hydrogenerated, the remainder coming from thermal plants. In actual production, thermal plants are responsible for two-thirds of the annual output, since hydroelectric plants can be turned on or off far more easily and are therefore often kept in reserve to deal with peak demand. Of the hydroelectric stations, the most important at Sun Moon Lake has a fall of 1,100 feet and a generating capacity of 200,000 kilowatts. Several other stations, connected to the centres of population and industry by a cross-island power line, are scattered along the steep east coast and further projects are in planning or under construction.

Table 5

Taiwan: Value of Exports by Commodities 1968 (unit: US$1,000,000)

	Amount		Percentage
Rice	13.9		
Bananas	57.2		
Others	38.2		
Agricultural products total		109.3	13.0
Sugar	50.5		
Tea	11.7		
Citronella oil	1.7		
Canned pineapple	19.0		
Canned mushrooms	30.7		
Canned asparagus	33.1		
Others	26.7		
Processed agricultural products total		173.4	20.6
Salt	1.0		
Building materials	7.0		
Cement	16.3		
Chemicals	24.7		
Metals and machinery	145.6		
Lumber and products	35.7		
Plywood	55.4		
Paper and pulp	6.8		
Textiles	183.1		
Others	83.5		
Industrial products total		559.1	66.4
Grand Total		841.8	100.0

From *Taiwan Statistical Data Book*, 1969.

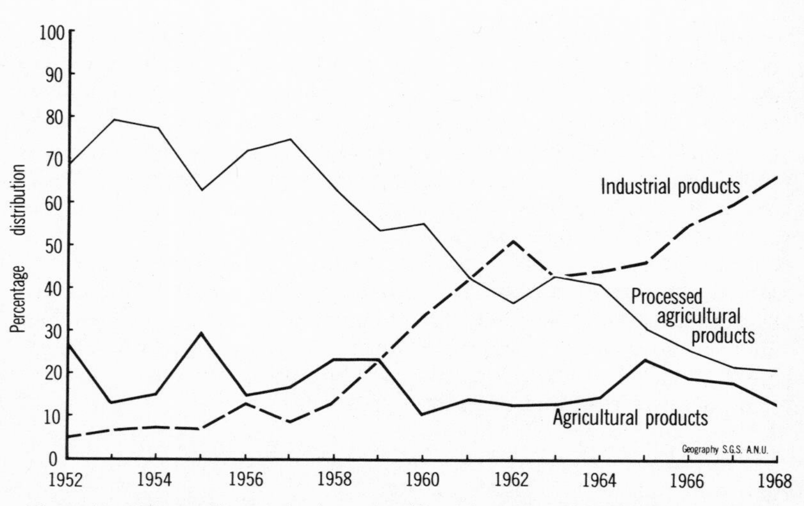

Figure 10 Taiwan: Changes in the composition of exports, 1952–68. (Based on *Taiwan Statistical Data Book*, 1969)

Table 6

Taiwan: Composition of Imports 1968 (unit: US$1,000,000)

	Amount	Percentage
Capital goods	361.7	35.2
Agricultural and industrial raw materials	588.6	57.4
Consumer goods	75.5	7.4
Total	1,025.8	100.0

From *Taiwan Statistical Data Book*, 1969.

The Taiwan Forestry Bureau controls a lumber industry worth more than 50,000,000 US dollars, or 10 per cent of exports. Cypress, which grows between 5,000 and 9,000 feet above sea-level, is the most valuable timber, but there are more than 200 economic species, including spruce and fir, hemlock and acacia. Camphor, which grows below 4,000 feet, provides an export industry of its own, and in the highest mountains, among the coniferous trees, there are fine stands of cedar. To balance the extraction of timber, the Bureau has introduced a programme of reafforestation. There is a Forest Research Institute controlled by the Bureau, and forestry departments at National Taiwan University in Taipei and Provincial Chung Hsing University in Taichung.

In a small, developing country, minerals, oil and power may quite naturally be the concerns of the government and such large extractive industries as fishery and forestry obviously need some central supervision or control. Besides these, however, the government has become involved in several secondary industrial enterprises, to supervise major sectors of the economy and to develop new fields in the future. The processing of sugar-cane, still worth more than 50,000,000 US dollars in exports, is handled by the Taiwan Sugar Corporation, which also promotes the research and development of new varieties. The Taiwan Fertiliser Company produces such materials as superphosphate, nitrophosphate, calcium cyanide and ammonium sulphate, and exports of fertiliser are worth some 5,000,000 US dollars a year, though imports are still three times that value.

Besides these established industries, the government controls the Taiwan Machinery Manufacturing Corporation which manufactures motor plants, steel and shipbuilding facilities, the Taiwan Aluminium Corporation which is involved with processing and refining, and the Taiwan Shipbuilding Corporation, based at Chilung, which is expanding production largely in the fields of rebuilding and refitting.

Such large-scale projects, however, while ambitious for the future, are in some respects less immediately important than the development of light industry which remains in private hands and which has shown a growth rate of over 10 per cent per annum. Chief of the light industrial products is textiles, whose value on the export

Plate 55 Kaohsiung, at the south end of the island, is the main port of Taiwan. The Kaohsiung Export Processing Zone, established in 1966, is intended to encourage manufacturing industry by granting exemption of import duty for raw materials brought in from overseas for processing and re-export as finished articles. *(Courtesy: Government of the Republic of China)*

market has increased from 2,000,000 US dollars in the middle 1950s to more than 70,000,000 US dollars in 1966, and is now the largest single earner of foreign exchange. Table 7 shows something of this development in the production both of natural fibres such as cotton and of artificial fabrics like rayon. Besides this development, which has led to the proliferation of a multitude of small plants, the major products of light industry are plastics, electrical appliances, paper and various forms of chemicals—all of them appropriate to small-scale manufacture with limited capital but high technical skill. The electronics industry, in particular, is booming, and Taiwan is becoming increasingly important in the manufacture of components for television sets and transistor radios.

Table 7

Taiwan: Output of Principal Industrial Products 1952 and 1966
(unit: 1000 metric tons unless otherwise specified)

	1952	1968
Electric power (million k.w.h.)	1,420	9,802
Coal	2,286	5,014
Sugar	520	847
Canned pineapple (1000 st. box)	490	4,060
Wheat flour	16	327
Alcoholic beverages (kilolitres)	5,581	14,770
Cigarettes (millions)	7,663	15,507
Cotton yarn	13.6	69.1
Cotton fabrics (1000 metres)	87,639	371,405
Rayon filament	—	2.9
Poly vinyl chloride	—	67.6
Paper	27.6	238.2
Caustic soda	9	91
Soda ash	0.6	34.7
Fertiliser	148	1,244
Crude oil refined (1000 kilolitres)	300	3,750
Plate glass (1000 st. box)	—	1,781
Cement	—	3,993
Pig iron	9.9	75.6
Steel bar	17.8	418.3
Aluminium ingot	3.8	20
General machinery	6	181
Sewing machines (1000 sets)	25	361
Electric fans (1000 sets)	10	349
Fluorescent lamps (1000 pieces)	—	5,551
Watthour meters (1000 pieces)	—	218
Shipbuilding (metric tons)	565	79,183

From *Taiwan Statistical Data Book*, 1969.

The greater part of this industry, naturally enough, is centred round Taipei, as it provides both a centre of population and a convenient outlet for overseas trade through the port of Chilung. Kaohsiung in the south of the island is the major international port, handling 7,000,000 metric tons of cargo in 1966 compared to some 3,000,000 at Chilung. Since the end of 1966, the Ministry of Economic Affairs has established the Kaohsiung Export Processing Zone, within which no import duties are levied on raw materials, components for manufacture, or plant equipment. The official plan is for 120 plants to be established, of which fifty are already approved, and for goods to be brought in, processed and manufactured, and then re-exported. The final investment in the zone should reach 18,000,000 US dollars, but the scheme itself is still only beginning.

Table 8

Taiwan: Plants Approved for the Kaohsiung Export Processing Zone 1967

Source of investment	*No. of Plants*	*Amount* (US$)	*Category of enterprise*
Domestic	13	1,970,525	electronics, chemicals, handicrafts, furniture, plastics, garments, packaging
Japan	1	200,000	candy
Hong Kong	14	2,310,000	plastics, knitting and weaving, packaging, electronics, furniture, leather goods, garments, handicrafts
Overseas Chinese (total)	15	2,510,000	
Japan	6	324,000	plastics, handicrafts, electronics, machinery
Israel	1	170,000	clothes
Holland	1	730,000	electronics
United States	4	2,437,000	plastics, electronics
Foreign (total)	12	3,661,000	
Joint investment—Sino-Japanese	4	625,000	metal manufactures, knitting and weaving, garments, toys
Grand Total	44	8,766,525	

From *China Yearbook*, 1966-7.

The Kaohsiung project shows the pattern of development for Taiwan's industrial economy: light manufacturing and processing of raw materials, particularly in those fields where skilled work is a high component of the added value—plastics, chemicals and electronics. With few natural resources suitable for heavy industry, the island is to a great extent dependent on overseas investment or aid. Capital comes mainly from the United States, with considerable private contribution from Overseas Chinese communities in Hong Kong and from Japan. For the foreseeable future, however, while secondary and extractive industries will become increasingly important as factors in the island's rising standard of living, agriculture will remain predominant, and the major problem will be whether the Taiwanese people can continue to feed themselves.

Offshore island

The history of Taiwan in the twentieth century has been dominated by geography and politics, chiefly because of the struggle of the great Pacific powers, America and Japan, to confine the apparent threat of China within the mainland of Asia. So long as Taiwan is held by a force opposed to the government at Peking, China is effectively barred from the Pacific, while if the Communists or any other powerful government succeeded in re-uniting the island with the mainland, then China would possess a salient into the island ring of the western ocean and would become a close and interested neighbour of Japan, Korea and the Philippines. It was for this reason that Taiwan became one of the first victims of Japanese imperialism in the late nineteenth century, and similar arguments must have influenced the American decision to maintain Taiwan as a Nationalist refuge in the aftermath of the Chinese civil war.

In the event, these circumstances of geopolitics have resulted in remarkable development in an island which would not normally be of any great importance either in size, population, natural resources or production. Both the Nationalist government and their American allies have been eager to make Taiwan a showplace of anti-Communist Asia, and comparison of key economic indicators between Taiwan and her neighbours may show that they have succeeded (table 9). It is arguable that much of Taiwan's development and present prosperity has been artificially induced by massive foreign aid, and it is certain that a great part of the island's economy is held under the firm control of a paternalistic and autocratic regime, but the achievement of the last twenty years still provides an example of what can be achieved by a determined government with adequate overseas assistance.

Table 9

Comparison of Key Economic Indices between Taiwan and her neighbours

	Taiwan	Japan	Indonesia (excl. West Irian)	Malaya (excl. Sabah and Sarawak)	Philippines
Area (1000 sq. miles)	14	143	575	50	115
Population (millions estimated in 1967)	13	100	110	9	35
Arable land as per cent of total area	25	21	7	16	25
Consumption of all sources of energy in kilograms of coal equivalent per inhabitant in 1967	726	2,323	99	424	236
Consumption of steel in kilograms per inhabitant in 1967	68	513	2	45	31

From *United Nations Statistical Yearbook*, 1968.

Barring major changes in the political situation, which are always possible but which are not the direct concern of a geographical study, the main threat to Taiwan's future development lies in the growth of population. The expansion of agricultural land has reached its limit, and the mineral resources of the island are comparatively poor. There are still good prospects for the development of light industries, but economic progress will be hampered almost to a standstill if advances in agricultural techniques and productivity fail to keep pace with the rise in population and compel the import of staple foods from abroad.

In recent years, the growth of population, almost entirely from natural increase, has been around 3 per cent a year and, while a great part of this increase has been due to a falling death-rate, the birth-rate is also high. Birth control programmes have been introduced with various degrees of success and the growth rate has shown some tendency to decline, but the next few years will show whether the great economic gains of the last two decades will be overthrown and lost among the demands of new mouths to feed, new minds to train, and new hands to find employment.

11 Government and Geography

Any government of China at this time would be faced with the same three basic problems: population, industrial progress, and the defence of the borders. The political ideology of the mainland Chinese government may have some effect on the means by which these problems are tackled, but it is not likely that any competent regime would accept significant restrictions on the final goal. There is no doubt that the Americans have shown far more generosity to the Nationalist government in Taiwan than the Soviet Union displayed to its comrades on the mainland: the United States gave vast amounts of money and aid, but Russian support came entirely in the form of interest-bearing loans which have since been repaid. On the other hand, nothing in Nationalist policy suggests that they would be any less intransigent on questions of China's sovereignty than their enemies in Peking, and maps printed in Taiwan today place the borders of China and Mongolia or India quite as far out as the lines on mainland maps, and sometimes even further.

The border territories of China, both north and south, are often undefined and frequently disputed, and the Chinese feel extremely vulnerable to attack in several places. By unfortunate circumstance, much of the resources and equipment needed for modern development are spread across country well within reach of a hostile army. Manchuria, the present centre for heavy industry, is particularly sensitive, but the new development at Paotow, Inner Mongolia, is also close to an international frontier. The atomic energy plants about Lop Nor (map 23, page 113) and Kansu are similarly exposed, and it is a strange trick of fate that set the bulk of China's known oil reserves in the far west of Dzungaria, so close to the Soviet Union.

For self-defence and to maintain some influence over her neighbours, China is developing atomic weapons, and there is every reason to believe that she will have, well before the end of the 1970s, a rocket system capable of delivering these. Despite her present low income per head, the size of the Gross National Product in a country with so many people is clearly sufficient to allow considerable investment in military technology. Over a period of time it is possible that similar investment in dams for hydroelectricity, drilling programmes and pipelines for oil, and plants for the peaceful use of atomic power may gradually lift the prosperity of the country. For the time being, however, while China is an atomic power in military terms, her industrial development is essentially dependent on coal; now something of an anachronism for a modern state. Admittedly, coal has served as the industrial base for all the advanced countries over the last centuries and is still the world's major source of generated power, but in economies such as that of the United States it is steadily being replaced by oil in most branches of industry, and the trend generally lies in this direction. As a result, China's industrial progress now rests heavily, and will continue to do so for some time to come, on a fuel which is being superseded elsewhere by cleaner and more efficient materials.

It is in some ways hard for the people of China to have to compete with the rest of the world in the development of heavy industry, for the great asset of the Chinese is rather their imagination and practical skill than the sheer strength of their machinery. As we have seen in the chapter on Taiwan, considerable progress may be made in the fields of light industry, particularly electrical goods of a sophisticated kind such as television sets and transistor radios. Visitors to factories in mainland China have remarked with awe that their trucks and tractors are put together with a careful attention to detail that rivals the Rolls-Royce. Chinese workmen, in fact, can be trained to deal skilfully with computers and atomic power, yet heavy plant needing large capital expenditure is often beyond their economic reach; so men must work in ill-equipped factories, and automatic control devices are used to guide clumsy and sometimes inefficient machinery.

This paradox has not been overlooked by the present rulers of China, and several propaganda campaigns over the years have encouraged the people to take an interest in their tools, to use them with skill, and to suggest improvements. Often, the sheer lack of technicians has made it necessary for apprentice and even more advanced training to be carried out on the factory floor under the guidance of experienced workmen. In many cases, as always in the past, projects requiring large-scale engineering such as the Ming Tombs Reservoir outside Peking or the flood-basins along the Yangtze have been carried through by the massive application of man-power rather than by machinery. Unfortunately, however, this necessity has been turned into a virtue, and to 'learn from the masses' and rely on mass participation became an ideological law. In 1958 and 1959, during the period of the Great Leap Forward, the People's Republic claimed that the organisation of a myriad individuals would place China in the forefront of world agriculture and industrial power. The establishment of the commune system for large-scale co-operative farming, and the building of blast furnaces, literally in back-yards, were attempts to mobilise the people in working units large enough to offer some economies of size, but yet not too big to be organised and inspired by local cadres.

The results were disastrous, and the Great Leap Forward tumbled into a welter of impossibly optimistic quotas, poor quality goods and meaningless statistics. The commune system and the home furnaces are now largely abandoned, iron and steel production continues in recognised foundries, and agriculture is slowly recovering from a series of bad harvests. The memory of the Great Leap Forward remains as an example of the desperation behind China's drive for progress, and its failure still rankles in the Party and the government. Some of the frustration caused by the country's slow economic advance has been heard again in the sound and fury of the Cultural Revolution, where true believers still claim that the 'experts' are wrong, and that 'red' ideals can break the bonds of reactionary economic reality.

Apart from the politics of the Cultural Revolution, other patterns may be seen in the events of recent years. Firstly, the Red Guards focused attention on both the youth and the impatience of great numbers of the Chinese people, who have a capacity for excitement and disruption no less than any of their contemporaries in the outside world. Secondly, and in some ways this is more interesting, the Chinese government's policy towards these groups has been to move them frequently from one part of the country to another, at first in the comfort of railway transport to mass demonstrations in Peking, Shanghai and other major cities, but more recently on foot in emulation of the famous Long March of the 1930s. At one time, the number of extra passengers threatened to disrupt the whole rail communications system of China. Now, supported by slogans encouraging them to share the life of the people and learn from the masses, whole schools of educated young people from the cities are living and working in the countryside or in the distant colonised regions of Outer China. There they are of real advantage to their country and their zeal may be tempered by practical work.

An economy based so heavily on agriculture can hardly afford the luxury of a great urban proletariat unless the labour force can be fully and profitably employed. Indeed, in Mainland China, not only the land and its products but also the people may be regarded as resources of skill or physical strength to be used for the common good. Frontier service has long been a punishment in China, and the present government has sent thousands of men and women for 'rehabilitation' to colonise the marginal lands of Central Asia. Husbands and wives with technical skills are separated to work in different places, an arrangement which not only spreads expert knowledge more widely but also has some effect in limiting the birth-rate. Recently the mass emigrations from the cities to the countryside, whether voluntary or compulsory, not only reduced the number of agitated mouths and unemployed hands in the great cities of the east, but also transferred responsibility for the supply of food to the provincial authorities and freed the central government for affairs of more national concern.

In the last few years, Australia and Canada have been among China's main trading partners, buying little but selling the Peking government great quantities of wheat. There are arguments whether the bulk purchase of food-grains year by year reflects a chronic weakness in China's agriculture, or whether they are imported so that other more profitable crops may be grown for cash export or to subsidise allies such as North Vietnam. There is a strong possibility that the problems of the central government in feeding the grain-hungry regions of the country have often been complicated by the reluctance of grain-surplus provinces to contribute their fair share to the common reserves.

As in all aspects of China's internal economy, figures are lacking and have been for years, but estimates of China's overseas trade based on statistics from her foreign partners calculate annual imports at 1,500,000,000 US dollars, with far the greater quantity spent on raw materials for processing and resale—food-grains, rubber, timber, oil products, chemical fertiliser and even cotton. Exports, some 1,750,000,000 US dollars, are chiefly light consumer goods, housegold tools, cotton and synthetic textiles, with the traditional products of hogs bristles, duck feathers, soybeans and tea. Only a comparatively small amount of exchange is available for heavy capital equipment, some bought from Russia and other Communist countries, but a good deal from Western Europe, particularly Britain, France and Germany. Hong Kong is the leading importer from China. It buys half its food from the mainland and serves as an export market for many of her goods. Japan is the chief trading partner, receiving each year some US $275 million and selling some US $300 million value of goods. Even so, Sino-Japanese trade was 16 per cent of China's overseas dealings in 1966, and little more than 3 per cent of Japan's.

To put Mainland China's foreign trade in perspective, it should be compared with Taiwan, whose imports in 1966-7 were more than US $550 million, and exports over the same period were US $500 million. Though her population is hardly one-sixtieth of her rival, Taiwan has fully a quarter the amount of Mainland China's total trade.

The People's Republic of China, then, is essentially self-reliant, and in both politics and economics her rulers would claim to be self-sufficient. Russian experts, who have been among China's most consistent critics since the break between their two countries, have given small credit to Peking's claims of industrial and agricultural success, and in January 1970 Tass News Agency remarked that the latest Chinese cereal harvest was judged no better than the average level ten or twelve years earlier, while the population of China in the last decade had increased 100,000,000. However biased the source, such criticism does point to China's chief danger for the future: food supplies must keep pace with expanding population, for there is as yet no reserve of profit from overseas trade to buy more food; and the people of China are increasing their numbers at a frightening rate.

Foreign estimates, generally no more than educated guesses, suggest that China's food production has increased from 100,000,000 tons to some 190,000,000 in the twenty years since the Communist government came to power, while the population in the same time has grown from 550,000,000 to more than 750,000,000. As in other aspects of production, much of this increase in annual harvests can be explained by the restoration of competent and efficient government after decades of war and disruption. The comparative failure of such ambitious short-cuts as the Great Leap Forward arouses anxiety lest the Chinese may not be able to develop their resources fast enough to achieve prosperity at home and peace with their neighbours. In recent months, however, there has been evidence that new strains of 'miracle' high-yield rice may have been brought through Hong Kong and have now been sown and harvested in China.* Some reports claim that production has doubled where the new grain has been tried and, if these tales are true and are not propaganda, then the Green Revolution may prove to be as important for China in the future as the triumph of the Communist Party twenty years ago.

---

*See, for example, the report of Tillman Durdin in Hong Kong, published in *The New York Times Weekly Review*, 2 November 1969, p. 8. It seems probable that the new seeds in China are related to those developed by the American-financed Rice Research Center at Los Banos in the Philippines.

Guide to Further Reading

The references below are in no way intended as a complete bibliography, but only as a possible introduction to individual topics of interest which are treated in the various chapters. Very full lists of scholarly and other works appear in George B. Cressey's *Land of the 500 Million*, in T. E. Tregear's *A Geography of China*, both cited below, and in Joseph E. Spencer's *Asia East by South*, John Wiley, New York, 1954. A particularly useful recent compilation is *The Geography of China: A Selected and Annotated Bibliography*, edited by Theodore Herman, Occasional Publication No. 7 of the Foreign Area Materials Center, University of the State of New York, New York, 1967.

Chapter 1

On the people of China and their history, two of the best introductory texts are C. P. Fitzgerald's *China: A Short Cultural History*, Cresset Press, Third Edition, 1961, and *Revolution in China*, Cresset Press, 1952, re-issued by Pelican Books in 1964 as *The Birth of Communist China*. Among other general histories, L. C. Goodrich's *A Short History of the Chinese People*, Allen and Unwin, Third Edition, 1969, gives a survey with considerable attention to technology and scientific history, while the two volumes of *East Asia, The Great Tradition* and *East Asia, The Modern Transformation* by Edwin O. Reischauer and John K. Fairbank, Allen and Unwin, 1960, and Houghton Mifflin, 1965, are generally recognised as the best histories of their kind readily available.

On the background to China's international position, there are useful sections in *A Geography of World Affairs*, by J. P. Cole, Pelican Books, 1965, and on the life and work of China's people under Communist rule there is nothing comparable for detail and sympathy with Jan Myrdal's *Report from a Chinese Village*, first published in Sweden in 1963, by Heinemann in 1965, and by Pelican Books in 1967. The same author has also written the text for *Chinese Journey*, with photography by Gun Kessle, published by Chatto and Windus, 1965. For general information, there is Nagel's remarkable encyclopediac-guide to *China*; the English edition was first published at Geneva in 1968.

For the southern colonisation movement of China's people over the centuries, Herold J. Wiens's *China's March Toward the Tropics*, Shoe String Press, Hamden, Connecticut, 1954, is a general scholarly survey, and on population in recent centuries there is Ho Ping-ti's work *Studies on the Population of China, 1368-1953*, Harvard University Press, Cambridge, Mass., 1959. Among a great many books and articles on the present population, the reliability of the 1953 census, and the dangers that may come from a high rate of increase in the years to come, the paper by Sripati Chandrasekhar on *China's Population: Census and Vital Statistics*, Hong Kong University Press, Second Edition, 1960, gives a survey of the situation by an expert in the demography of Asian countries, based on the figures of 1953 and a visit made in 1958.

Chapter 2

The best general geography of China is still that of George B. Cressey, *Land of the 500 Million, A Geography of China*, McGraw-Hill, 1955, while a most useful recent work is *A Geography of China*, by T. R. Tregear, University of London Press, 1965. *China Proper*, (British) Naval Intelligence Division, B.R.530 (Restricted), three volumes, 1944-5, is particularly strong on physical data.

Physical maps in fair detail are most readily available in *The Times Atlas of the World*, either the Mid Century Edition, Volume 1, 1958, or the Comprehensive Edition, 1967. *The National Atlas of China*, published by The National War College of Taiwan in co-operation with The Chinese Geographical Institute and edited by Chang Chi-yün, 1964-7, comprises four volumes of regional and provincial maps, with a fifth volume containing general maps of natural resources, economic development, communications and demography; the editor claims that details since the Nationalist exile from the mainland have been filled in with data gathered from reconnaissance flights by spy-planes. *China in Maps*, Philipps, 1968, contains some short general articles and statistical estimates, with useful maps and diagrams.

On the vital question of land use and agriculture, two major works are *Land Utilization in China*, by John Lossing Buck, Commercial Press, Shanghai, three volumes, 1937, which presents the results of a detailed survey carried out by a team from the University of Nanking, and which is still the only work of its kind on China Proper; and *Food and Agriculture* in Communist China, being four essays by John Lossing Buck, Owen L. Dawson and Yüan-li Wu, Praeger, New York, 1966, which is a valuable reference source on the question of China's present-day food supply.

Rhodes Murphey's 'China's Transport Problem and Communist Planning', in *Economic Geography* 32, 1956, pp. 22-8, is an important survey of possible communication methods and their value in linking one region of the country to another.

Chapter 3

On the physical features of China, including climate and soil, and particularly on the hydrography of the great rivers, a most valuable source of data is *The Physical Geography of China*, published by the USSR Academy of Sciences, Moscow, 1964, English translation published by Praeger, New York.

Two articles in the *Geographical Review*, journal of the American Geographical Society, New York, describe the Hwang Ho and work on its control: 'The Hwang Ho, Yellow River', by Frederick G. Clapp, in Volume 12, 1922, pp. 1-18, and 'The Yellow River Reharnessed', by Oliver J. Todd, in Volume 39, 1949, pp. 38-56. The latter is by an expert in flood control, who supervised the closing of the great breach, first opened in 1938 to impede the Japanese advance, and not finally controlled until 1947. The same writer has a more popular, well-illustrated article 'Taming "Flood Dragons" Along China's Hwang Ho' in *National Geographic Magazine* 81, 1942, pp. 205-24. More recently, the *Report on the Multi-purpose Plan for Permanently Controlling the Yellow River and Exploiting its Water Resources*, Foreign Languages Press, Peking, 1955, describes the problems of water control and the government's plans to deal with them in an official publication by Teng Tse-hui, then Vice-Premier of the State Council.

On features of loess soil, a valuable article is that by George B. Barbour, 'Recent Observations on the Loess of North China', in *Geographical Journal*, published by the Royal Geographical Society, London, Volume 86, 1935, pp. 54-64.

Chapter 4

The famous novel of Pearl S. Buck, *The Good Earth*, John Day, New York, 1931, gives an imaginative and effective picture of the traditional life of the Chinese peasant on the North China Plain in the years before Communist government, and in *The Chinese People and the Chinese Earth* by Keith Buchanan, G. Bell and Sons, London, 1966, there is a favourable view of development under the Communist regime and the commune system, as seen in two visits made during 1958 and 1964.

On the historical functions of the traditional Chinese city, there is an article by Wolfram Eberhard, 'Data on the Structure of Chinese Cities in the Pre-Industrial Period' in *Economic Development and*

Cultural Change, Volume 4, 1955-6, pp. 253-68, and on particular communities there are the works of Martin C. Yang, *A Chinese Village*, Columbia University Press, New York, 1945, which describes the author's native village in Shantung, and S. D. Gamble, *Ting Hsien: a North China Rural Community*, Institute of Pacific Relations, New York, 1954. On the patterns of towns and markets, an important recent article is G. William Skinner's 'Marketing and Social Structure in Rural China', in *Journal of Asian Studies* 24, 1964-5, pp. 3-43, 195-228 and 363-99.

Chapter 5

'Manchurian Railway Development', by Norton S. Ginsberg, in *Far Eastern Quarterly* 8, 1949, pp. 398-411, describes the history of railway construction and its influence on agriculture and economics in the period up to the end of World War II. 'The Iron and Steel Industry of China', by Musaffer Erselzuk, in *Economic Geography* 32, 1956, pp. 347-71, covers the whole field of China's heavy industrial development, but naturally gives particular attention to the Manchurian Region and to the complex at An-shan. Covering the same area, the article 'The Present State of the Chinese Iron and Steel Industry', in *Soviet Geography*, published by the American Geographical Society, Volume 8, October 1960, gives a regional survey of China by two Russian geographers then at Peking University.

Chapter 6

One of the most important and exciting works on Chinese history, and certainly on Outer China, is Owen Lattimore's *Inner Asian Frontiers of China*, American Geographical Society, New York, 1940, Second Edition, 1951.

Further pieces by Professor Lattimore are contained in his *Studies in Frontier History: Collected Papers 1928-1958*, Oxford University Press, London, 1962.

Among a multitude of books and articles on Mongolia, Tibet and Central Asia, those listed below deal with specific regions:

Cable, Mildred, and French, Francesca, *The Gobi Desert*, Hodder and Stoughton, London, 1942, reprinted 1950

Chang Chih-yi, 'Land Utilization and Settlement Possibilities in Sinkiang', *Geographical Review* 39, 1949, pp. 57-75

Fleming, Peter, *News from Tartary: a Journey from Peking to Kashmir*, Cape, London, 1936

Harrer, Heinrich, *Seven Years in Tibet*, Dutton, New York, 1953

Jackson, W. A. Douglas, *The Russo-Chinese Borderlands*, van Nostrand, New York, 1962.

Liu En-lan, 'The Ho-si [i.e. Kansu] Corridor', *Economic Geography* 28, 1952, pp. 51-6

Moseley, George, *A Sino-Soviet Cultural Frontier: The Ili Kazakh Autonomous Chou*, Harvard East Asian Monographs 22, Cambridge, Mass., 1966 (on the problems of Chinese pressure against the non-Chinese peoples in one part of Dzungaria)

Wiens, Herold J., 'Cultivation, Development and Expansion in China's Colonial Realm in Central Asia', *Journal of Asian Studies* 26, 1966, pp. 67-88

A general work on human geography and environment, with a section on the nomads of Central Asia, is *Habitat, Economy and Society: a geographical introduction to ethnology*, by C. Daryll Forde, Methuen, London, Sixth Edition, 1948.

Chapter 7

George B. Barbour, 'The Physiographic History of the Yangtze', in *Geographical Journal* 87, 1936, pp. 17-34, discusses the course of the river, its bedrock structure, subsidence and sediment in the lower reaches, and the theories on its evolution.

Regional studies of territories in the upper Yangtze and Szechwan basins are:

Fitzgerald, C. P., *The Tower of Five Glories*, Cresset, London, 1941 (on the non-Chinese peoples of Tali in Yunnan)

Jones, Fred O., 'Tukiangyen: China's Ancient Irrigation System', in *Geographical Review* 44, 1954, pp. 543-59 (on the Min Kiang irrigation system near Chengtu)

Spencer, Joseph E., 'Kueichow: an Internal Chinese Colony', in *Pacific Affairs* 13, 1940, pp. 162-72

—— 'The Szechwan Village Fair', in *Economic Geography* 16, 1940, pp. 48-58

Stevenson, P. H., 'Notes on the Human Geography of the Chinese Tibetian Borderland', in *Geographical Review* 22, 1932, pp. 599-616

Weins, Herold J., 'The Shu Tao or Road to Szechwan', in *Geographical Review* 39, 1949, pp. 584-604

Jan Myrdal and Gun Kessle's *Chinese Journey*, referred to in the notes to Chapter 1, contains a short essay and photographs of country near the Sino-Burmese border.

A survey of all the flora of China, including the great variety found in Szechwan, is 'The Plants of China and Their Usefulness to Man', by Edbert H. Walker, in the *Annual Report of the Smithsonian Institution*, Washington, D.C., 1943, pp. 325-61.

Chapter 8

C. S. Worcester, *The Junks and Sampans of the Yangtze: a study in Chinese nautical research*, two volumes, Maritime Customs, Shanghai, 1947-8, gives a fascinating picture of the life and trade of these people, with detailed drawings of their craft, relating each local type to the rivers and lakes where they are designed to sail. On village life in the south, there are *Peasant Life in China*, by Fei Hsiao-t'ung, Routledge, London, 1939, describing the author's native village in southern Kiangsu, near Shanghai; and 'The Fenghsien Landscape', by George B. Cressey, in *Geographical Review* 26, 1936, pp. 396-413, on settlement, farming, fishing and salt-collection in reclaimed dyke and polder land on the north of Hangchow Bay.

'Shanghai', by John E. Orchard, in *Geographical Review* 26, 1936, pp. 1-31, describes the treaty port in its hinterland of the Yangtze valley while Fei Hsiao-t'ung, in his *China's Gentry*, University of Chicago Press, 1953, discusses the development of the traditional Chinese city and compares it to the treaty ports as outposts of the alien West on Chinese soil. For a picture of Shanghai in Communist times, there is *Shanghai: Key to Modern China*, by Rhodes Murphey, Harvard University Press, Cambridge, Mass., 1953, and also sections in *China Observed*, by C. P. Mackerras and N. J. Hunter, Nelson, Melbourne, 1968.

'Salt in China', in *Geographical Review* 25, 1935, pp. 158-66, was written by Joseph E. Spencer, a former official of the Salt Administration, and describes all the sources of manufacture and mining, together with trade and transport.

Chapter 9

'Yunnan and the West River of China', by E. C. Wilton, in *Geographical Journal* 49, 1917, describes what was almost a pioneering exploration of the Yunnan-Kwangsi Region, and is still valuable today. 'Field Observations on the Canton Delta of South China', by Glenn T. Trewartha, in *Economic Geography* 15, 1939, pp. 1-10, describes land use in the hills and alluvial lowland about Canton. 'The Chinese Fishing Industry', by H. Robinson, in *Geography* 41, 1956, pp. 158-66, describes deep-sea, inshore and inland fishing, and the government's plans to increase production.

On the British Crown Colony of Hong Kong, the most accessible source of information and statistics is the annual report of the administration. For an intelligent tourist's view of the region, including Macau, there is *Asia's Bright Balconies*, by Colin Simpson, Angus and Robertson, 1962; and for a scholarly report on the current situation, read 'Hong Kong Revisited', by V. C. Funnell, in *Australian Outlook*, Journal of the Australian Institute of International Affairs, Volume 23, 1969, pp. 279-93.

Chapter 10

Volume I of the *National Atlas of China*, cited in the notes to Chapter 2, is devoted to the island province of Taiwan, and the Nationalist government also publishes regularly the *China Yearbook* and the *Taiwan Statistical Data Book*, published by the China Council for International Economic Co-operation and Development, Executive Yüan, Republic of China, Taipei, 1969. As a member of the United Nations, details of the Republic of China are included in the publications of that organisation.

Formosa, A Study in Chinese History, by W. G. Goddard, Macmillan, 1966, is a historical and geographical description of the island under Nationalist rule, strongly in favour of President Chiang Kai-shek.

On the vital problem of population, there is an important article by William Petersen in *Asia's Population Problems*, edited by S. Chandrasekhar, Allen and Unwin, London, 1967.

A detailed study of the physical geography of the island, *Taiwan (Formosa): A Geographical Appreciation*, was published in 1952, by the Department of Mines and Technical Surveys Geographical Branch, Ottawa, Canada, as No. 5 of the Foreign Geography Information Series, and is still valuable today.

Chapter 11

Political events in China have a habit of disproving pundits within months of their work being published, and much that is written is strongly influenced by the author's political interests. Books with a strongly pro-Communist bias, irrespective of the contact their writers may have had with China, are almost without exception valueless, though mainland magazines, such as *China Reconstructs* and *China Pictorial*, are still useful, despite elements of propaganda, for the items of information which the government wishes to emphasise and for their superb photographs of Chinese life and work. On the other side, the interesting *Orbit of China*, by Harrison E. Salisbury, Secker and Warburg, 1967, is a survey of the Communist regime from the neighbouring countries, though like many other books of this kind it is to some extent distorted by the author's outside viewpoint and by the fears of the people he talked to.

Useful surveys are those of *China, New Age and New Outlook*, by Ping-chia Kuo, Penguin Books, 1960, a favourable picture of mainland administration up to the time of the Great Leap Forward, and more important *A Quarter of Mankind, An Anatomy of China Today*, by Dick Wilson, Penguin Books, 1968, which presents the balanced view of an experienced China-watcher in more recent years.

One of the best collections of regular factual information may be found in the yearbooks of the *Far Eastern Economic Review*, published in Hong Kong each December. Closer to home, there are frequent articles in the Australian daily papers and news magazines, but *The New York Times Weekly Review*, in particular, has regular notes and occasional full-page articles on developments in Hong Kong, Taiwan and the mainland.

Index

Page references in italics refer to maps and figures.